Laboratory Manual

PHYSICS

R. Terrance Egolf • Richard A. Seeley • Linda E. Shumate

Teacher's Edition

Second Edition

BJU PRESS

Greenville, South Carolina

PLEASE NOTE:

You are legally responsible for the safety of your students in the lab. Insist that they follow safe lab practices. Do not leave them unattended while they are working on any experiment or project in the lab.

You may want to consult with your school lawyer to determine whether any local or state safety regulations should be taken into consideration. Rules regarding laboratory safety are constantly changing. Safety procedures in this lab manual should be regarded as only generalized suggestions. You should consult the safety laws in your own state and community, as well as the most recent OSHA guidelines.

Although you may not appreciate the intrusion of the government into your classroom, your example will influence the attitude of your students with regard to personal safety and a Christian s responsibility to government.

Note:
The fact that materials produced by other publishers may be referred to in this volume does not constitute an endorsement of the content or theological position of materials produced by such publishers. Any references and ancillary materials are listed as an aid to the student or the teacher and in an attempt to maintain the accepted academic standards of the publishing industry.

Laboratory Manual:
PHYSICS Teacher's Edition
Second Edition

R. Terrance Egolf, CDR, USN (Ret.)
Richard A. Seeley, M.S.
Linda E. Shumate

Editor
Robert E. Grass

Design
Patricia A. Tirado

Composition
Monotype Composition Company

Cover Design
Elly Kalagayan

Photo Credits
The following agencies and individuals have furnished materials to meet the photographic needs of this textbook. We wish to express our gratitude to them for their important contribution.

CERN
Egolf, R. Terrance
Fisher Science Education
Lawrence Berkeley National Laboratory

PhotoDisc, Inc.
Sargent-Welch/CENCO
Science Kit & Boreal Laboratories
USAF Photo

FRONT COVER
Top Section: PhotoDisc, Inc. (top left); USAF Photo by Tom Reynolds (top right); Bottom Section: CERN photo (top left); Lawrence Berkeley National Laboratory (middle left); PhotoDisc, Inc. (top right, bottom left to right)

UNIT 2
Photography Courtesy of Sargent-Welch/CENCO 19, 58; Science Kit & Boreal Laboratories 25 (both); Egolf, R. Terrance 83

UNIT 3
Fisher Science Education 106 (left); Sargent-Welch/CENCO 106 (right); Sargent-Welch/CENCO 107 (main photo and right

UNIT 4
Egolf, R. Terrance 207

UNIT 5
Lawrence Berkeley National Laboratory 277

BACK COVER
Lawrence Berkeley National Laboratory (entire)

OF NOTE
Schematics and diagrams are based on the EP-50 Electronic Playground & Learning Center manual. Copyright Elenco Electronics Inc. Used by Permission.

Produced in cooperation with the Division of Natural Science of the Bob Jones University College of Arts and Science and the Center for Educational Technology (BJ LINC).

' 2002 Bob Jones University Press
Greenville, South Carolina 29614

First Edition ' 1988, 1999

Printed in the United States of America
All rights reserved

ISBN 978-1-57924-630-3

20 19 18 17 16 15 14 13 12 11 10 9 8 7 6 5 4 3

Contents

Introduction

Physics. What does that word mean to you? You have probably developed very definite mental associations with this area of science. Visions of Albert Einstein, levers and pulleys, high-energy lasers, or supercomputers may come to mind. Physics is a broad area of science that overlaps most of the other major scientific disciplines. It concerns the origins, transformation, and uses of energy, as well as the interaction of energy with matter. Physics traditionally includes the study of motion (mechanics), energy transformations (thermodynamics and cryogenics), sound (acoustics), uses of light (optics), the effects of electric and magnetic energy, nuclear particle physics, and cosmology. As you can see, physics touches on nearly every aspect of your life. As you strive to conform to the image of Christ, it is essential that your awareness of His creation include a basic knowledge of the way it works.

A textbook study of physics by itself would be tedious and would likely result in an unrealistic view of the way the world functions. For this reason, you have the opportunity to validate the principles and laws of physics in a laboratory setting. There are many benefits to performing labs that go beyond merely showing that $F = ma$, for example. You can be assured that with proper preparation, attention to detail, and just plain hard work, you will academically succeed in this course. You will also be better prepared for the future and be a better witness for Christ.

Purposes

This laboratory manual was developed to help you

- *understand how science works.* True science is nothing more than an organized method of gathering information and solving problems that relate to the physical universe. You will not imitate a scientist in this course; you will actually *be* a scientist. You will see firsthand how science works, what it can do, and where its limitations lie.
- *remember the information in your textbook.* You can remember information more easily when you use it than when you simply memorize it. The laboratory exercises in this manual allow you to review, apply, and observe the principles you have encountered in your textbook.
- *develop scientific attitudes.* Are you curious? Do you make decisions based on facts? How do you react when a scientific observation seems to contradict one of your beliefs or your experience? A scientific attitude will help you make reasonable decisions in areas as different as buying clothes, forming opinions about ecology, and choosing which courses to take in school.
- *build problem-solving skills.* Throughout your life you will be solving some sort of problem. This laboratory manual will guide you in making accurate observations and sound judgments as you investigate scientific problems. You will also learn to follow detailed written and oral instructions, which will benefit you in many activities as an adult.
- *learn laboratory skills.* The activities in this manual will teach you to make accurate measurements and use common laboratory equipment correctly.

Procedures

No book nor any person can force you to learn. *You* are responsible for the benefit you gain from each lab period. Keeping in mind the ultimate purpose for learning, you need to be consistent in your preparations. Adhering to the following principles will assure you of success.

Before the lab period

1. Read the entire lab when it is assigned. The Prelab Homework will require you to demonstrate your understanding of the practical and theoretical points of the lab. You will be more efficient during lab because you will know what you are supposed to be doing.
2. Review the textbook material that corresponds to the topic of the investigation. Also review any appendices that may apply to the assigned lab.
3. Plan ahead. Use the diagrams provided to help you visualize the steps of the lab procedure.
4. Bring all necessary supplies with you to class. Besides your lab manual and calculator, you will often need various kinds of paper, a ruler, or drawing instruments.

During the lab period

1. Carefully follow all of the instructions given by your teacher as well as the written instructions in this manual. Do not proceed with the lab until you are told to do so.

2. Work efficiently. Restrict your talking to questions that will help you work better.
3. Ask questions if you are not sure what to do. The time you spend getting your questions answered will be far less than the time you spend having to perform a procedure over again to obtain the required data.
4. Record your results accurately. Observations should be recorded as soon as possible after they are made. Most calculations and the analysis of the data can take place outside class.
5. At the completion of the lab, disassemble the lab apparatus and follow your teacher's instructions for putting away equipment and cleaning up.

After the lab period

1. Promptly complete the Postlab Exercises and the Postlab Analysis when assigned. Although the observations and data you obtain will usually be the same as your partner's, never copy his calculations or answers. Aside from the dishonesty of such an action, the work you copy may be wrong!
2. Written mathematical solutions should show enough steps that your teacher can follow your thought process. You should never write down only the result of a calculation without supporting your work either on the lab report pages or on an attached sheet of paper.
3. Answer free-response questions in complete, thoughtful sentences whenever possible. Try to explain *why* your answer is true, using the concepts you have learned.
4. Promptly turn in your report to your teacher on or before the date assigned.
5. File your completed and graded work. **Note:** It is important that you retain the entire lab in a notebook because later labs often refer back to instructions provided in earlier labs.

Laboratory Policies

When you walk into a laboratory, you are walking into a potentially dangerous place. Although the experiments contained in this manual are not inherently dangerous, the laboratory or classroom may be used for other lab courses, and hazardous materials and expensive equipment may be present. Obey the following rules and any other guidelines your teacher establishes for your laboratory.

1. Never engage in unruly or athletic behavior in any laboratory, even if a lab activity is not in progress.
2. Never perform unauthorized experiments. It is good to be curious, but you should never operate devices or apparatus unsupervised "just to see what will happen."
3. Know where fire blankets, emergency showers, and fire extinguishers are located and learn how to use them.
4. Avoid handling containers of chemicals stored in the lab. Never taste, smell, or allow your eyes to be exposed to laboratory chemicals.
5. Secure long hair and loose clothing that could interfere with your work.
6. Never heat a closed container. When heating a test tube or flask, point the open end away from yourself and anyone else in the room.
7. Keep your work space neat and uncluttered.
8. Report any accident, however minor it may seem, to the teacher.
9. Keep combustible materials away from open flames.
10. Handle delicate measuring instruments with care. Use two hands to carry heavier instruments.

Hopefully, you will have an interesting and exciting year of studying science, one that will provide you with valuable information and experience. This lab manual will help you achieve goals that you have set for yourself, but more importantly, it will open doors for you into areas of science you may not have known existed. Even if you do not enter a career in science, you will undoubtedly face many situations in which a basic knowledge of science is crucial.

Laboratory Activity

Name _____

Date _____ Hour _____

MEASUREMENT

Purpose

You must be able to perform measurements and make calculations from lab data in this physics course. The purpose of this exercise is to

- practice various laboratory measuring techniques.
- practice reading the scales on various kinds of laboratory instruments to the proper precision.
- practice organizing data into useful tables.
- practice using significant digits in arithmetic calculations.

Prelab Discussion

Recall that **density** is the mass of a specific volume of matter. It is usually described by the formula

$$\rho = \frac{m}{V},$$

where ρ (Greek letter rho) is the density of the substance, m is the mass of the substance, and V is the volume of the substance.

You can find the density of a substance by determining its mass and volume and then using the above formula. Thus, the units for density must be some form of mass units divided by volume units. For example, you might find units such as grams per milliliter (g/mL), kilograms per liter (kg/L), grams per cubic centimeter (g/cm^3), or pounds per cubic foot (lb/ft^3). The density of water is one gram per cubic centimeter. Objects or substances more dense than water will sink in water, but those less dense will float. You will study this concept in a later lab exercise.

Volumes can be expressed by two different units in the metric system. Volumes of solids are usually measured in cubic centimeters, while volumes of fluids (liquids and gases) are measured in milliliters. Also, recall that one cubic centimeter and one milliliter are equivalent volumes. Thus, it is simple to convert from liquid to solid volumes in metric units. Conversions are much more difficult in the English system. For example, one gallon is not equal to one cubic foot.

Mass is measured on a *laboratory balance*. The triple-beam balance recommended for this exercise measures mass in grams. The graduated scale is subdivided into tenths of a gram. Measuring masses greater than 10 grams requires the use of the sliders on the other two notched beams. Always ensure that the sliders are engaged in the notches before determining the mass. The *precision* of the balance is assumed to be tenths of a gram, which means it will give measurements to the tenth gram consistently through many measurements by one person or different people. Measurements with this instrument should always be estimated to hundredths of a gram. *Accuracy,* an indication of how close a measurement is to the accepted value, is different from precision. The *manufacturer* determines the basic accuracy of the balance by how accurately the sliding masses are machined and how accurately the beams and scales are marked. The *user* maximizes accuracy for a given instrument by setting the balance to zero ("zeroing the balance") before use. This is accomplished by adjusting the screw knob located just under the pan on the end of the arm.

You will also use a laboratory instrument that you are more familiar with—a *metric ruler.* A metric ruler 1 meter long is commonly called a *meter stick.* Since the ruled scale is marked in tenths of a centimeter, you will normally estimate measurements to the hundredth of a centimeter (a tenth of a millimeter) unless otherwise instructed.

Required Equipment

balance
brass cylinder or other object
graduated cylinder, 100 mL
metric ruler
string
water

Optional Equipment

metric mass set (for double-pan balance)

Prelab Discussion

- Review the prerequisites for Lab 1-1 in the back of this manual. Ensure that you have discussed Appendix A prior to performing this lab.

- The natural tendency for students using scientific calculators is to express the results of calculations to an excessive number of significant digits (SDs). This textbook strives to limit the answers given in the Teacher's Edition to the correct number of SDs. The following conventions should help you ascertain what method was used to round the final results. For answers that are exact or require no rounding, the symbol "=" is used. If displayed answers are truncated or rounded calculator results and the correct number of SDs is implied, the symbol "≐" is used. For results that are explicitly rounded to conform to the significant digit rules given in Appendix A, the symbol "≈" is used.

Equipment and Setup

- The instruments in this lab should be familiar to most of your students.

- If you have the other specific gravity cylinders that usually come in a set, you may want to use them for this lab as well. The accepted values for their densities are as follows:

aluminum	2.64 g/cm^3
copper	8.94 g/cm^3
steel	7.86 g/cm^3

- If you wish, you may use a glass marble (a sphere) instead of the brass cylinder. The accepted value for the density of glass is about 2.6 g/cm³. Record only the diameter for dimensions in Table 1.

- Following is a brief description of the correct use of a triple-beam balance.

  1. Start with all sliding masses in the leftmost position. The 100 g and 10 g sliders are on notched beams.

  2. Zero the balance prior to use by turning the knob under the pan (for Ohaus balances) clockwise to lower the pointer or counter-clockwise to raise the pointer.

  3. Gently place the object to be measured on the pan; then, starting with the largest, move the notched sliders until the arm drops below the zero mark. When this occurs, move the slider to the left one notch.

  4. Adjust, from largest to smallest, the remaining sliders until the arm rests at the zero point.

  5. The mass of the object is the sum of the positions of the 100 g, 10 g, and 1 g sliders. Read the graduated scale to the nearest hundredth gram.

- Your school may have two-pan balances. If so, you will have to modify the instructions in the lab to accommodate this change, but the results will be unaffected for balances with precision equivalent to the recommended balance.

Procedure

- Point out to your students that when the procedures require measurements for length, mass, and volume, they do not have to physically make the measurements independently; they just have to read the instrument independently.

- If your class is small, you should treat the class as one group in order to obtain the advantages of averaging results to improve precision.

- Emphasize the proper use of SDs in all measurements and calculations. Repeated practice will make using SDs second nature.

The third instrument in this laboratory exercise is called a *graduated cylinder*. The scale imprinted on the side of a 100-milliliter cylinder has markings in one-milliliter increments, so measurements should be estimated to tenths of a milliliter. The attraction (or repulsion) of liquids to the sides of a glass container forms a curved liquid surface called a **meniscus.** Always measure liquid volume by observing the center of the meniscus against the scale.

Since volume can be measured in cubic centimeters, making careful dimensional measurements of a regularly shaped object (cube, cylinder, etc.) will enable you to calculate its volume in cubic centimeters, using a formula. This method of determining volume is often called the **linear-measurement method.** Several familiar formulas for regular objects follow.

Cube	$V = s^3$
Rectangular prism (parallelepiped)	$V = lwh$
Cylinder	$V = \pi r^2 h$
Sphere	$V = (4/3)\pi r^3$

Not all objects are regularly shaped, however. If an object is irregular, you can use the **water-displacement method** for determining the volume. There are two basic methods of accomplishing this. The first method requires that you fill a container to the brim with water, add the object, and catch the overflow liquid in another container. This overflow liquid occupies the same volume as the irregularly shaped object. The second method requires that you fill a measuring vessel, such as a graduated cylinder, with a predetermined volume of liquid, add the solid object, and determine the *change* in liquid level. The latter method will be used with a graduated cylinder in this exercise. The starting volume of the water must be sufficient to completely cover the object being measured, but not so great that the water level is forced past the top mark on the scale.

One objective in this lab is to calculate the density of a regularly shaped object—a brass cylinder. You will use the linear-measurement method (Method 1) and the water-displacement method (Method 2) to determine the volume. After using both methods to compute the density, you will compare your results with an accepted value for the density of brass.

Table 1 helps chart out your "plan of attack." Each person in your group will make the indicated measurements. Record all measurements of the brass cylinder in the appropriate table. Be sure to get this much done before your class period is over. You can complete the calculations later.

Procedure

1. Measure the length and the diameter of the brass cylinder. Every lab group member should make each measurement *independently* (that is, without conferring with anyone else or otherwise revealing the results until everyone has finished). Record the dimensions (in centimeters) obtained by each group member in Table 1.

2. Determine the mass of the brass cylinder. Every member of your group should make the measurement *independently*. After all have finished the measurement, record the mass (in grams) obtained by each group member in Table 1.

3. Pour water into the graduated cylinder to some easily read mark. Every member of your group should read this volume *independently* prior to Step 4. Record the volume (in milliliters) for each group member as the initial volume (V_i) in Table 1.

4. Tie a string to the brass cylinder. Gently lower the cylinder into the water. All members of your group should read the new level of the water *independently*. Record the volume (in milliliters) for each group member as the final volume (V_f) in Table 1.

Data

Table 1
Measurements (Record values using proper significant digits.)

Student Name	Linear Measurement			Water Displacement	
	Length, h	Diameter, d	Mass, m	Initial Volume, V_i	Final Volume, V_f
1.	cm	cm	g	mL	mL
2.	cm	cm	g	mL	mL
3.	cm	cm	g	mL	mL
4.	cm	cm	g	mL	mL
Average	cm	cm	g	mL	mL

Data in Table 1 will vary.

Postlab Exercises

1. Calculate the averages for each column in Table 1 by adding together all of the values and dividing by the number of students in your group. Record the average values in the last row of Table 1.

2. Calculate the volume (V_1) of the cylinder in cubic centimeters from the length and diameter measurements. Use the formula

$$V_1 = \pi r^2 h.$$

   Note: When calculating the radius, ensure that $d/2$ does not have a precision greater than the original diameter measurement. (Review the discussion of precision and significant digits in Appendix A.)

   Record the values for V_1 in Table 2 for each member of your group.

3. Determine the *displacement volume* (V_2), using the V_i and V_f measurements recorded in Table 1.

$$V_2 = V_f - V_i$$

   Record the values of V_2 in Table 2 for each member of your group.

4. Calculate the density, using V_1 from Table 2 and m from Table 1. Record the value in Table 2 as ρ_1 for each member of your group.

5. Calculate the density, using V_2 from Table 2 and m from Table 1. Record the value in Table 2 as ρ_2 for each member of your group.

6. Determine the **percentage of error** in your density measurements and calculations for each member of your group and the group average, using the following formula:

$$\text{percent error} = \frac{(\text{experimental value} - \text{accepted value})}{\text{accepted value}} \times 100\%.$$

   The *accepted value* for the density of yellow brass is approximately 8.47 g/cm³. This value varies from sample to sample, depending on the exact composition of the alloy, but it will be sufficient for your purposes. Notice that the percent error is negative if your value is less than the accepted value and positive if your value is greater than the accepted value. The *experimental value* is what you recorded as ρ_1 and ρ_2 in Table 2. The percent error is a method of calculating the *accuracy* of your group.

Prelab Homework

- Assign and collect the Prelab Homework before performing the lab. You may want to give a brief quiz before beginning.

- Remind your students that they will receive maximum benefit from the labs if they are properly prepared beforehand. The prelab assignments are designed to exercise the students in all the skills they will need to successfully complete the lab.

Table 2
Calculation of Density, Percent Error, and Percent Difference

Student Name	Linear Measurement (Method 1)			Displacement Volume (Method 2)			Percent Difference
	V_1	ρ_1	Percent Error	V_2	ρ_2	Percent Error	
1.	cm³	g/cm³	%	mL	g/cm³	%	
2.	cm³	g/cm³	%	mL	g/cm³	%	
3.	cm³	g/cm³	%	mL	g/cm³	%	
4.	cm³	g/cm³	%	mL	g/cm³	%	
Average	cm³	g/cm³	%	mL	g/cm³	%	%

Answers will vary, but percent error and percent difference should be 5% or less.

7. You can now calculate the *precision* of your results.

   a. Enter the values of ρ_1 and ρ_2 for each person in the applicable columns of Table 3.

   b. Enter the average values for ρ_1 and ρ_2 ($\rho_{1_{av}}$, $\rho_{2_{av}}$) for each person in your group in the applicable columns in Table 3.

   c. Find the absolute value of the difference between each person's density and the average density of the group for both methods. Refer to Table 3.

   d. To determine the precision for each method, calculate the average of the differences found in Step 7c. Refer to Table 3. The precision is the *mean average deviation* (see Appendix A). It indicates the quality or repeatability of the measurements performed by the group.

Table 3
Calculating Precision of Density Measurements

Student Name	ρ_1	$\rho_{1_{av}}$	$\lvert\rho_1 - \rho_{1_{av}}\rvert$	ρ_2	$\rho_{2_{av}}$	$\lvert\rho_2 - \rho_{2_{av}}\rvert$
1.						
2.						
3.						
4.						
Precision			±			±

Answers will vary, but precision should be within ±0.5 g/cm³.

8. Another helpful evaluation tool is to find the **percent difference** in the values determined using two different methods. In this exercise you determined the density by using a linear-measurement method and a water-displacement method. The percent difference between two methods of measurement is often used to determine whether they are equivalent. If the percent difference is small, either method is satisfactory. If the percent difference is great, the method that is closer to the accepted value is better.

$$\text{percent difference} = \frac{|\text{difference of the two measurements}|}{\text{average of the two measurements}} \times 100\%$$

Calculate the percent difference between the *average* of your group's values for ρ_1 ($\rho_{1_{av}}$ from Table 2) and the *average* of your group's values for ρ_2 ($\rho_{2_{av}}$ from Table 2). Record your percent difference in the Percent Difference column of Table 2.

Postlab Analysis

1. ____Ans. vary.____ What is the accuracy of your group for Method 1? (Enter the average percent error from Table 2 for Method 1.)

2. ____Ans. vary.____ What is the accuracy of your group for Method 2? (Enter the average percent error from Table 2 for Method 2.)

3. ____Ans. vary.____ What is the precision of your group for Method 1? (Enter the precision for Method 1 from Table 3.)

4. ____Ans. vary.____ What is the precision of your group for Method 2? (Enter the precision for Method 2 from Table 3.)

5. Which of the two methods produced results nearer to the accepted value for the density of your metal sample?

   Answers will vary, but normally Method 1 will be more accurate.

6. If the *precision* of your group is good but the *accuracy* of your group members is poor, what would you expect the most likely source of error to be—human or equipment? Explain.

   Since everyone obtained nearly the same answer, the problem probably was in a piece of equipment that was not set at zero, was not well made, or was not working properly.

7. If the *accuracy* of your group is good but the *precision* is poor, what would you expect the probable source of error to be—human or equipment? Explain the reason for your choice and what was done to reduce this source of error.

   Since the accuracy was good, the variation of results is probably due to human error. Averaging results is effective in eliminating precision errors, especially if all experimenters used the same equipment.

8. As noted above, there are two likely sources of error in this experiment—human and equipment. List at least three examples of human error.

   Accept any three of the following: carelessness in reading the instrument; failure to follow instructions; defective instructions; mathematical computational errors; rounding errors; recording data improperly.

9. List at least two potential equipment errors that would contribute to a lack of accuracy.

   The prelab discussion mentioned manufacturing problems with the mass balance. Other correct answers include wrong-sized graduations on scales, manufacturing defects, damage, wear, and corrosion.

10. Discuss a potential problem when determining the density of a porous object, using the water-displacement method.

The porous material may retain gas pockets when submerged, which could give an erroneously large indication of volume and therefore a lower density. If the pores are sealed so that they are an integral part of the material structure, then the lower density is a property of the material.

11. Discuss a problem with using the water-displacement method to determine the density of an object that is less dense than water.

The object would float, which means some arrangement would have to be made to force it underwater without affecting the indicated displaced volume.

Name _____

Date _____ Hour _____

PRELAB HOMEWORK

1. An object with a density of 1.34 g/cm³ will (float/sink) when immersed in water. (Circle one.)

2. To what precision will you estimate measurements made with the following instruments?
   a. Triple-beam balance calibrated in tenth-gram graduations _____0.01 g_____
   b. Metric ruler having tenth-centimeter graduations _____0.01 cm or 0.1 mm_____
   c. Graduated cylinder having one-milliliter graduations _____0.1 mL_____
   d. Thermometer calibrated in two-degree graduations _1° (The smallest *decimal* grad-uation is 10°. See Appendix A.)_____

3. The laboratory instrument designed to measure *mass* is the _____laboratory balance_____.

4. One method for determining the volume of a small, irregularly shaped object is the _____water-displacement_____ method.

5. _____c_____ Which of the following choices would be an appropriate unit for density?

   a. $\dfrac{g}{cg}$ b. $\dfrac{mL}{g}$ c. $\dfrac{kg}{L}$ d. $\dfrac{kL}{g}$ e. kg·m

6. _____5.5 cm³_____ A graduated cylinder contains 27.0 mL of water. After lowering an object into the cylinder, the water level is 32.5 mL. What is the volume of the object in cubic centimeters? Show your work.

   Given: V_i = 27.0 mL; V_f = 32.5 mL; V = ?
   Formula: $V = V_f - V_i$
   Solution: V = 32.5 mL − 27.0 mL = 5.5 mL
   $$\frac{5.5 \text{ mL}}{} \left| \frac{1 \text{ cm}^3}{1 \text{ mL}} \right. = 5.5 \text{ cm}^3$$

7. _____1.16 g/mL_____ If the mass of an object is 25.2 g and its volume is 21.7 mL, what is the density in grams per milliliter?

   Given: m = 25.2 g; V = 21.7 mL; ρ = ?
   Formula: $\rho = \dfrac{m}{V}$

   Solution: $\rho = \dfrac{25.2 \text{ g}}{21.7 \text{ mL}} \approx 1.16 \ \frac{g}{mL}$ (3 SDs allowed)

8. _____7.1 mL_____ Given that the length of a brass cylinder is 5.00 cm and its diameter is 1.33 cm, calculate its volume in milliliters. Show your work.

   Given: h = 5.00 cm; d = 1.33 cm; $r = \dfrac{d}{2} = \dfrac{1.33 \text{ cm}}{2} = 0.665$ cm; V = ?
   Formula: $V = \pi r^2 h$
   Solution: (The radius cannot have greater precision than original measurement—round to $r \approx 0.67$ cm.)
   $V = \pi(0.67 \text{ cm})^2(5.00 \text{ cm}) \doteq 7.051 \text{ cm}^3 \approx 7.1 \text{ cm}^3$ (2 SDs allowed)
   $$\frac{7.1 \text{ cm}^3}{} \left| \frac{1 \text{ mL}}{1 \text{ cm}^3} \right. = 7.1 \text{ mL}$$

9. What problem could occur if you were to drop a heavy object into a *glass* graduated cylinder?

   The object could break the bottom out of the cylinder.

10. If you use the water-displacement method to determine the density of a porous material such as wood or sandstone, what could be the consequences of determining its volume before its mass?

    If you immerse it first to determine volume, it may soak up some water, which
    would increase its apparent mass. The calculated density would be higher than
    the actual density.

Name _____

Date _____ Hour ____

VECTORS

Purpose

This laboratory exercise is designed to give you practice with concepts related to vectors. The purpose is to

Required Equipment
metric ruler
protractor

- determine the resultant of two vectors that have been added together.
- determine the resultant of one vector subtracted from another.
- find the x- and y-components of a given vector.
- become familiar with methods for indicating direction.

Prelab Discussion

Vectors are quantities that can be *fully* defined only by giving both magnitude and direction. Geometrically, a vector is "a directed line segment." Therefore, we can use these geometric devices to visually represent abstract quantities having magnitude and direction in one, two, or three dimensions. We will draw vectors as arrows. The tail of the arrow is the **initial point** and the head of the arrow is the **terminal point.** Vectors are printed in a textbook using bold roman characters, such as vector **A.** The magnitude of a vector is represented by either A or $|A|$. You should write vectors by hand with the conventional vector half-arrow over the symbol, such as $\vec{A}$, and write the vector magnitudes without the half-arrow.

An understanding of vectors is vital to the study of physics. You will use them to represent displacement, velocity, force, acceleration, magnetic fields, electric fields, and many other quantities. Both magnitude and direction must be stated for any of these to be fully defined. **Scalars** are nondirectional quantities. We can say 10 kg, 6 m in circumference, and 40 cm. Notice that there is no direction associated with these measurements. However, to say that a car is traveling 60 miles per hour (scalar) only partly describes the motion of the vehicle. To completely understand its movement, the *direction* of motion must be stated— 60 miles per hour *north* (vector). A vector is quantified by its length and direction. For example, vector **V** that is 5.0 cm long pointing 135° could be expressed as **V** = 5.0 cm at 135°. This notation will be used in this lab.

Vectors may be added, subtracted, or multiplied together. They may also be multiplied or divided by scalars. It is not the intent of this manual to discuss in detail all of the mathematical operations involving vectors. You should refer to your textbook and mathematical texts for that information. You must take note of the fact, however, that the sum, difference, and product of vectors are considerably different from the results of arithmetic addition, subtraction, and multiplication. The sum (and difference) of two vectors is called a **resultant.** We can add and subtract vectors, using either graphic or analytic techniques. **Graphic solutions** involve physically drawing vectors on graph paper. **Analytic solutions** involve the use of trigonometry or vector algebra. The latter method is commonly used in calculus. You will primarily use trigonometry in order to find analytic solutions to vector sums in this course.

When indicating the direction of a vector, either **Cartesian** or **compass directions** may be used. In two-dimensional Cartesian geometry, angles are normally measured from the positive x-axis on the Cartesian coordinate system. Angles may be measured either in the counterclockwise or clockwise direction. Angles measured counterclockwise are considered positive; angles measured clockwise are negative. There is no limit to the size of the angle in a purely Cartesian setting—an angle of 524° is perfectly reasonable. We will use θ (Greek letter theta) to represent a Cartesian angle. An application of Cartesian angle measurement is determining elevation and depression angles in the *vertical* plane. **Elevation angle** is an angle measured above the horizontal (+θ), while **depression angle**

Prelab Discussion

- Review the prerequisites for Lab 1-2 in the back of this manual. Be sure that you have discussed the textbook topics of vectors, vector components, vector addition and subtraction, and vector notation prior to performing this lab.

- This lab may be assigned for homework if your class is well grounded in trigonometry and graphing. Experience has shown, however, that it is profitable to have a structured class time in which students can work together to solve basic vector problems.

- It is anticipated that students will already be familiar with the Cartesian method of angle measurement, so discussion of those details is limited. Using compass directions is probably less familiar to students, so more information is provided regarding conventions and terminology.

- The concepts of reference triangles and reference angles is presented clearly in *ALGEBRA 2 for Christian Schools,* Second Edition.

Procedure

- Graphic solutions of the four exercises are straightforward. Students should not report resultant magnitudes to a greater precision than the original measurements. Angles should be estimated to the nearest tenth degree, but this may be difficult when using small protractors.

- Remind students that trigonometric ratios are pure numbers. The product or quotient of a measurement and a trig ratio should not increase or decrease the *precision* of the original measurement; however, the number of SDs may change.

• Collect and grade the graphs, giving maximum credit for following instructions, using proper SDs, including units in answers, and following specified conventions for notation. Students who obtain small percent differences between geometric and analytic results should also be rewarded.

is an angle measured below the horizontal ($-\theta$). The range of elevation and depression angles is limited (0° to ±90°).

Two-dimensional physical processes in the *horizontal* plane often refer to directions based on a compass. The reference direction for a compass is true north, or the direction to the geographic North Pole. Compass directions are always positive and angles are always less than 360°. Directions are measured *clockwise* around the compass from 000T to 359.9 T. Notice that the capital "T" denotes that the angle is a compass direction referenced to true north. Various terms are used for compass directions. When reporting the direction to an object from the observer, the term **bearing** is used. When reporting the direction an object or person is facing, a **heading** is given. The direction in which a vehicle or vessel is moving is called its **course.**

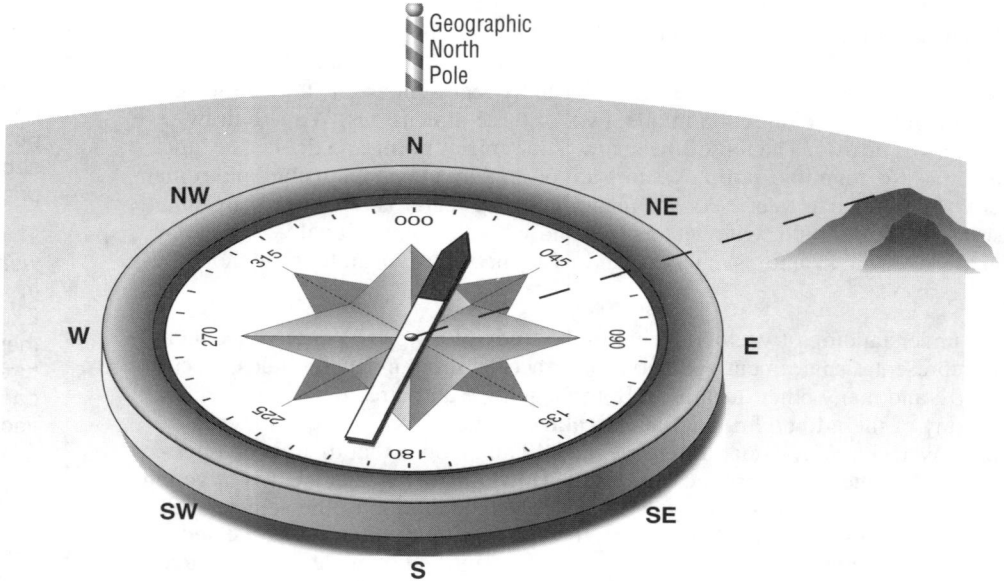

The bearing to the mountain is 060 True.

Figure 1

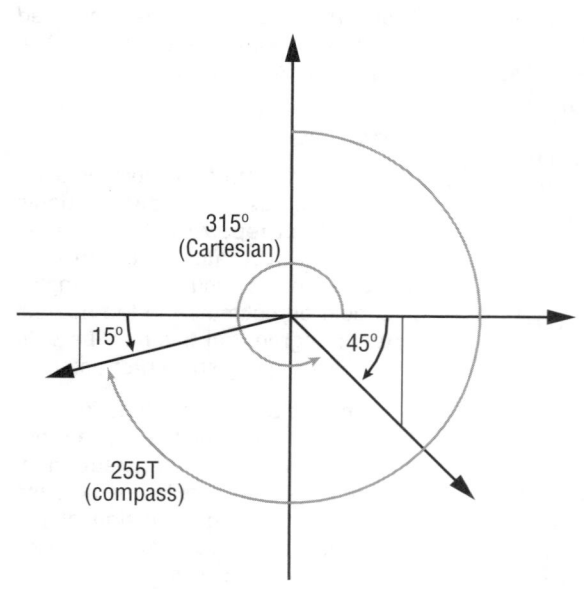

Figure 2

If you have studied trigonometry in an algebra course, you learned that any angle on a Cartesian plane (or a map using compass directions) can be analyzed using a **reference triangle.** In a reference triangle, the **reference angle** is measured from the *x*-axis (represented by the directions 090T and 270T on a map) and is always between 0° and 90°. For example, on the Cartesian plane, the reference angle for a vector with an angle of 315° is 45°, and the reference angle for a vector pointing −165° is 15°. On a map, a car heading 135T also has a 45° reference angle (135° − 090°), and a mountain peak bearing 255T has a reference angle of 15° (270° − 255°). See Figure 2. After a little practice, you will quickly see the reference angles for each situation.

Components of vectors will be either positive or negative values. Assume that the reference horizontal direction is east (090T) and positive with respect to the *x*-axis, and that the reference vertical direction is north (000T) and positive with respect to the *y*-axis. Also, the notations A_y (Cartesian) and A_N (compass) will denote vertical components, and A_x (Cartesian) and A_E (compass) will denote horizontal components. *Vector components that point in a reference direction are positive, and components that point in the direction opposite to a reference direction are negative.*

The system of angular measurement used in this lab, either Cartesian or compass, will be evident from the context of the exercise. To summarize, if directions are given with reference to a Cartesian coordinate system (*x*- and *y*-axes), then positive angles are measured counterclockwise from the positive *x*-axis. If the word *bearing, heading,* or *course* is used, then the exercise is based on compass directions, and you should measure these angles clockwise from the north direction (positive *y*-axis).

> When vector quantities using compass directions must be analyzed, convert the compass directions to Cartesian angles for each vector first, find the solution by using Cartesian graphic or analytic methods, and then convert the answer back to compass directions if the exercise requires it.

Procedure

Graphic Techniques

Complete the following exercises, using graphic techniques. Use the blank graphs on the following pages, a metric ruler, and a protractor. Choose an appropriate scale so that each unit in the exercise is equal to 1 cm (for example, 1 cm = 1 km). Write the scale at the bottom of the graph in the scale legend in the margin. *Use the graph grids only as a guide for direction and angular measurements, not for length measurements.* Record the magnitude and direction for each exercise in Table 1 in the Graphic column. Record all directions in degrees to the nearest tenth degree.

Exercises

Sketch out each situation as accurately as possible. Be particularly alert to the method of angular measurement.

1. Suppose a man walked a distance of 6.5 km heading east and then 10.0 km heading north. Using a ruler and protractor, determine as accurately as possible the magnitude and compass bearing of the displacement vector from his starting point to his destination. Sketch your drawing on Graph 1.

2. A golfer putts a ball to a point 22.0 ft east of his position. The ball passed south of the hole. In order to sink the ball into the hole from his new location, the golfer will have to putt the ball 7.0 ft on a bearing of 302T. How many feet away from the hole was he before he made his first putt, and what was the compass bearing to the hole before his first putt? Sketch your drawing on Graph 2.

3. A hiker walks 13.0 mi heading northeast (045T). She then turns 15° toward the east of her original direction and continues for an additional 15.0 mi. Determine the displacement and bearing of her destination from her starting point. Sketch your drawing on Graph 3.

4. Vector **A** is 20.0 cm long and points −15°. Vector **B** is 11.0 cm long and points −52°. Using your ruler and protractor, subtract **B** from **A**. Sketch your drawing on Graph 4.

Analytic Techniques

Vector addition and subtraction can also be accomplished by analytic techniques. Complete the four exercises above, using trigonometry as discussed in your text. Show your work in the unused graph space. Find both magnitude and direction for each exercise. Record your answers in the Analytic column of Table 1 to the nearest tenth unit for magnitude and to the nearest tenth degree for angular measures.

Once you have solved for the unknown values both graphically and analytically, you can compare the two methods as you did in Lab 1-1. The formula for calculating percent difference is

$$\text{percent difference} = \frac{|\text{difference of the two values}|}{\text{average of the two values}} \times 100\%.$$

Calculate the percent difference for both magnitude and direction for all four exercises. Show your work in unused graph space for each exercise. Record the percent difference in Table 1 to the nearest hundredth percent.

Table 1
Graphic and Trigonometric Solutions

Exercise	Quantity	Graphic	Analytic	Percent Difference
1	**Magnitude**	11.9 ± 0.5 km	11.9 km	*
	Direction	033T ± 1.5T	033.0T	*
2	**Magnitude**	16.5 ± 0.8 ft	16.5 ft	*
	Direction	077T ± 4T	077.1T	*
3	**Magnitude**	27.8 ± 1.0 mi	27.8 mi	*
	Direction	053T ± 2.5T	053.0T	*
4	**Magnitude**	13.0 ± 0.6 cm	13.0 cm	*
	Direction	15.6° ± 1°	15.6°	*

All answers in Table 1 are based on actual analytic solutions. Student graphic answers will vary.

*Percent differences should be less than 5%.

Graph 1
Exercise 1

East

North

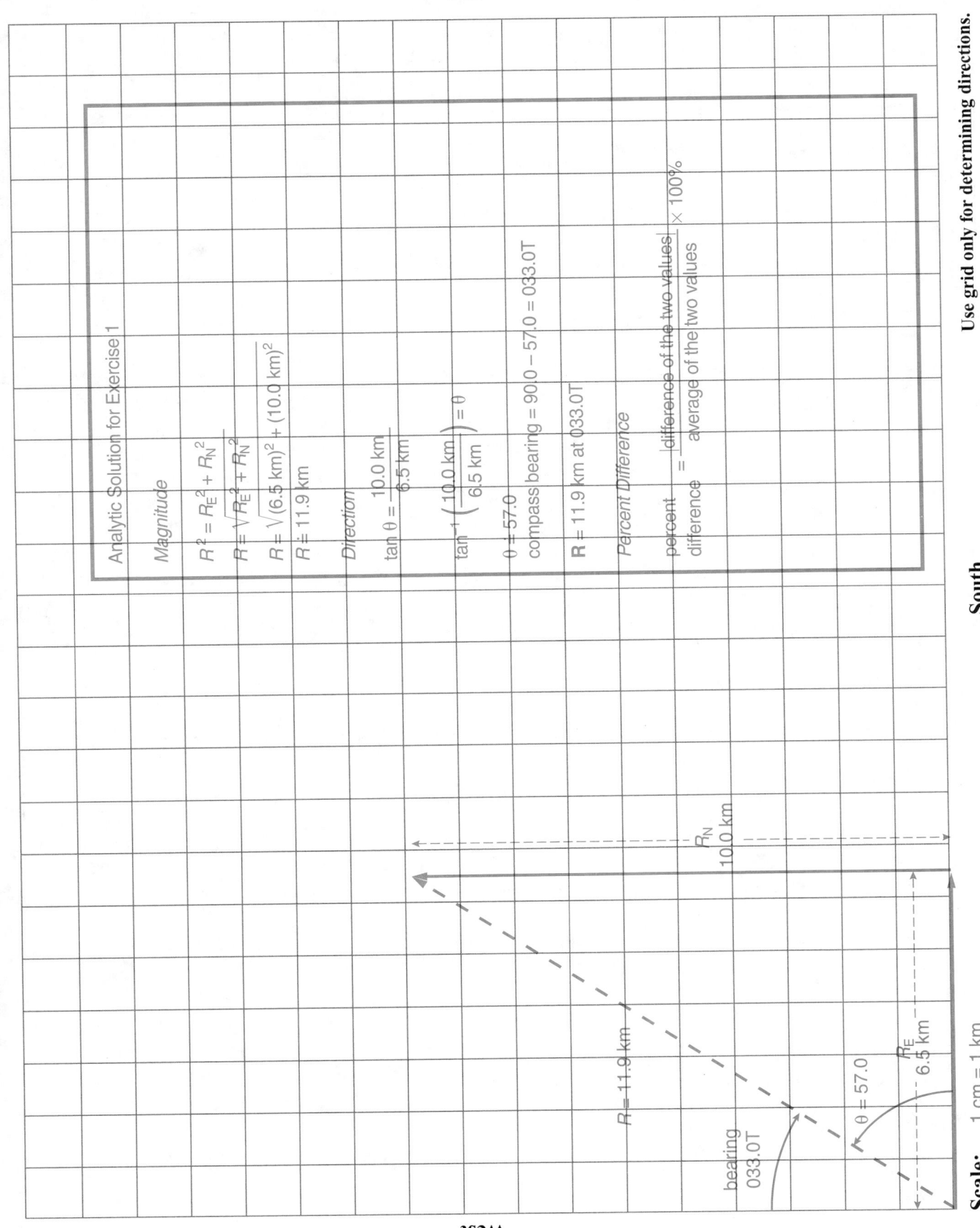

Analytic Solution for Exercise 1

Magnitude

$R^2 = R_E^2 + R_N^2$

$R = \sqrt{R_E^2 + R_N^2}$

$R = \sqrt{(6.5 \text{ km})^2 + (10.0 \text{ km})^2}$

$R \doteq 11.9 \text{ km}$

Direction

$\tan \theta = \dfrac{10.0 \text{ km}}{6.5 \text{ km}}$

$\tan^{-1}\left(\dfrac{10.0 \text{ km}}{6.5 \text{ km}}\right) = \theta$

$\theta \doteq 57.0$

compass bearing $= 90.0 - 57.0 = 033.0\text{T}$

$\mathbf{R} = 11.9 \text{ km at } 033.0\text{T}$

Percent Difference

$\text{percent difference} = \dfrac{|\text{difference of the two values}|}{\text{average of the two values}} \times 100\%$

West

South

Use grid only for determining directions.

R_N 10.0 km

$R = 11.9 \text{ km}$

$\theta = 57.0$

R_E 6.5 km

bearing 033.0T

Scale: 1 cm = 1 km

13

Graph 2
Exercise 2

West

North

East

South

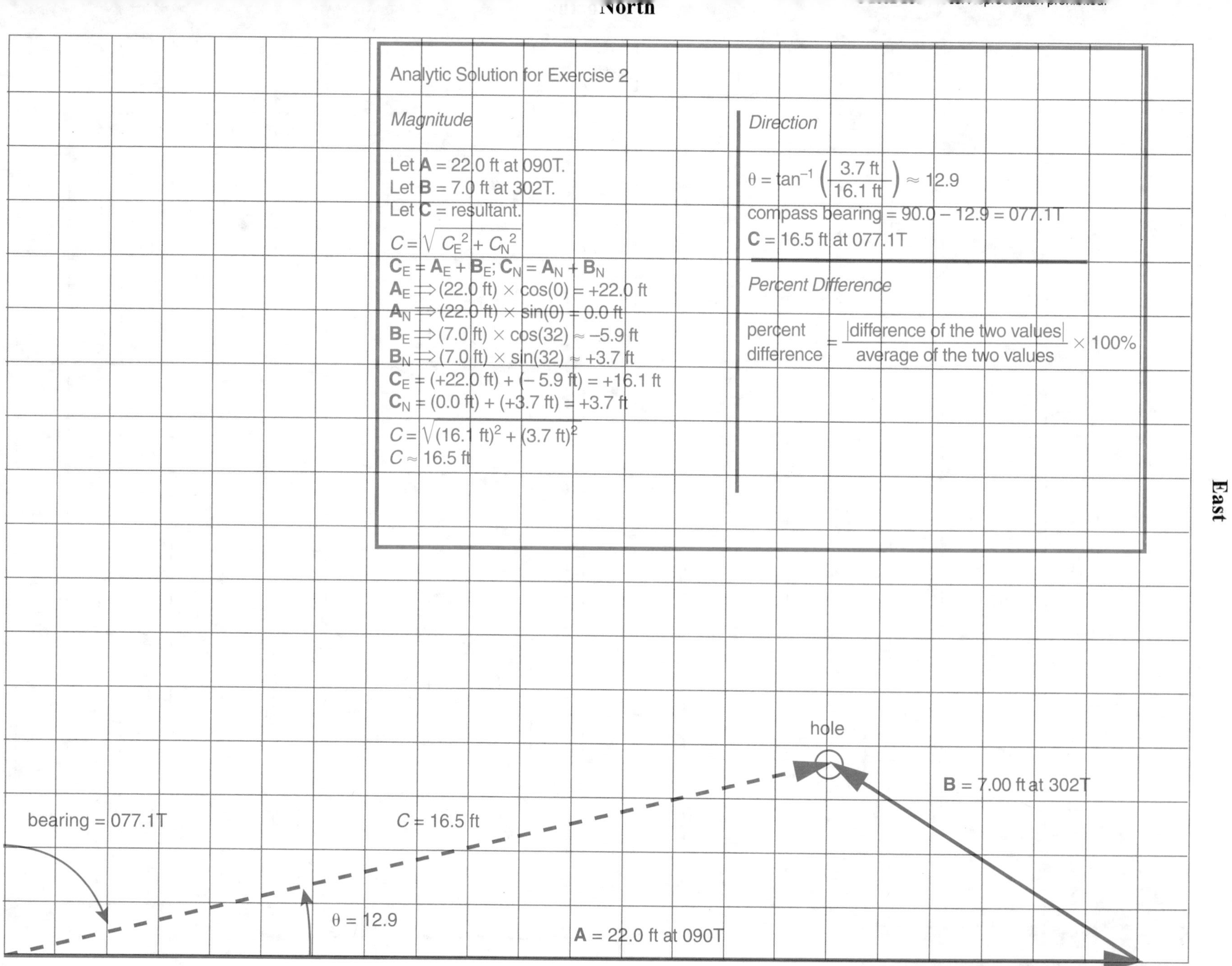

Scale:

1 cm = 1 ft

Use grid only for determining directions.

bearing = 077.1T

θ = 12.9

C = 16.5 ft

A = 22.0 ft at 090T

B = 7.00 ft at 302T

hole

Analytic Solution for Exercise 2

Let **A** = 22.0 ft at 090T.
Let **B** = 7.0 ft at 302T.
Let **C** = resultant.

Magnitude	Direction

$C = \sqrt{C_E^2 + C_N^2}$

$C_E = A_E + B_E;\ C_N = A_N + B_N$

$A_E \Rightarrow (22.0\ \text{ft}) \times \cos(0) = +22.0\ \text{ft}$

$A_N \Rightarrow (22.0\ \text{ft}) \times \sin(0) = 0.0\ \text{ft}$

$B_E \Rightarrow (7.0\ \text{ft}) \times \cos(32) \approx -5.9\ \text{ft}$

$B_N \Rightarrow (7.0\ \text{ft}) \times \sin(32) \approx +3.7\ \text{ft}$

$C_E = (+22.0\ \text{ft}) + (-5.9\ \text{ft}) = +16.1\ \text{ft}$

$C_N = (0.0\ \text{ft}) + (+3.7\ \text{ft}) = +3.7\ \text{ft}$

$C = \sqrt{(16.1\ \text{ft})^2 + (3.7\ \text{ft})^2}$

$C \approx 16.5\ \text{ft}$

$\theta = \tan^{-1}\left(\dfrac{3.7\ \text{ft}}{16.1\ \text{ft}}\right) \approx 12.9$

compass bearing = 90.0 − 12.9 = 077.1T

C = 16.5 ft at 077.1T

Percent Difference

$\text{percent difference} = \dfrac{|\text{difference of the two values}|}{\text{average of the two values}} \times 100\%$

Graph 3
Exercise 3

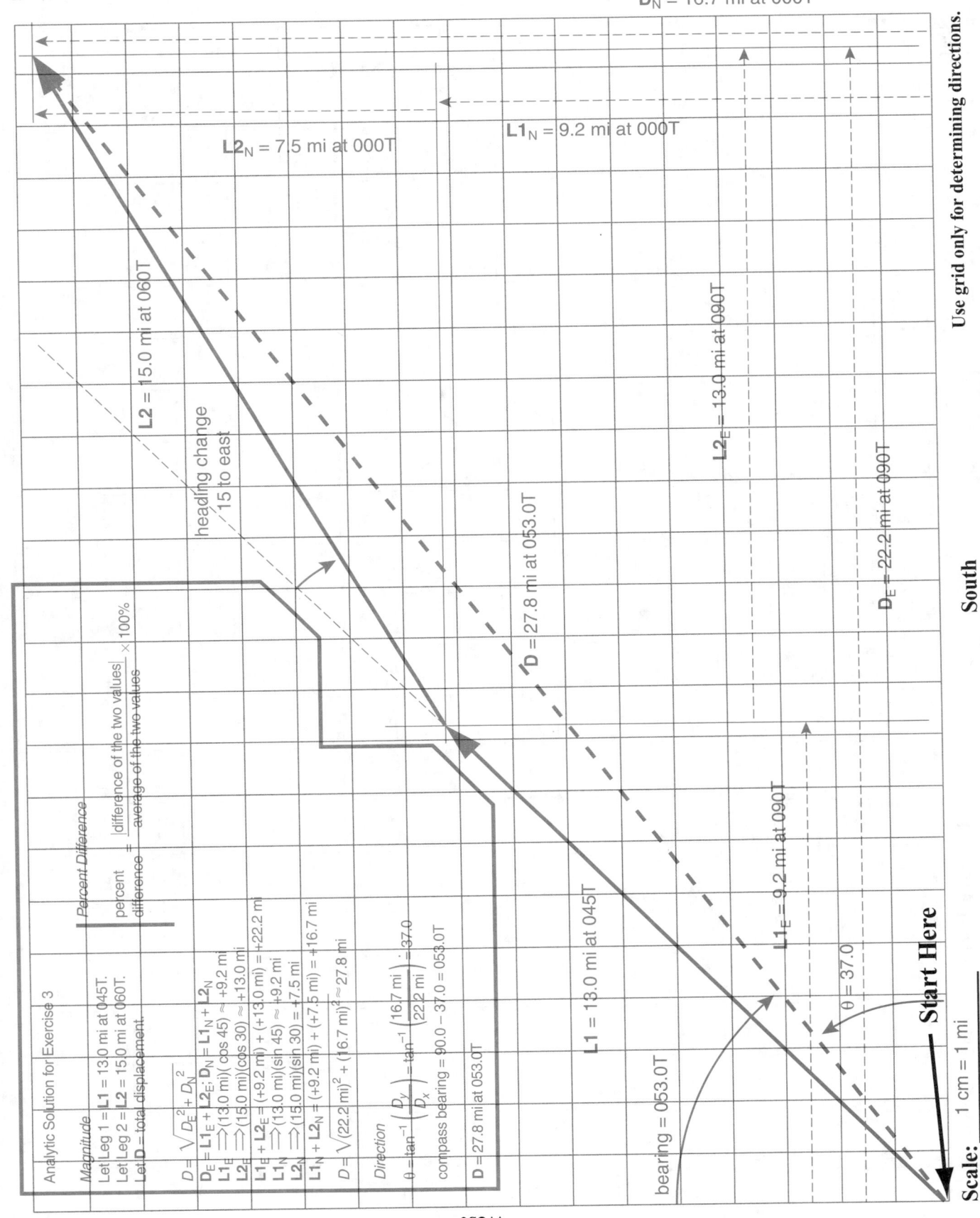

East

$D_N = 16.7$ mi at 000T

Use grid only for determining directions.

$L2_N = 7.5$ mi at 000T

$L1_N = 9.2$ mi at 000T

$L2 = 15.0$ mi at 060T

heading change
15 to east

$D = 27.8$ mi at 053.0T

North

$L2_E = 13.0$ mi at 090T

$D_E = 22.2$ mi at 090T

South

Analytic Solution for Exercise 3

Magnitude

Let Leg 1 = **L1** = 13.0 mi at 045T.
Let Leg 2 = **L2** = 15.0 mi at 060T.
Let **D** = total displacement.

$D = \sqrt{D_E^2 + D_N^2}$

$D_E = L1_E + L2_E; \; D_N = L1_N + L2_N$
$L1_E \Rightarrow (13.0 \text{ mi})(\cos 45) \approx +9.2 \text{ mi}$
$L2_E \Rightarrow (15.0 \text{ mi})(\cos 30) \approx +13.0 \text{ mi}$
$L1_E + L2_E = (+9.2 \text{ mi}) + (+13.0 \text{ mi}) = +22.2 \text{ mi}$
$L1_N \Rightarrow (13.0 \text{ mi})(\sin 45) \approx +9.2 \text{ mi}$
$L2_N \Rightarrow (15.0 \text{ mi})(\sin 30) = +7.5 \text{ mi}$
$L1_N + L2_N = (+9.2 \text{ mi}) + (+7.5 \text{ mi}) = +16.7 \text{ mi}$

$D = \sqrt{(22.2 \text{ mi})^2 + (16.7 \text{ mi})^2} \approx 27.8 \text{ mi}$

Direction

$\theta = \tan^{-1}\left(\dfrac{D_y}{D_x}\right) = \tan^{-1}\left(\dfrac{16.7 \text{ mi}}{22.2 \text{ mi}}\right) \cdot 37.0$

compass bearing $= 90.0 - 37.0 = 053.0$T

$D = 27.8$ mi at 053.0T

Percent Difference

$\text{percent difference} = \dfrac{|\text{difference of the two values}|}{\text{average of the two values}} \times 100\%$

$L1 = 13.0$ mi at 045T

$L1_E = 9.2$ mi at 090T

$\theta = 37.0$

bearing = 053.0T

Start Here

Scale: 1 cm = 1 mi

West

15

Graph 4
Exercise 4

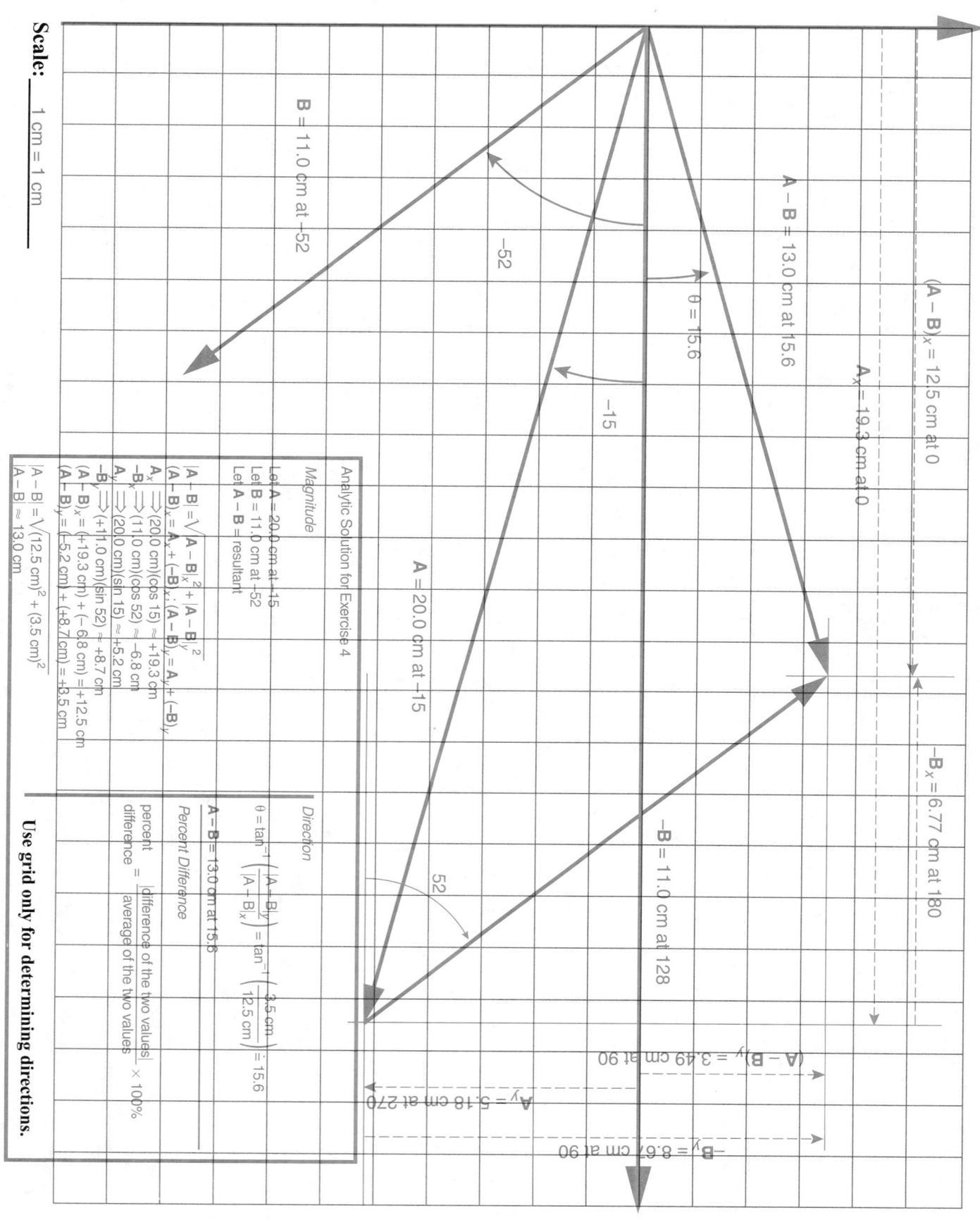

Scale: _____ 1 cm = 1 cm

$(A - B)_x$ = 12.5 cm at 0

A_x = 19.3 cm at 0

$-B_x$ = 6.77 cm at 180

$A - B$ = 13.0 cm at 15.6

$\theta = 15.6$

-52

-15

52

B = 11.0 cm at -52

A = 20.0 cm at -15

$-B$ = 11.0 cm at 128

$(A - B)_y$ = 3.49 cm at 90

A_y = 5.18 cm at 270

$-B_y$ = 8.67 cm at 90

x

y

Analytic Solution for Exercise 4

Let **A** = 20.0 cm at -15
Let **B** = 11.0 cm at -52
Let **A** − **B** = resultant

Magnitude

$|A - B| = \sqrt{|A - B|_x^2 + |A - B|_y^2}$

$(A - B)_x = A_x + (-B)_x; (A - B)_y = A_y + (-B)_y$

$A_x \Longrightarrow (20.0 \text{ cm})(\cos 15) \approx +19.3 \text{ cm}$
$-B_x \Longrightarrow (11.0 \text{ cm})(\cos 52) \approx -6.8 \text{ cm}$
$A_y \Longrightarrow (20.0 \text{ cm})(\sin 15) \approx +5.2 \text{ cm}$
$-B_y \Longrightarrow (+11.0 \text{ cm})(\sin 52) \approx +8.7 \text{ cm}$
$(A - B)_x = (+19.3 \text{ cm}) + (-6.8 \text{ cm}) = +12.5 \text{ cm}$
$(A - B)_y = (-5.2 \text{ cm}) + (+8.7 \text{ cm}) = +3.5 \text{ cm}$

$|A - B| = \sqrt{(12.5 \text{ cm})^2 + (3.5 \text{ cm})^2}$
$|A - B| \approx 13.0 \text{ cm}$

Direction

$\theta = \tan^{-1}\left(\dfrac{|A - B|_y}{|A - B|_x}\right) = \tan^{-1}\left(\dfrac{3.5 \text{ cm}}{12.5 \text{ cm}}\right) = 15.6$

$A - B = 13.0 \text{ cm at } 15.6$

Percent Difference

percent
difference = $\dfrac{|\text{difference of the two values}|}{\text{average of the two values}} \times 100\%$

Use grid only for determining directions.

Name _____

Date _____ Hour ____

PRELAB HOMEWORK

1. A scalar can be described completely by stating its _____magnitude_____.

2. A vector can be described completely by stating its _____magnitude and direction_____.

3. Explain how scalars are added together.
   Scalars are added by adding their magnitudes together.

4. The sum of a set of vectors is called a(n) _____resultant_____.

5. Explain how two vectors are added graphically.
   When adding two vectors graphically, the initial point of the second vector is placed at the terminal point of the first vector. The resultant proceeds from the initial point of the first vector to the terminal point of the second.

6. Explain how vectors are added together analytically.
   Vectors are added by first finding their vertical and horizontal components and then adding the related components algebraically. The net vertical and horizontal components are used to find the resultant magnitude and direction.

7. What is the geometric difference between the vectors $\mathbf{A}$ and $-\mathbf{A}$?
   Vector $\mathbf{A}$ points in the opposite direction from vector $-\mathbf{A}$.

8. Determine the reference angles for the following Cartesian and compass directions. (Hint: First sketch the angle using the associated direction system; then determine the reference angle.)

   a. 045T ___45°___   c. 190° ___10°___   e. 145° ___35°___   g. 320T ___50°___

   b. $-120°$ ___60°___   d. 025T ___65°___   f. 166T ___76°___   h. $-26°$ ___26°___

9. Determine the components of the following vector quantities. Show your work and include correct units and SDs in your answers.

   a. $\mathbf{A} = 45.0$ km at 060T $A_N = $ ___22.5 km___ at ___000T___ ; $A_E = $ ___39.0 km___ at ___090T___
   $A_N = (45.0 \text{ km})(\sin 30°) = 22.5 \text{ km}; A_E = (45.0 \text{ km})(\cos 30°) \approx 39.0 \text{ km}$

   b. $\mathbf{B} = 26.0$ N at $-140°$ $B_y = $ ___16.7 N___ at ___$-90°$___ ; $B_x = $ ___19.9 N___ at ___180°___
   $B_y = (26.0 \text{ N})(\sin 40°) \approx 16.7 \text{ N}; B_x = (26.0 \text{ N})(\cos 40°) \approx 19.9 \text{ N}$

   c. $\mathbf{C} = 18.6$ cm at 255T $C_N = $ ___4.8 cm___ at ___180T___ ; $C_E = $ ___18.0 cm___ at ___270T___
   $C_N = (18.6 \text{ cm})(\sin 15°) \approx 4.8 \text{ cm}; C_E = (18.6 \text{ cm})(\cos 15°) \approx 18.0 \text{ cm}$

10. ___32.1 cm___ Determine the *magnitude* of a resultant ($\mathbf{R}$) of the sum of vector $\mathbf{K}$ that is 13.0 cm long at an angle of 63° and vector $\mathbf{M}$ that is 20.0 cm long at an angle of 90°.

   $K_x = (13.0 \text{ cm})(\cos 63°) \approx 5.9 \text{ cm}$ $K_y = (13.0 \text{ cm})(\sin 63°) \approx 11.6 \text{ cm}$
   $M_x = (20.0 \text{ cm})(\cos 90°) = 0.0 \text{ cm}$ $M_y = (20.0 \text{ cm})(\sin 90°) = 20.0 \text{ cm}$
   $R_x = K_x + M_x = 5.9 \text{ cm} + 0.0 \text{ cm} = 5.9 \text{ cm}$
   $R_y = K_y + M_y = 11.6 \text{ cm} + 20.0 \text{ cm} = 31.6 \text{ cm}$
   $R = \sqrt{R_x^2 + R_y^2} = \sqrt{(5.9 \text{ cm})^2 + (31.6 \text{ cm})^2} \approx 32.1 \text{ cm}$

Name _____

Date _____ Hour ____

BALANCED AND UNBALANCED FORCES

Purpose

This laboratory exercise is designed to give you practice using a force board and determining both resultant and equilibrant forces. The purpose is to

- reinforce what you learned about vector addition, resultants, and equilibrants.
- give you experience using a simple force board.

Prelab Discussion

You will need to be thoroughly familiar with forces and resolving vectors as presented in your textbook in order to obtain maximum benefit from this activity. Using correct notation is very important when working with vectors. (Review the guidelines given in Lab 1-2.)

The sum of two or more vectors is called a **resultant,** and an **equilibrant** is a vector that can exactly balance the resultant. If three forces act in opposition to one another so that they are balanced, any one of the three forces can be considered the equilibrant of the other two. The sum of the other two forces (their resultant), on the other hand, would have the same magnitude as the equilibrant but would act in a direction 180° from the equilibrant.

A **force board** or **force table** is a device that can be used to demonstrate the addition of vectors. It consists of a rigid, circular surface, usually graduated in degrees around its perimeter. It includes a small ring placed over a peg in the center of the board. Forces may be added to the ring in such a way that they center the ring over the peg. At that point, all forces are balanced. If you are using the recommended force board (see Figure 1), you will start with two known forces that are produced by certain predetermined masses. These forces will act against each other at an angle that can be measured on the face of the force board. Finding the force that exactly balances these forces, using the weight of a third mass, gives you an experimental method for determining the equilibrant of the two forces. You will also calculate the equilibrant of the two forces, using trigonometry, and compare the results of the two methods.

Procedure

Setup

1. Support the force board with books so that the masses can hang freely. If your force board has legs, this step may not be necessary.

2. Fasten three strings to the ring by tying a small loop in each string as shown in Figure 2.

3. Place the ring with its three strings over the center peg of the force board.

4. Thread the loose ends of the strings over the pulleys. Tie a loop at the end of each string.

Trial 1

5. Add masses to the three strings.

   a. If you are using metric masses, add 200. g to the free ends of both string 1 and string 2 (in Figure 2). Add 350. g to string 3.

   b. If you are not using metric masses, add 10 washers to both string 1 and string 2, using paper clips as hooks. Add 15 washers to string 3. In order

Required Equipment

force board and accessories
 (including 3 pulley clamps)
metric mass set

Optional Equipment

balance
metal washers
paper clips

Prelab Discussion

- Review the prerequisites for Lab 2-1 in the back of this manual.

- Point out the need to use the correct notation. The homework and lab procedures require close attention to the notation in order to understand what is being discussed.

Figure 1

Equipment and Setup

- There are several types of force boards available from science suppliers. These instructions assume you are using one similar to the BJU Press model, but any type will work. Make any necessary adjustments to the instructions. Use three pulley clamps (BJUP #121160) as discussed in the lab. They are not expensive, and they will greatly enhance the accuracy of this and other mechanics lab exercises.

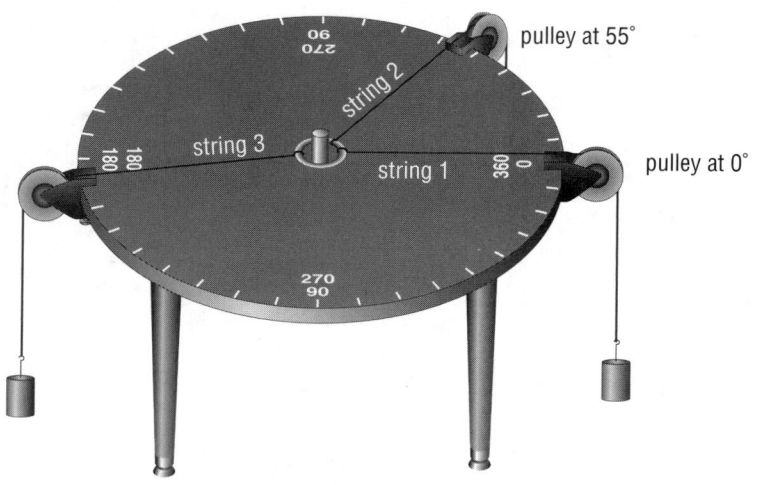

pulley at 55°

string 2

string 3

string 1

pulley at 0°

Figure 2

Procedure

• Prior to the lab, discuss the Prelab exercise to ensure that students understand how to compute the forces exerted by the masses (their weights) and how to determine the equilibrant of two forces.

• The lab results will be more consistent (and easier to grade) if your students orient their force boards so that the zero angle mark points to their right and angles are measured counterclockwise as with the Cartesian coordinate system.

to find the force exerted on each string, determine the mass of each group of washers along with the paper clip used to hang them.

6. Arrange the pulleys so that string 1 is positioned directly over the 0° mark (oriented to your right as you face the force board) and string 2 is positioned over the 55.0° mark (*counterclockwise* from the 0° mark). Move the third pulley to the left or right until the ring in the center is exactly centered over the peg. You may need to add more mass to string 3 in the form of paper clips or washers. Do not add additional masses to strings 1 and 2 and do not change their angular position.

7. Estimate the angular position of the string 3 to the nearest tenth degree and record the measurement under Direction of F_3 in Table 1. All angles should be measured to 0.1° precision.

8. Record the magnitude of the force (in newtons) on each of the three strings in Table 1 (F_1 for string 1, F_2 for string 2, etc.). If applicable, you will need to determine the mass of the washers and paper clips that you added to string 3 and then add that mass to the mass suspended from the string in order to determine the force exerted on string 3.

Trial 2

9. Replace the mass on string 1 with a mass of 150. g. Keep the pulley at 0°. Add 50. g to the 200. g mass on string 2 and move its pulley to 65.0° (counterclockwise from 0°). Place approximately 340. g on string 3.

10. Move the pulley containing string 3 to the left or right and add additional mass to the string as necessary until the ring is centered over the peg.

11. Record the magnitude of the force for each string and the direction of the third string in Table 1.

Data

Table 1
Data for Determining Equilibrants

Trial	F_1	Direction of F_1	F_2	Direction of F_2	F_3	Direction of F_3
1	1.96 N	0.0 °	1.96 N	55.0 °	~3.48 N	~207.6 °
2	1.47 N	0.0 °	2.45 N	65.0 °	~3.35 N	~221.5 °

F_1 and F_2 data in Table 1 are determined from the lab. Student F_3 data will vary.

• The masses and angles stipulated for $\mathbf{F}_1$ and $\mathbf{F}_2$ require that some small additional weight be added to the third mass to establish equilibrium, so be sure to have spare washers and paper clips available. The students need to remember to include the mass of these additional items when computing $\mathbf{F}_3$.

• Assume that the metric masses are precise to the nearest gram.

Postlab Exercises

1. Using trigonometric formulas, calculate the equilibrant of $\mathbf{F}_1$ and $\mathbf{F}_2$ for Trials 1 and 2. Use the information in Table 1 to draw the vectors and find the resultant (the sum of the forces). From the resultant you should be able to describe the equilibrant. Show your work in the space allotted for solutions. Record the magnitudes in Table 2 to 3 SDs; record directions to the nearest tenth degree.

2. Determine the percent differences between your measured and calculated values for the equilibrants. Record the percentages in Table 2. Recall that

values for the equilibrants. Record the percentages in Table 2. Recall that

Table 2
Calculated Equilibrants and Percent Errors

Trial	F_3	Force Percent Difference	Direction of F_3	Direction Percent Difference
1	3.48 N	≤ 5 %	207.6 °	≤ 5 %
2	3.35 N	≤ 5 %	221.5 °	≤ 5 %

F_3 answers are based on conditions specified in the lab.

$$\text{percent difference} = \frac{|\text{difference of the two values}|}{} \times 100\%.$$

Solutions

Show all formulas and significant steps. Use correct SDs and units.

Trial 1 Calculations

$R^2 = (F_1 + F_2)_x^2 + (F_1 + F_2)_y^2$

$R = \sqrt{(F_1 + F_2)_x^2 + (F_1 + F_2)_y^2}$

$R = \sqrt{(3.08 \text{ N})^2 + (1.61 \text{ N})^2}$

$R \approx 3.48 \text{ N}$

$\tan \theta_R = \dfrac{(F_1 + F_2)_y}{(F_1 + F_2)_x}$

$\tan^{-1}\left[\dfrac{(F_1 + F_2)_y}{(F_1 + F_2)_x}\right] = \theta_R$

$\tan^{-1}\left(\dfrac{1.61 \text{ N}}{3.08 \text{ N}}\right) = \theta_R$

$\theta_R \doteq 27.6°$

$F_3 = R = 3.48 \text{ N}$

$\theta_3 = \theta_R + 180° = 27.6° + 180.0°$

$\theta_3 = 207.6°$

Postlab Exercises

- Instruct the students to complete their analytic solutions, including sketches of the force vectors, in the Solutions section of the Postlab Exercises.

- Percent error should be less than 5%, especially if the pulley clamps were used.

Home School Notes

- Force Boards are simple to make. You need an 18 in. circular disk. Cut it out of smooth 1/4 in. or thicker plywood. A nail, screw, or short piece of dowel should be inserted in the center in such a way that it holds firmly and sticks up at least 1/2 in. above the board.

- In lieu of pulley clamps, you may bend 8 in. sections of glass tubing at 90° angles. Thread the strings through the tubing before tying the loops for the masses. Plastic straws can be substituted for the glass tubes, but you may lose some accuracy with straws.

- A circular ring about 1 in. in diameter (such as those used for curtain hangers) completes the apparatus.

- To make the force board simpler to use, add 360 marks around the outer edge to indicate the angle at which the strings should be placed. Label every fifth mark. Be as accurate as possible with these marks. If you have access to a copy machine, you can copy and enlarge a protractor until your copy is large enough to fit on your circular disk.

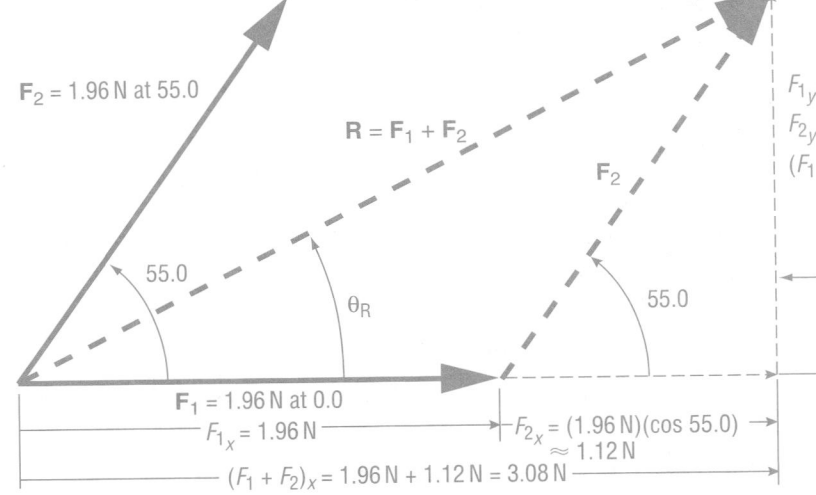

$F_2 = 1.96 \text{ N at } 55.0$

$R = F_1 + F_2$

F_2

$F_{1y} = (1.96 \text{ N})(\sin 0.0) = 0 \text{ N}$
$F_{2y} = (1.96 \text{ N})(\sin 55.0) \approx 1.61 \text{ N}$
$(F_1 + F_2)_y = 0 \text{ N} + 1.61 \text{ N}$
$\qquad = 1.61 \text{ N}$

θ_R

55.0

55.0

$F_1 = 1.96 \text{ N at } 0.0$

$F_{1x} = 1.96 \text{ N}$

$F_{2x} = (1.96 \text{ N})(\cos 55.0)$
$\qquad \approx 1.12 \text{ N}$

$(F_1 + F_2)_x = 1.96 \text{ N} + 1.12 \text{ N} = 3.08 \text{ N}$

Trial 2 Calculations

$$R^2 = (F_1 + F_2)_x^2 + (F_1 + F_2)_y^2$$

$$R = \sqrt{(F_1 + F_2)_x^2 + (F_1 + F_2)_y^2}$$

$$R = (2.51 \text{ N})^2 + (2.22 \text{ N})^2$$

$$R \approx 3.35 \text{ N}$$

$$\tan \theta_R = \frac{(F_1 + F_2)_y}{(F_1 + F_2)_x}$$

$$\tan^{-1}\left[\frac{(F_1 + F_2)_y}{(F_1 + F_2)_x}\right] = \theta_R$$

$$\tan^{-1}\left(\frac{2.22 \text{ N}}{2.51 \text{ N}}\right) = \theta_R$$

$$\theta_R \doteq 41.5°$$

$$F_3 = R = 3.35 \text{ N}$$

$$\theta_3 = \theta_R + 180° = 41.5° + 180.0°$$

$$\theta_3 = 221.5°$$

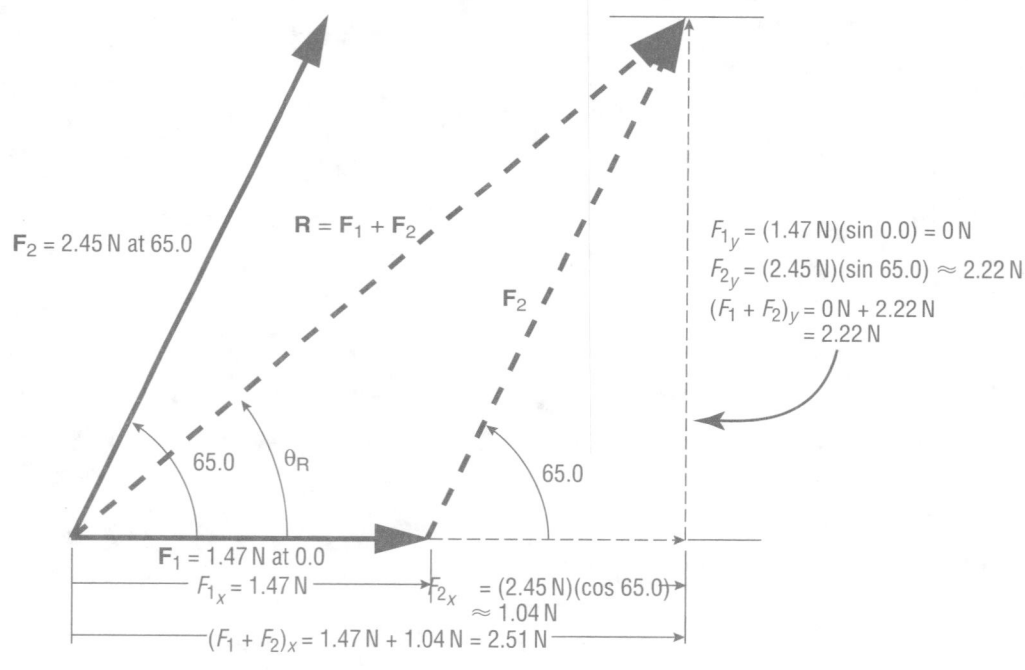

$F_2 = 2.45$ N at 65.0

$\mathbf{R} = \mathbf{F_1} + \mathbf{F_2}$

$\mathbf{F_2}$

65.0 θ_R

65.0

$\mathbf{F_1} = 1.47$ N at 0.0

$F_{1x} = 1.47$ N

$F_{2x} = (2.45 \text{ N})(\cos 65.0)$
≈ 1.04 N

$(F_1 + F_2)_x = 1.47 \text{ N} + 1.04 \text{ N} = 2.51 \text{ N}$

$F_{1y} = (1.47 \text{ N})(\sin 0.0) = 0 \text{ N}$
$F_{2y} = (2.45 \text{ N})(\sin 65.0) \approx 2.22 \text{ N}$
$(F_1 + F_2)_y = 0 \text{ N} + 2.22 \text{ N}$
$= 2.22 \text{ N}$

Name _____

Date _____ Hour ____

PRELAB HOMEWORK

1. The sum of two forces is called the _____resultant_____.

2. The force that will balance the above force is called the _____equilibrant_____.

3. The term _____equilibrium_____ describes the condition when all forces on an object are balanced.

4. A device used in the laboratory to demonstrate vector addition is called a ___force board___.

5. The angle between the resultant of two forces and their equilibrant is ___180°___.

6. ___1.96 N___ What is the magnitude (in newtons) of the downward force exerted by a 200.0 g mass to 3 SDs?

$$F = mg = \frac{200.0 \text{ g}}{} \cdot \frac{1 \text{ kg}}{1000 \text{ g}} \cdot \frac{9.81 \text{ N}}{\text{kg}} = 1.96 \text{ N}$$

7. ___67.6 N___ A force of 30.0 N (F_1) acts along the horizontal. Another force of 45.0 N (F_2) acts 52.5° above the horizontal. Calculate the magnitude of the *resultant* (R). Report the magnitude in newtons to 3 SDs. Show your work in the Solutions section at the bottom of the page and write your answer in the blank.

8. ___31.9°___ Calculate the angle of the *resultant* (θ_R) in Question 7.

9. ___67.6 N___ Determine the magnitude of the *equilibrant* (F_3) for the forces in Question 7. Report in newtons to 3 SDs.

10. ___211.9°___ Determine the angle of the *equilibrant* (θ_3).

Solutions
Show all formulas and significant steps. Use correct SDs and units.

7. $R^2 = (F_1 + F_2)_x^2 + (F_1 + F_2)_y^2$

$R = \sqrt{(F_1 + F_2)_x^2 + (F_1 + F_2)_y^2}$

$R = \sqrt{(57.4 \text{ N})^2 + (35.7 \text{ N})^2}$

$R \approx 67.6 \text{ N}$

8. $\tan \theta_R = \dfrac{(F_1 + F_2)_y}{(F_1 + F_2)_x}$

$\tan^{-1}\left[\dfrac{(F_1 + F_2)_y}{(F_1 + F_2)_x}\right] = \theta_R$

$\tan^{-1}\left(\dfrac{35.7 \text{ N}}{57.4 \text{ N}}\right) = \theta_R$

$\theta_R \doteq 31.9°$

10. $\theta_3 = \theta_R + 180° = 31.9° + 180.0°$

$\theta_3 = 211.9°$

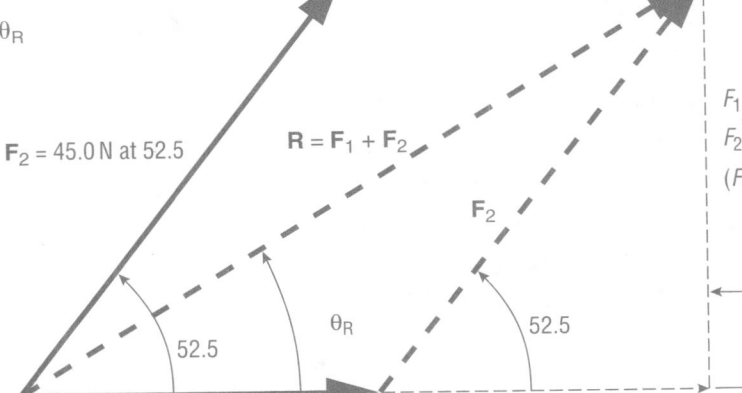

$F_{1y} = (30.0 \text{ N})(\sin 0.0) = 0 \text{ N}$
$F_{2y} = (45.0 \text{ N})(\sin 52.5) \approx 35.7 \text{ N}$
$(F_1 + F_2)_y = 0 \text{ N} + 35.7 \text{ N}$
$= 35.7 \text{ N}$

$F_2 = 45.0$ N at 52.5

$R = F_1 + F_2$

θ_R

52.5

$F_1 = 30.0$ N at 0.0

$F_{1x} = 30.0$ N

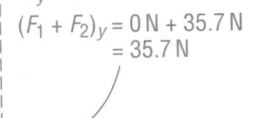
$F_{2x} = (45.0 \text{ N})(\cos 52.5)$
$\approx 27.4 \text{ N}$

$(F_1 + F_2)_x = 30.0 \text{ N} + 27.4 \text{ N} = 57.4 \text{ N}$

Name _____

Date _____ Hour _____

THE RECORDING TIMER

Purpose

Science often requires the use of specialized equipment in order to obtain specific data. The purpose of this exercise is to

- introduce the various types of recording timers.
- describe the function of a recording timer.
- calibrate a recording timer for use in future activities.
- provide practice using a recording timer.

Prelab Discussion

In this laboratory activity you will become familiar with the recording timer (see Figures 1 and 2). The timer is a simple electrical device that has either a motor and wheel arrangement or a mechanism similar to a doorbell buzzer. Its function is to mark a paper tape that is drawn through it. Carbon paper is inserted between the timing tape and the marking device, which creates a dot on the tape each time the wheel rotates or the arm moves up and down. A recording timer makes dots at a constant rate on the tape moving through it. The time between dots is assumed to be constant, but the distance between dots varies with the speed that the tape moves through the timer. The timer that you are using, whether DC (Figure 1) or AC (Figure 2), needs to be experimentally tested in order to determine how many dots are imprinted on the tape in one second. This is accomplished by dropping a heavy object that has a specific length of timing tape attached to it. If the time it takes for the length of tape to pass through the timer is known, you can easily compute the rate at which dots are imprinted on the tape.

You are aware that the longer an object falls, the faster it moves. This change of speed over time is called **acceleration (a).** The acceleration of a falling object near the surface of the earth is approximately 9.81 m/s^2. The time that an object *starting at rest* takes to fall through a known distance can be calculated using the formula

$$t = \sqrt{\frac{2d}{a}}, \tag{1}$$

where t is the time of fall, d is the distance or length traveled, and a is the acceleration.

Since you know the acceleration due to gravity and the length of the tape, you can calculate the time the tape requires to move through the timer. By counting the number of dots recorded on the tape during this period of time, you have the data needed to calculate the number of dots made in one second. The timer can then be used to determine the displacement, velocity, and acceleration of a moving dynamics cart (used in future exercises) in a wide range of experimental conditions.

Procedure

1. Assemble the recording timer as instructed. The specific details vary among models. The timing tape must be able to move freely as the flywheel spins or the marking arm vibrates. If your timer is a DC model, it should be connected to just *one* fresh battery. Your teacher will demonstrate the correct arrangement for you.

2. Tape a hooked 200 g mass to one end of a strip of timing tape that has been precut to 2.1 m.

Required Equipment
graph paper
masking tape
mass, 200 g
metric ruler
recording timer and accessories

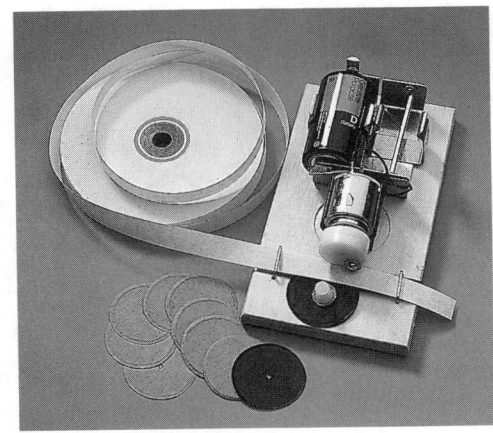

Figure 1

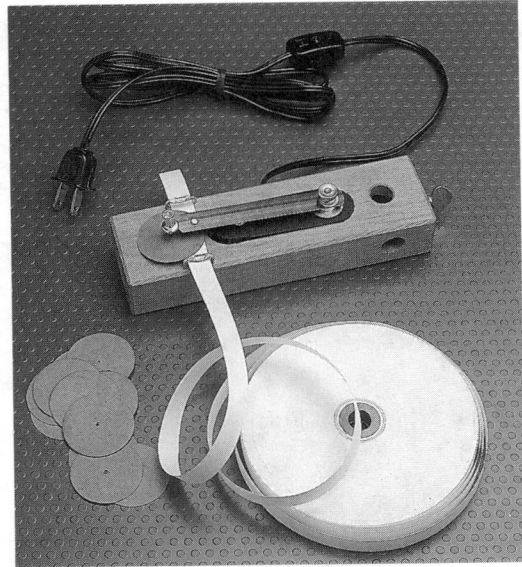

Figure 2

Prelab Discussion

- Review the prerequisites for Lab 2-2 in the back of this manual and be sure you have discussed the basic definitions for time intervals, distance, speed, and acceleration.

Students need not have learned Newton's Laws of motion or the three equations of motion at this point.

- Demonstrate the setup and use of a recording timer on the day prior to the lab, if possible. First, discuss the operation of the recording timer, including how to replace the carbon disks, how to thread the timing tape, and how to turn it on and off. If the recording timer will be clamped to a door or ladder, demonstrate that process also.

- Also discuss step-by-step the calibration of the timer and the procedure for obtaining the data. Having a marked tape to show the class is beneficial.

Equipment and Setup

- The recording timer is an essential piece of equipment that cannot be easily substituted. The device is discussed and pictured in the body of the lab. AC and DC versions are available, and both have positive and negative features.

- DC timers are generally simpler to use than AC because they do not need an extension cord. This may be an important consideration if you have a large class using many timers simultaneously. To mark the tape, DC timers use a wheel-like device, which is simple and reliable. On the other hand, their dependence on a battery produces variability in frequency output when battery voltage changes. In fact, for future labs involving recording timers, you should plan to have students run a quick check on DC timer calibration at the beginning of the lab, using this lab procedure.

- The key advantage of AC timers is that their frequency is the same as power grid frequency (60 Hz), which is very stable, so the output of the timer is consistently reproducible. However, besides needing electrical outlets, some AC timer models have a flimsy marking arm that tends to flex excessively, causing multiple marks. They also tend to destroy the carbon disks quickly. You can contact other teachers in your school's association and obtain their opinion of which model works best.

3. Cut the other end of the tape with a scissors so that the end is straight and squared off.

4. Measure exactly 2.00 m (200. cm) from the cut end of the tape toward the mass and draw a line across the tape at that point. Your mark will be about 0.1 m from the mass.

5. Thread the cut end of the tape into the timer until the line on the timing tape is directly under the arm or wheel that makes the dots on the tape. You may clamp the timer to a high object, such as the top of a door, or you may hold it, but the hanging mass must be more than 2.1 m from the floor.

6. Station an observer on a ladder or chair in order to verify that the tape is starting on the mark.

7. Hold the timer high enough above the floor that the mass can pull the tape completely out of the timer. Be sure that the marking arm or rotating wheel is directly over your mark. Start the motor on the timer. Drop the mass so that it will pull the tape cleanly through the timer. If the tape jams or obviously drags, the trial will have to be repeated. Turn off the timer.

8. Perform the experiment five times, using a clean piece of tape for each trial. (Label each tape with the trial number at the end opposite the mass.)

9. Record the number that is on your timer in the box to the right of Table 1. Each of the timers in your class may run at a slightly different rate, so this number will permit your teacher to record the calibration for the timer you used.

10. Use your tape segments to complete the Postlab Exercises below. If possible, complete the Postlab Exercises during the lab period.

Data

Table 1
Timer Calibration

Trial	Number of Dots per 2 m segment	Number of Dots per second
1		
2		
3		
4		
5		
Average		

Data in Table 1 will vary with each timer.

Timer Number _____

_____ $\dfrac{\text{dots}}{\text{s}}$

Postlab Exercises

1. For each tape, count the number of dots that the timer marked on the 2 m segment.

2. Record your data in Table 1.

3. Determine the number of dots per second for each trial (see Prelab Homework Question 7).

4. Calculate the average of each of the columns in Table 1 and record the results in the last row. Round to the nearest tenth. Record the average number of dots per second, rounded to the nearest tenth, in the Timer Number box also.

5. Choose the tape that has values closest to the two averages in Table 1 to use for Lab 2-4. Clearly label the tape to be retained with the names of the individuals in your lab team. You will not need the other tapes any longer, *but your teacher may ask you to turn them in with this report for his review.*

- Check all timers to verify that they work properly. Be sure to install fresh batteries in DC timers. The recording timer supplied by BJUP has a two-battery holder, but it is recommended that the shorting rod provided with the timer be installed in one of the holders in order to reduce the marking frequency to 30 to 50 dots per second.

- If using AC timers, ensure that there is an electrical supply near each station or that a sufficient number of extension cords are available.

- Ensure that sufficient rolls of timing tape and replacement carbon paper disks are available to the class.

- If you have never performed the frequency calibration on the timers, print up calibration labels similar to the form provided in the Data section and affix them to the timers.

Procedure

- This activity tends to be noisy, especially if you are using AC timers, so encourage the students to work with a minimum of talking.

- The most technically challenging part of the lab is ensuring that the tape is at the starting mark when it is released. This may require several attempts before a successful trial is obtained.

Postlab Exercises

- Once the data is collected, review the procedure for performing calculations with the data in order to obtain timer frequency.

- Collect and retain one data tape from each lab team for Lab 2-4. Check the results for timer calibration and write the calibration (in dots/s) on each timer label.

Name _____

Date _____ Hour _____

PRELAB HOMEWORK

1. Look at the photographs in Figures 1 and 2. What are some obvious differences between the AC and DC recording timers?

   The most obvious difference is that the DC timer has a battery and that the AC timer uses an electric cord. Students may also note that the DC timer has a marking wheel, while the AC timer uses a vibrating arm.

2. What would happen to the data on the tape if the timer were not held high enough during a trial and the hooked mass hit the floor before the tape pulled out of the timer?

   The tape would slow or stop before it had pulled free from the timer. The number of dots imprinted could not be related to a specific time interval determined by an object falling a certain distance.

3. What is one basic assumption that is made about the recorder timer as it imprints dots on the tape?

   It is assumed that the timer produces dots at a constant rate.

4. ___9.81 m/s²___ What is the accepted magnitude (to 3 SDs) for the acceleration due to gravity in units of meters per second squared?

5. Write the formula for determining the time it takes an object to accelerate through a certain distance, starting from rest.

   $$t = \sqrt{\frac{2d}{a}}$$

6. ___0.639 s___ How long, in seconds, would it take for an object to fall 2.00 m from a rest position?

   Given: $d = 2.00$ m; $a = 9.81 \frac{m}{s^2}$; $t = ?$

   Formula: $t = \sqrt{\frac{2d}{a}}$

   Solution: $t = \sqrt{\frac{2(2.00 \text{ m})}{9.81 \frac{m}{s^2}}} \approx 0.639$ s (3 SDs allowed)

7. ___53.2 dots/s___ If the object in Question 6 is allowed to pull a 2.00 m length of timing tape through a recording timer and you count 34 dots on the tape in the 2.00 m interval, how many dots would be recorded on the tape in one second?

   34 dots ÷ 0.639 s ≈ 53.2 dots/s (3 SDs allowed because counted numbers do not determine SDs)

Name _____

Date _____ Hour ____

TRANSMITTED FORCES

Purpose

This laboratory exercise is designed to help you visualize Newton's second law and gain experience solving problems involving transmitted forces. The purpose is to

- give you additional experience using a recording timer.
- practice observing and recording experimental data.
- use formulas related to velocity and acceleration.
- analyze the effects of transmitted forces.
- observe Newton's second law of motion in action.

Prelab Discussion

Study the section in your textbook pertaining to **transmitted forces**—forces that are transferred from one point to another that may or may not lie in line with the original force. The example in the textbook discusses two objects connected by an **ideal string.** One of the objects rests on a frictionless table, and the other object is supported by the string. The string moves over a pulley at the edge of the table, thus changing the direction of the forces imposed on and by the two objects. In that example you must determine the acceleration of the system of objects in which the force that produces acceleration (gravitational attraction of the hanging block) is applied to the mass of the entire system. No other forces affect the system.

The circumstances will be somewhat different in this lab because you will use an inclined plane instead of a horizontal table. The object supported by the inclined plane will be a dynamics cart, which will approximate frictionless motion on ball-bearing wheels. While the normal force exerted by a horizontal surface supports all of the weight of the object resting on it, the inclined plane supports only part of the weight of the cart. A component of the cart's weight will act down the plane. When determining the sum of the forces on the cart, you must take into account the downhill component of the cart's weight. This force is calculated by $F_{wc} \sin \theta$, where θ is the angle that the inclined plane makes with the horizontal, and F_{wc} is the weight of the cart.

Required Equipment
C-clamps, 2
dynamics cart
inclined plane or board
masking tape
masses, 1 kg, 3
meter stick
protractor
pulley clamp
recording timer and accessories
right-angle clamp
string
support rod
support stand, heavy-duty

Prelab Discussion

- Review the prerequisites for Lab 2-3 in the back of this manual. Ensure that your students have studied and discussed free-body diagrams in class before performing this lab.

- Discuss the theoretical aspects of the lab, referring to the box in the Prelab Discussion that explains the derivation of the theoretical acceleration formula. You will need to refer to the textbook to fill in the steps that identify the *x*- and *y*-components in each free-body diagram (see Figure 1). The box shows only the applicable steps.

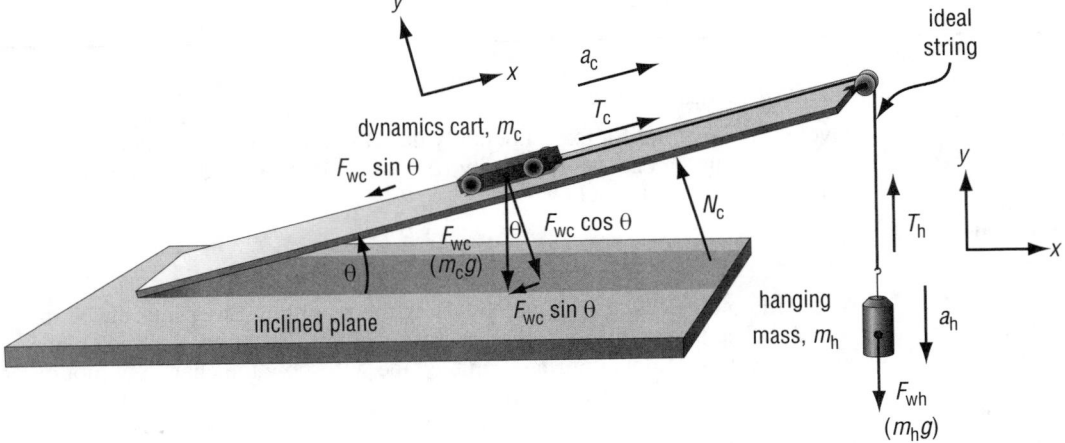

Figure 1

Mathematical Analysis

Determining the acceleration mathematically is similar to the example problem in your text. Since $\Sigma \mathbf{F} = m\mathbf{a}$ applies to each object in a system, you need to

- Remind students that the component of the cart's weight perpendicular to the inclined plane and the normal reaction force cancel each other out, so they do not appear in the final equation for the forces acting on the cart.

Equipment and Setup

- The recommended equipment consists of a commercial kinetics inclined plane with built-in pulley, a 1 × 6 plank about 1.5 m long with a pulley clamp at the upper end, or a home-built ramp using an integral

consider all of the forces acting on each object separately. Recall that the first step in any free-body problem is to choose reference directions for each object so that you can assign the correct signs to the scalar values of the vectors stated in the problem. For the cart, the frame of reference will be oriented so that the *y*-axis is perpendicular to the inclined plane and the positive *x*-axis is *up* the plane. The frame of reference for the hanging mass will be the usual orientation with the *y*-axis vertical and the positive *x*-axis horizontal, pointing away from the inclined plane (see Figure 1). The next step is to make an assumption about the direction of the unknown acceleration (**a**). If your assumption is wrong, then the magnitude of the calculated result will be a negative number. This should alert you to a problem because *magnitudes* are always positive. We will assume that the hanging mass accelerates in the downward (negative *y*-direction), which means the cart will accelerate up the inclined plane in the positive *x*-direction. Refer to the discussion in the textbook for a complete explanation of the solution for the *theoretical acceleration* of the system shown in the box below.

Sum of the forces on the *cart* ($\Sigma \mathbf{F}_c$)

Let the weight of the cart be $\mathbf{F}_{wc} = m_c\mathbf{g}$.

$\Sigma \mathbf{F}_c = \mathbf{F}_{wc} + \mathbf{N} + \mathbf{T}_c = m_c\mathbf{a}_c$

$\mathbf{F}_{wc} = \mathbf{F}_{wc\,norm} + \mathbf{F}_{wc\,incline}$

$F_{wc\,norm} = -F_{wc}\cos\theta;\ F_{wc\,incline} = -F_{wc}\sin\theta$

   (signs reflect directions of vectors)

Only the components in the *x*-direction are important.

$\Sigma F_{cx} = T_c - F_{wc}\sin\theta = m_c a_c$

$T_c - m_c g\sin\theta = m_c a_c$

Simplify.

$T = m_c a + m_c g\sin\theta$

Substitute T into the hanging mass equation.

Sum of the forces on the *hanging mass* ($\Sigma \mathbf{F}_h$)

Let the weight of the hanging mass be $\mathbf{F}_{wh} = m_h\mathbf{g}$.

$\Sigma \mathbf{F}_h = \mathbf{F}_{wh} + \mathbf{T}_h = m_h\mathbf{a}_h$

$\Sigma F_h = T_h - F_{wh} = -m_h a_h$

   (signs reflect directions of vectors)

The forces act only in the *y*-direction.

$T_h = F_{wh} - m_h a_h$

$T_h = m_h g - m_h a_h$

$$T_c = T_h = T;\ a_c = a_h = a$$

Simplify.

$T = m_h g - m_h a$

$\Rightarrow$

$m_c a + m_c g\sin\theta = m_h g - m_h a$

$m_c a + m_h a = m_h g - m_c g\sin\theta$

$a(m_c + m_h) = (m_h - m_c\sin\theta)g$

$$a = \left(\frac{m_h - m_c\sin\theta}{m_h + m_c}\right)g \tag{1}$$

---

thread spool for a pulley. See the diagram at the end of this lab for construction details.

- Four-wheel dynamics carts are recommended for this experiment, but any three- or four-wheel dynamics cart provided by science equipment suppliers will work.

- The inclined plane may be supported by a short metal rod clamped to either a heavy-duty lab support stand (the typical chemistry support stands are generally too lightweight for this lab) or a support rod set into a socket in the tabletop. A stack of books may be substituted for the stand.

- Clamp the inclined plane to the support rod in order to keep it stable

Experimental Analysis

Overall, the method for experimentally determining cart acceleration (a) requires finding the change in velocity (Δv) of the cart in a measured time interval (Δt), using the formula

$$a = \frac{\Delta v}{\Delta t}. \tag{2}$$

You will obtain acceleration data by using the recording timer introduced in Lab 2-2. The tape will be attached to the dynamics cart on the inclined plane, and the pattern of dots imprinted on the tape will show the change in motion of the cart as it accelerates up the incline. Figure 2 shows the arrangement of the equipment. Setting up and performing the experiment will be discussed in the procedure, but it is helpful to understand how the data will be analyzed so that the reasons for the procedures will be clear.

After the tape has been imprinted, choose the first dot that can be clearly defined at the beginning of the tape to be the starting point (P_0). Assume that the velocity at this point (v_1) is 0 m/s. Finding the final velocity (v_2) is more difficult because

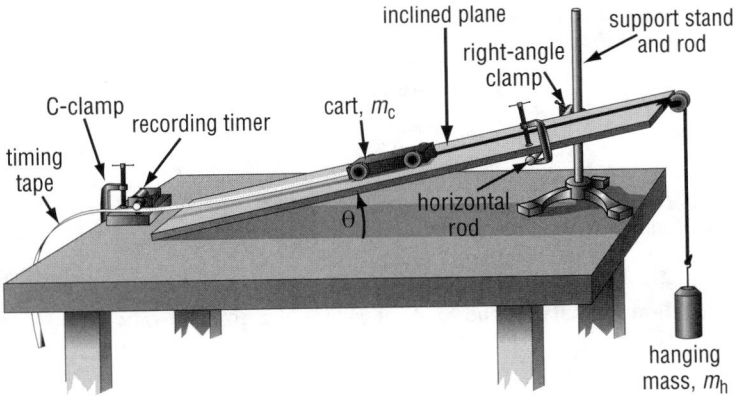

Figure 2

the velocity changes constantly as the cart moves up the plane. There are three methods for determining instantaneous velocity at a point in time: using advanced math (calculus), finding the tangent to the curve on a displacement-time graph, and finding the average velocity between two close points. Most high-school students lack the math background to use calculus, and graphing is tedious and somewhat inaccurate, so we will use the third method.

during the trials. This precaution will usually prevent changes in the angle of the inclined plane also.

- Caution your students about using too much weight in the hanging mass. A cart with a large mass attached to it may damage the pulley mechanism if it is allowed to hit the pulley.

- Timer accessories include timing tape, carbon disks, batteries, a shorting rod, and an extension cord, as applicable.

- Determine an appropriate length for the timing tapes by setting the cart at the top of the inclined plane and measuring back to the recording timer. The end of the tapes should be cut just short of the timer.

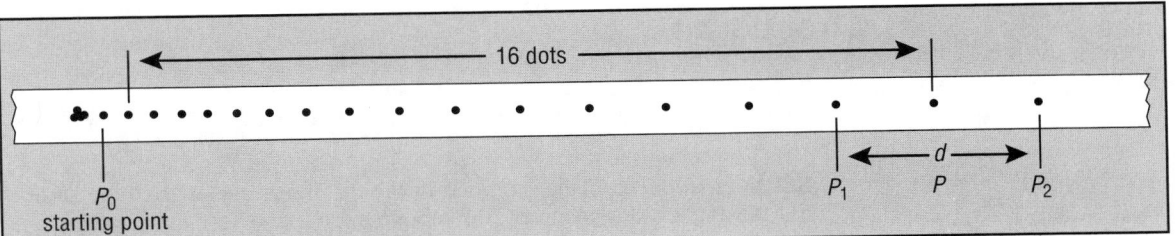

Figure 3

Figure 3 is an example of a typical timing tape for this kind of experiment. Refer to it for this explanation. We can assume that the *average velocity* during a very short time interval defined by points P_1 and P_2 is a good approximation of the instantaneous velocity at point P, which was marked at the midpoint of the *time* interval. You will choose a dot near the end of the timing tape that will represent the moment of interest. The result of calculating the average velocity between the two surrounding dots (P_1 and P_2) will then represent the velocity at point P. Average velocity is calculated simply by dividing the distance traveled by the time interval of the displacement,

$$v_{av} = \frac{d}{\Delta t}. \tag{3}$$

The distance between points P_1 and P_2 can be measured with a metric ruler. In Figure 3, the distance (d) is 2.70 cm (0.0270 m). The time interval can be found using the recording timer calibration determined in Lab 2-2 (or just before beginning this lab). For this example, assume that the timer produces 53.0 dots/s. From P_1 there are two dots to P_2. The time interval can be found by using unit analysis.

$$\Delta t = \frac{2 \text{ dots}}{} \left| \frac{1 \text{ s}}{53.0 \text{ dots}} \doteq 0.0377 \text{ s.}\right.$$

Procedure

- Students will have to develop a method for releasing the cart that does not retard it or give it any additional velocity upon release. Using a "hold-back" string tied to a back axle is often useful when setting up the masses and starting the timer. When everything is ready for the trial, release the string. If a tack or nail is fastened to the bottom of the incline, the string may be tied to it and cut with a scissors to release the cart.

- The main objective for the lab period is to obtain the three timing tapes and the data they contain. The calculations can be performed later.

Postlab Exercises

- You may instruct the lab teams to submit their data tapes with their papers so that you can verify that the data was analyzed correctly.

- Consider awarding extra credit for percent differences below a certain value, such as 5%.

Substituting into Equation (3), the average velocity for the interval P_1 to P_2 (and the assumed instantaneous velocity at P) is

$$v = \frac{0.0270 \text{ m}}{0.0377 \text{ s}} \doteq 0.716 \text{ m/s}.$$

After obtaining the two velocities ($v_1 = 0$ m/s at the start of the tape and $v_2 = 0.716$ m/s at point P), you can calculate Δv, which is $v_2 - v_1 = 0.716$ m/s. But what is the change in time between those two points? As before, we can use the timer calibration and the number of dots from P_0 to P to determine Δt. There are 16 dots printed from *after* the starting point to point P. The dot at P_0 is not counted. Using unit analysis, the time interval is determined to be 0.302 s.

$$\Delta t = \frac{16 \text{ dots}}{} \left| \frac{1 \text{ s}}{53.0 \text{ dots}} \right. \doteq 0.302 \text{ s}$$

Finally, the *experimental acceleration* can be estimated by dividing Δv (0.716 m/s) by Δt (0.302 s) to yield 2.37 m/s². Remember that these are not the values you will use. They are simply sample calculations performed to show you the proper procedure based on the tape in Figure 3. Your tape will be different.

Comparing this *experimental* value for acceleration to the *mathematical* value will be interesting. The difference will be due to factors such as friction, human error, and equipment precision and accuracy.

Procedure

Setup

1. Determine the mass of the cart (m_c). Record the mass in Table 1 for Trials 1 and 2.

2. Set up the inclined plane (pictured in Figure 2) near the edge of the table. Set the angle of the plane at 20.0° above the horizontal.

3. Clamp the recording timer to the table so that it won't move during the trials.

4. Choose a hanging mass (m_h) for Trial 1 that is approximately twice the mass of the cart. For most carts, a mass of 1 kg will work well. (If you are using a roller skate for your cart, you may need to use several 1 kg masses. Just make sure that the mass is large enough to make the cart accelerate up the plane.)

5. Tie a length of string to the mass. Tie the free end of the string to a paper clip.

6. Cut the timing tapes into appropriate lengths so that they will exit the recording timer just before the cart must be stopped. This will help you to avoid including ambiguous dots from the end of the cart's run in your analysis.

7. The mass must be able to fall freely until the cart leaves the inclined plane during the trial. You may want to place something under the mass to keep it from marring the floor.

8. Record the calibration of your timer in Table 1.

Data Collection

9. Label a timing tape with the appropriate trial number. Tape one end of the tape to the cart and thread the other end through the timer. Position the cart at the bottom of the inclined plane and take up the slack in the tape through the timer.

10. Tie a loop of thread around the back axle of the cart long enough so that it can be grasped. The cart will be held in place until released by this loop of thread.

11. Hook the string that is attached to the hanging mass to the front end of the cart.

12. Start the timer.

13. Release the string holding back the cart. You need to release the cart in such a way that it is not impeded or accelerated when released.

    Caution: The cart will tend to fly off the end of the inclined plane. You or your lab partner must be ready to catch it. Also, depending on the configuration of the cart and the inclined plane, the cart may strike the pulley at the end of ramp. In that case you must stop the cart before it strikes in order to avoid damaging the pulley.

14. For Trial 2, repeat Steps 9–13, using a hanging mass that is about 1 kg heavier than the mass in Trial 1, but keep the mass of the cart the same. If the cart accelerates too rapidly, decrease the hanging mass until you can successfully produce an acceptable tape for each trial. The size of the hanging mass is not important as long as it is larger for Trial 2 than for Trial 1. Record the hanging mass and the mass of the cart in Table 1. Before performing the trial, verify that the angle of incline has not changed.

15. For Trial 3, keep the same hanging mass that you used in Trial 2, but increase the cart mass by 1 kg. Record the hanging mass and the mass of the cart in Table 1. Before performing the trial, verify that the angle of incline has not changed.

16. Be sure to complete the three trials in the allotted class time. You can perform the analysis of the tapes after class if necessary.

Data

Table 1
Trial Data

Trial	Cart Mass, m_c	Hanging Mass, m_h	Number of Dots (P_0 to P)	Distance, d	Timer Calibration
1	kg	kg		m	
2	kg	kg		m	dots/s
3	kg	kg		m	

Data in Table 1 will vary.

Postlab Exercises

1. Mark the starting point (P_0) and a convenient final point (point P) on each tape. Be sure to select point P such that there is at least one additional dot before the cart began to slow down at the end of the trial.

2. Mark P_1 and P_2 on each tape. These will be the dots on either side of P.

3. Count the number of dots recorded on the tape starting from the dot after P_0 to P. Record the number in Table 1.

4. Measure distance (d) between P_1 and P_2 for each trial. Record the distance in meters in Table 1.

5. For each trial, calculate the time required to travel from P_1 to P_2. Record the value in Table 2.

6. Determine the average velocity of the cart between P_1 and P_2 for each trial. Record the value in Table 2 as the estimated velocity at P (v_2).

7. Record the change in velocity (Δv) for each trial in Table 2.

8. Calculate the time required to travel from P_0 to P for each trial. Record your results in Table 2. (See Prelab Homework Question 6.)

9. Determine the *experimental* rate of acceleration for each trial. Record your answers in Table 2.

10. Determine the *calculated* rate of acceleration for each trial. Use Equation (1) from the Prelab Discussion. Record your results in Table 2.

11. Determine the percent difference between the experimental and calculated accelerations. Record your results in Table 2.

Table 2
Calculations and Comparisons

Trial	Δt P_1 to P_2	Velocity at p, v_2	Initial Velocity v_1	Δv ($v_2 - v_1$)	Δt P_0 to P	a Calculated	a Experimental	Percent Difference
1	s	m/s	0 m/s	m/s	s	m/s^2	m/s^2	%
2	s	m/s	0 m/s	m/s	s	m/s^2	m/s^2	%
3	s	m/s	0 m/s	m/s	s	m/s^2	m/s^2	%

Answers in Table 2 will vary.

An apparatus can be made to substitute for the inclined plane and pulley. A bolt or threaded rod can serve as an axle, which can be mounted onto an inclined plane as shown below.

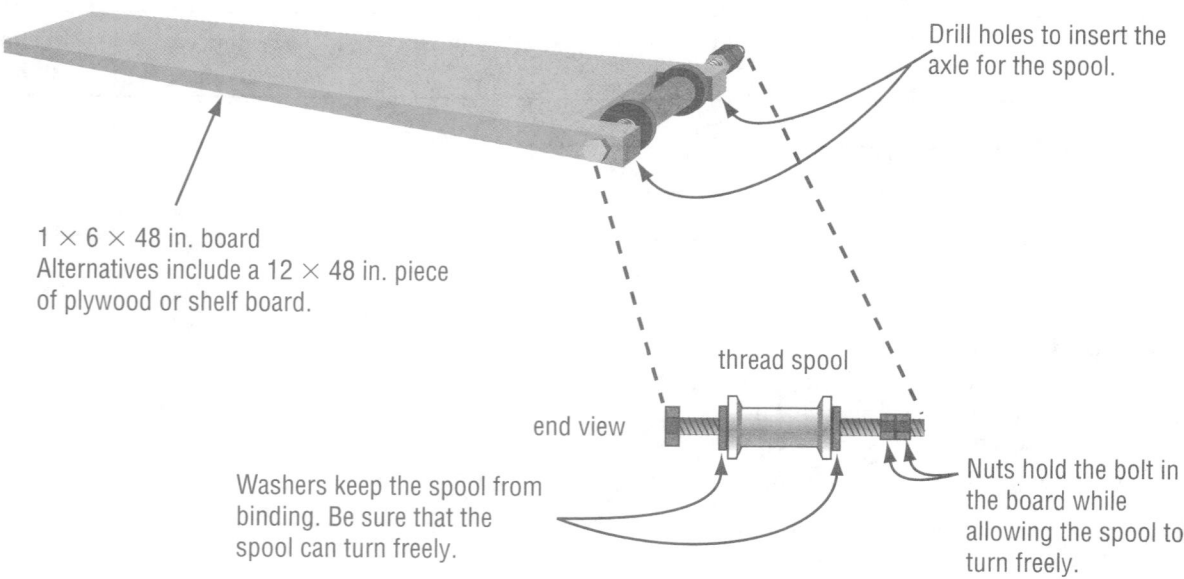

Drill holes to insert the axle for the spool.

1 × 6 × 48 in. board
Alternatives include a 12 × 48 in. piece of plywood or shelf board.

thread spool

end view

Washers keep the spool from binding. Be sure that the spool can turn freely.

Nuts hold the bolt in the board while allowing the spool to turn freely.

Postlab Analysis

1. What would happen to the magnitude of the acceleration if the slope of the incline increased and everything else remained the same? Explain your answer.

   The acceleration of the system of masses would decrease because the force of gravity on the hanging weight would be counterbalanced by the greater downhill component of the cart's weight acting through the string.

2. What would happen to the magnitude of the acceleration if the hanging mass increased and everything else remained the same? Explain your answer.

   The acceleration of the system of masses would increase because the gravitational force acting on the hanging mass would increase while the downhill component of the cart's weight remains the same. The increase in net force is somewhat offset by the increase in mass of the system.

3. What would happen to the magnitude of the acceleration if the mass of the cart increased and everything else remained the same? Explain your answer.

   The acceleration of the system of masses would decrease because the downhill component of the cart's weight would increase while the gravitational force on the hanging mass remains the same. The effect of reduced net force on acceleration is disproportionately greater due to the increase in the mass of the system.

4. State two specific sources of *equipment* error that may have contributed to large percent differences between the calculated and experimental methods for determining system acceleration.

   Answers may include inaccurate calibration of the recording timer, drag induced by the timing tape, friction in either the cart's wheels or the pulley mechanism, failure of the apparatus during a trial, or inaccurate metric masses.

5. State two specific sources of *human* error that may have occurred in this experiment.

   Answers may include misreading the protractor, failure to note a change in the angle of the inclined plane, failure to follow verbal instructions or the written procedure, errors using the information on the tapes, or calculation errors.

Name _____

Date _____ Hour _____

PRELAB HOMEWORK

1. ____5.80 m/s²____ A 1.500 kg mass is suspended from a string. The string, which runs over a pulley, is attached to a dynamics cart weighing 546 g and resting on an inclined plane with an angle of 32.0° from the horizontal. What is the magnitude of the acceleration of the cart up the plane in meters per second squared?

Given: $m_c = 0.546$ kg; $m_h = 1.500$ kg; $\theta = 32.0°$; $a = ?$

Formula: $a = \left(\dfrac{m_h - m_c \sin \theta}{m_h + m_c} \right) g$

Solution: $a = \left[\dfrac{1.500 \text{ kg} - (0.546 \text{ kg})(\sin 32.0°)}{1.500 \text{ kg} + 0.546 \text{ kg}} \right] (9.81 \tfrac{m}{s^2}) \doteq 5.80 \tfrac{m}{s^2}$

2. ____0.0333 s____ Suppose you use the apparatus pictured in Figure 2 to experimentally determine the acceleration on the cart. Assume that you produce a tape like the tape pictured in Figure 3. The distance from P_1 to P_2 is 3.25 cm. Assume that your timer imprints 60.0 dots/s. How long (in seconds) does the cart take to travel from P_1 to P_2?

$t = \dfrac{2 \text{ dots}}{} \left| \dfrac{1 \text{ s}}{60.0 \text{ dots}} \doteq 0.0333 \text{ s} \right.$

3. ____0.976 m/s____ Using the data from Question 2, calculate the *average velocity* during the time interval P_1 to P_2 in meters per second.

Given: $d = 0.0325$ m; $\Delta t = 0.0333$ s; $v = ?$

Formula: $v = \dfrac{d}{\Delta t}$

Solution: $v = \dfrac{0.0325 \text{ m}}{0.0333 \text{ s}} \doteq 0.976 \tfrac{m}{s}$

4. ____0.976 m/s____ What would be the estimated *instantaneous velocity* at point P in meters per second?

5. ____0.976 m/s____ What is the change in velocity during the entire time interval (P_0 to P)?

Given: $v_1 = 0 \tfrac{m}{s}$; $v_2 = 0.976 \tfrac{m}{s}$; $\Delta v = ?$

Formula: $\Delta v = v_2 - v_1$

Solution: $\Delta v = 0.976 \tfrac{m}{s} - 0 \tfrac{m}{s} = 0.976 \tfrac{m}{s}$

6. ____0.333 s____ Suppose there were 20 dots between P_0 and P. What would be the time required for the cart to travel that distance?

$t = \dfrac{2 \text{ dots}}{} \left| \dfrac{1 \text{ s}}{60.0 \text{ dots}} \doteq 0.0333 \text{ s} \right.$

7. ____2.93 m/s²____ What would be the acceleration during the time interval determined in Question 6?

Given: $\Delta v = 0.976 \tfrac{m}{s}$; $\Delta t = 0.333$ s; $a = ?$

Formula: $a = \dfrac{\Delta v}{\Delta t}$

Solution: $a = \dfrac{0.976 \tfrac{m}{s}}{0.333 \text{ s}} \doteq 2.93 \tfrac{m}{s^2}$

8. _____3.10 m/s²_____ Suppose that the mass of the cart is 0.500 kg and that the slope of the inclined plane is 35.0°. Assume that the hanging mass is 0.650 kg. Calculate the *magnitude* of the acceleration of the hanging mass.

Given: $m_c = 0.500$ kg; $m_h = 0.650$ kg; $\theta = 35.0°$; $a_h = ?$

Formula: Use Equation (1).

Solution: $a_h = \left[\dfrac{0.650 \text{ kg} - (0.500 \text{ kg})(\sin 35.0°)}{0.650 \text{ kg} + 0.500 \text{ kg}} \right]\left(9.81 \, \tfrac{m}{s^2}\right) \approx 3.10 \, \tfrac{m}{s^2}$

(3 SDs allowed)

9. _____5.6%_____ What is the percent difference between the two acceleration values determined in Questions 7 and 8?

$$\text{percent difference} = \frac{|\text{difference of the two values}|}{\text{average of the two values}} \times 100\%$$

$$= \frac{\left|2.93 \, \tfrac{m}{s^2} - 3.10 \, \tfrac{m}{s^2}\right|}{\left(\dfrac{2.93 \, \tfrac{m}{s^2} + 3.10 \, \tfrac{m}{s^2}}{2}\right)} \times 100\% = \frac{\left|-0.17 \, \tfrac{m}{s^2}\right|}{3.02 \, \tfrac{m}{s^2}} \times 100\% \approx 5.6\%$$

(2 SDs allowed)

Name _____

Date _____ Hour ____

DISPLACEMENT, VELOCITY, AND ACCELERATION

Required Equipment
metric ruler

Purpose

The study of velocity and acceleration in one dimension is the foundation for understanding mechanical motion. The purpose of this lab is to give you experience

- using formulas related to velocity and acceleration.
- translating experimental data into useful graphs.
- obtaining information from graphic analysis.
- experimentally determining the acceleration due to gravity, *g*.

Prelab Discussion

From your studies thus far, you know that a **displacement** is a change of position within the frame of reference of the system you are considering. In the real universe, a displacement always takes a finite amount of **time.** The **average velocity** (v_{av}) during a one-dimensional displacement can be determined by the formula

$$v_{av} = \frac{d}{\Delta t} = \frac{x_2 - x_1}{\Delta t}.$$

Note that the positions are measured at the beginning and the end of the time interval. The intermediate positions are not taken into consideration when calculating average velocity; therefore, velocity at any given moment, or **instantaneous velocity,** may change continuously during the time interval. If the velocity of an object changes during a time interval, the object experiences an acceleration. If velocity increases, we say that the object is accelerating, and if its velocity decreases, it is decelerating. The **average acceleration (a_{av})** of the object during an interval of time can be calculated from the formula

$$a_{av} = \frac{\Delta v}{\Delta t} = \frac{v_2 - v_1}{\Delta t}. \tag{1}$$

Only the instantaneous velocities at the beginning and the end of the time interval are considered when finding average acceleration. The average velocity during the interval is of no concern, and instantaneous velocities during the interval cannot be determined accurately without the use of calculus or an advanced graphic analysis program. This lab approximates differentiation in calculus by graphically estimating the instantaneous velocity along the displacement-time curve at regular time intervals. The acceleration producing the displacement may then be determined. To accomplish this task, you will interpret and graph the data obtained during Lab 2-2.

Procedure

1. Divide the tape retained from Lab 2-2 into 0.10 s intervals. For example, if your timer makes 30 dots/s or 3.0 dots every 0.10 s, draw a line across the tape at every third dot. If it makes 5.7 dots every 0.10 s, draw a line at 7/10 of the distance between the fifth and sixth dots, another line at 4/10 of the distance between the eleventh and twelfth dots, and so on. See Figure 1 for assistance in making this determination. Each 0.10 s interval along the tape in the diagram equals 5.7 dot intervals. Take care to draw the lines perpendicular to the sides of the tape so that your measurements in Step 2 will be accurate. (If your timer leaves multiple marks at each point, refer to the mark closest to the beginning of the tape in each group.)

2. This step measures the total displacement at the end of each 0.10 s interval. Measure the displacement from the starting point of the tape to the first

Prelab Discussion

- Review the prerequisites for Lab 2-4 in the back of this manual and be sure you have discussed the three equations of motion presented in the textbook.

- The term *velocity* is used throughout the lab when it is the *magnitude* of velocity (speed) that is being considered. However, since the motion is one-dimensional (downward), it is not inappropriate to consider it as a velocity.

Procedure

- This lab uses the recording timer tapes obtained in Lab 2-2. If they are not available for some reason, you can quickly produce new tapes by repeating the Lab 2-2 data collection procedure.

- The graphed curves should be smooth and should fit the data points closely. Instruct students to check for smoothness by looking along the curve with the graph paper horizontal near eye level. Irregularities in the curves will quickly become evident.

- The explanation of the basis for graphically determining instantaneous velocity at a point may be confused with the definition of average velocity at the beginning of the Prelab Discussion. You may want to provide the calculus differential for velocity (dv/dt) to illustrate the difference.

- Some students may have difficulty graphing two sets of data on the same graph. Explain that the vertical scale factor will be different for the two graphs.

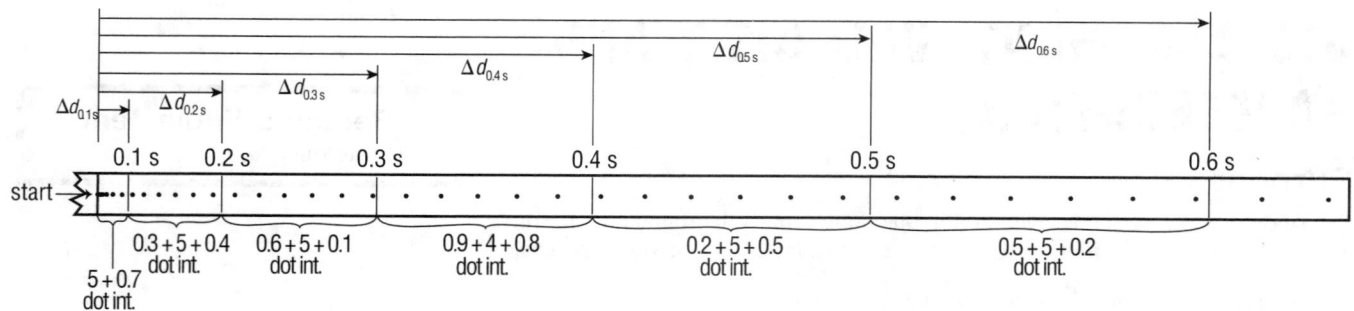

Figure 1

- Emphasize neatness on the graphs. Thin, sharp lines will produce the best results.

- To complete Steps 3 and 4 of the Postlab Exercises, you will need to display on the board the average accelerations and precisions for all teams. Collect the assignment after giving students the opportunity to complete these calculations.

0.10 s line ($\Delta d_{0.1 \text{ s}}$), from the starting point to the second line ($\Delta d_{0.2 \text{ s}}$), and so on until you have measured the displacement from the starting point to every line. Write the displacement at each time mark on the tape (see Figure 1).

3. Record the displacement for each 0.10 s mark in Table 1.

4. Table 1 now contains a list of ordered pairs of numbers—time and displacement. Plot these values as points on Graph 1 producing a graph of **displacement vs. time.** Determine the best scales for the dependent (displacement, y-axis) and independent (time, x-axis) variables so that you use as much of the graphing area as possible. The larger the graph, the more accurate your estimates will be. Use a pencil to plot this data. Mark and label the graph axes with the scales that you choose.

5. Beginning at the origin, carefully sketch a *smooth,* best-fit curve as close as possible to the displacement-time data points. There should not be any sharp bends or flat spots in the curve. The line of the curve should be thin, sharp, and clean.

6. Make a small dot on the curve at every 0.10 s. This is determined by extending the time scale on the x-axis up to the curve.

7. In the next few steps, you will estimate the instantaneous velocity of the falling mass. Draw a thin, crisp tangent line at each of the points marked on the curve such that the tangent line just touches the curve. The angles formed between the tangent line and the curve should appear to be equal on both sides of the point.

8. The *slope of the tangent line* (m) is equivalent to the instantaneous velocity at the point of tangency marking the end of the 0.10 s interval. Estimate the velocity as follows:

   a. For each tangent line, create a right triangle, using the tangent line for the hypotenuse and choosing a vertical and a horizontal grid line for the legs of the triangle. The larger the triangle, the more accurate the results.

   b. Determine the scale factors for the vertical and horizontal axes. For example, the vertical displacement scale factor may be 0.050 m/block, while the horizontal time scale factor may be 0.025 s/block.

   c. Measure the length of each side of the triangle in terms of grid blocks and multiply by the appropriate scale factor in order to obtain Δd (in the y-direction) and Δt (in the x-direction) for that time mark. (Note that the *actual* Δd and Δt of the curve at the point are infinitesimally small. The tangent line helps you visualize what is happening on an extremely small scale at the point of tangency.)

d. Determine the estimated instantaneous velocity from the slope ($m = \Delta d/\Delta t = $ v). (Calculus does this through differentiation.)

9. Record the instantaneous velocity for each 0.10 s in Table 1.

10. Table 1 now lists ordered pairs of values for time and velocity. Using a pen or pencil with a contrasting color, plot these values as points on Graph 1 as a graph of **velocity vs. time,** using the same graphing area as the displacement-time graph. Determine the best scale for the dependent variable (velocity, *y*-axis) so that you use as much of the graph as possible. Use the same time scale as the original graph. Label the *x*-axis and the second *y*-axis scale in the contrasting color. Write any missing labels on the graph in colored pencil or ink.

11. Draw the line that best fits the plotted velocity-time points. This line should be essentially straight. The slope at every point along a velocity-time graph is the instantaneous acceleration. Since the slope of a straight line is constant, you may conclude that the average acceleration, which is the acceleration due to gravity, is constant through the entire time interval. This is a reasonable conclusion because earth's gravity is not observed to change with time.

Data

Table 1
Displacement and Velocity

Time Mark	Displacement		Instantaneous Velocity (Displacement-Time Graph Slope)	
0.00 s	0.0000	m	0	m/s
0.10 s	0.0522	m	1.0	m/s
0.20 s	0.2070	m	2.0	m/s
0.30 s	0.4515	m	2.9	m/s
0.40 s	0.7900	m	4.0	m/s
0.50 s	1.2320	m	5.0	m/s
0.60 s	1.7700	m	unable to determine	m/s

Data shown in Table 1 is typical. Actual data will vary.
Check for correct SDs in measurements and calculations.

Postlab Exercises

1. Determine the average acceleration by determining the slope of the line from the velocity-time graph and record your result in meters per second squared.

   <u>   10.0 m/s^2 </u> (Answer is based on typical data.)
   The average acceleration will vary, but it should be within a range of 9.3 to 10.3 m/s^2.

2. Compare your average acceleration with the accepted value of 9.81 m/s^2 by calculating your percent error. Show your calculations below, using this formula:

   $$\text{percent error} = \frac{(\text{experimental value} - \text{accepted value})}{\text{accepted value}} \times 100\%.$$

   The percent error should be 5% or less.

   Percent error <u>   Ans. vary.   </u> %

3. Find the average acceleration from the results of your entire class. Then use that value to find the *percent error*. Show your calculations below.

The average acceleration should be within a range of 9.3 to 10.3 m/s².

The percent error should be 5% or less.

Class average acceleration ___Ans. vary.___ m/s²

Class average percent error ___Ans. vary.___ %

4. Find the class *precision*. Refer to Lab 1-1 and Appendix A for the procedure. Show your calculations below.

Class precision within ±0.5 m/s² should be commended.

Class average acceleration ± ___Ans. vary.___ m/s²

Postlab Analysis

1. Describe the shape of your displacement-time graph.

The graph rises to the right with increasing slope.

2. If a portion of a displacement-time graph were straight, it would indicate

that the velocity during that interval is ___constant___ .

3. Describe the shape of your velocity-time graph.

The graph should be a straight line. Students may note some

nonlinearity.

4. A straight portion of a curve on a velocity-time graph indicates that the ac-

celeration during that time interval is ___constant___ .

5. Why is it easier to approximate instantaneous velocity when a displacement-time graph is a straight line than when it is a curve?

The tangent to a curved line is difficult to estimate accurately by sight.

Therefore, the slope of the tangent line as an estimate of the instan-

taneous velocity on a curved graph will be less accurate than those

quantities determined from the slope of a straight-line graph.

6. How would using a larger mass have affected the results?

Theoretically, it should not change the results, but the larger force ex-

erted by the mass would proportionately diminish the effect of friction

in the timer and therefore increase the experimental acceleration.

7. List two possible sources of human error.

Answers will vary but may include errors reading the instrument, er-

rors counting the dots, errors recording the values, calculation errors,

rounding errors, or failure to follow directions.

8. List two possible sources of equipment error.

Answers will vary but may include variable battery voltage in the DC

recording timer (if applicable), friction between tape and timer guides,

measuring inaccuracies caused by the metric ruler ends being dam-

aged, failure of the carbon disk to mark a dot, the timer making mul-

tiple marks, and the inability to determine the exact starting point on

the tape.

Graph 1
Displacement vs. Time
Velocity vs. Time

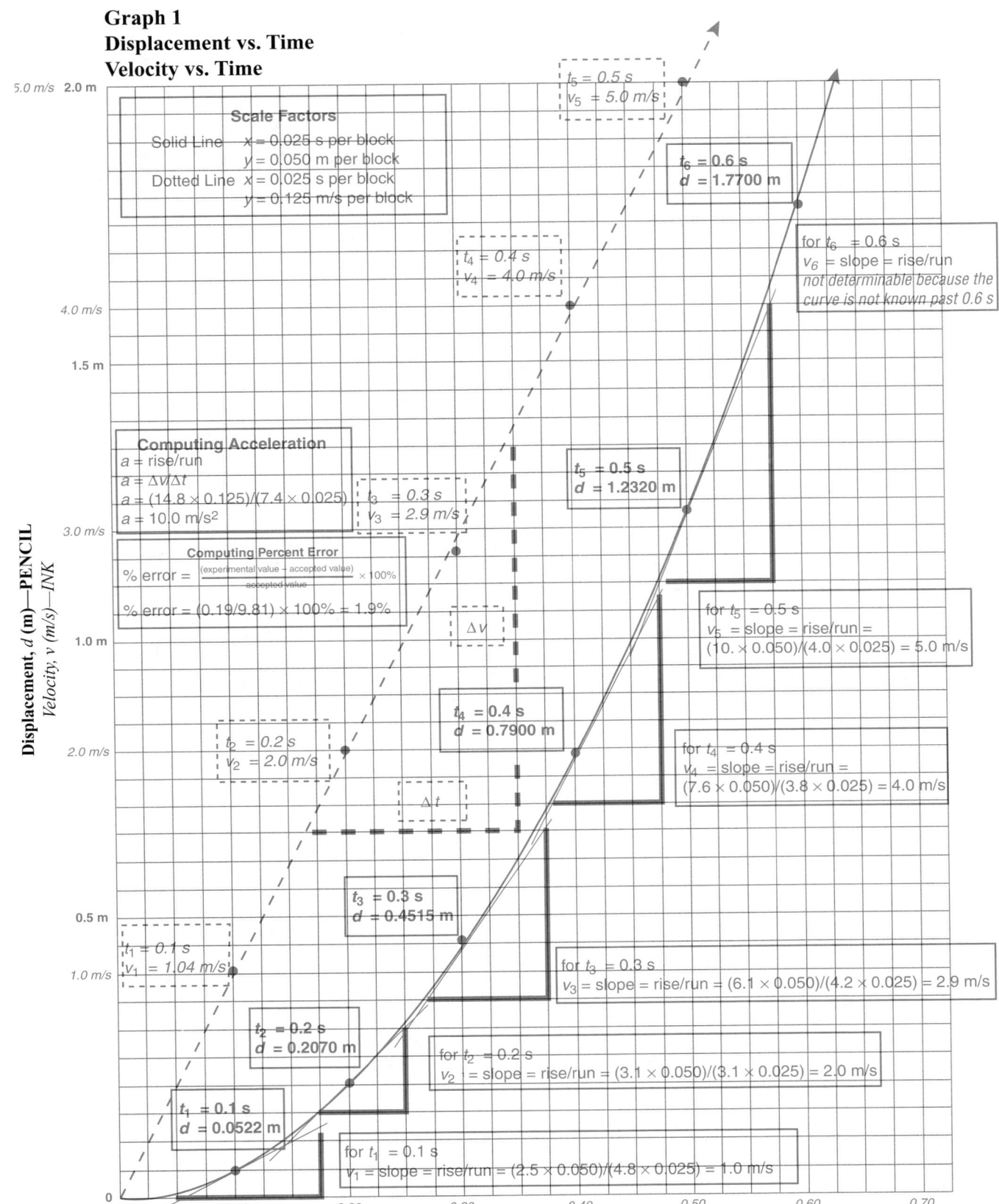

Scale Factors

Solid Line $x = 0.025$ s per block
$y = 0.050$ m per block

Dotted Line $x = 0.025$ s per block
$y = 0.125$ m/s per block

$t_5 = 0.5$ s
$v_5 = 5.0$ m/s

$t_6 = 0.6$ s
$d = 1.7700$ m

for $t_6 = 0.6$ s
$v_6 = $ slope = rise/run
not determinable because the curve is not known past 0.6 s

$t_4 = 0.4$ s
$v_4 = 4.0$ m/s

Computing Acceleration
$a = $ rise/run
$a = \Delta v/\Delta t$
$a = (14.8 \times 0.125)/(7.4 \times 0.025)$
$a = 10.0$ m/s^2

$t_3 = 0.3$ s
$v_3 = 2.9$ m/s

$t_5 = 0.5$ s
$d = 1.2320$ m

Computing Percent Error
% error = $\frac{(\text{experimental value} - \text{accepted value})}{\text{accepted value}} \times 100\%$

% error = $(0.19/9.81) \times 100\% = 1.9\%$

Δv

for $t_5 = 0.5$ s
$v_5 = $ slope = rise/run =
$(10. \times 0.050)/(4.0 \times 0.025) = 5.0$ m/s

$t_4 = 0.4$ s
$d = 0.7900$ m

for $t_4 = 0.4$ s
$v_4 = $ slope = rise/run =
$(7.6 \times 0.050)/(3.8 \times 0.025) = 4.0$ m/s

$t_2 = 0.2$ s
$v_2 = 2.0$ m/s

Δt

$t_3 = 0.3$ s
$d = 0.4515$ m

$t_1 = 0.1$ s
$v_1 = 1.04$ m/s

for $t_3 = 0.3$ s
$v_3 = $ slope = rise/run = $(6.1 \times 0.050)/(4.2 \times 0.025) = 2.9$ m/s

$t_2 = 0.2$ s
$d = 0.2070$ m

for $t_2 = 0.2$ s
$v_2 = $ slope = rise/run = $(3.1 \times 0.050)/(3.1 \times 0.025) = 2.0$ m/s

$t_1 = 0.1$ s
$d = 0.0522$ m

for $t_1 = 0.1$ s
$v_1 = $ slope = rise/run = $(2.5 \times 0.050)/(4.8 \times 0.025) = 1.0$ m/s

Displacement, d (m)—PENCIL
Velocity, v (m/s)—INK

Time, t (s)
Displacement-Time Graph—PENCIL (Solid Line)
*Velocity-Time Graph—***INK** (Dashed Line)

45

Name _____

Date _____ Hour _____

PRELAB HOMEWORK

1. ____0.18 m/s____ Assume that your recording timer imprints 53 dots/s. Suppose that the distance covered by 8 consecutive dots on the tape was 2.7 cm. What is the *average* velocity of the mass during that interval in meters per second?

    Average velocity is found by multiplying the average displacement per dot by the rate at which the dots are imprinted.

    $$v = \frac{2.7 \text{ cm}}{8 \text{ dots}} \left| \frac{53 \text{ dots}}{1 \text{ s}} \right| \frac{1 \text{ m}}{100 \text{ cm}} \doteq 0.18 \tfrac{m}{s}$$

2. How is the *instantaneous* velocity of a moving object estimated in this exercise?

    Instantaneous velocity is estimated by determining the slope of the line tangent to

    the point on a displacement-time graph.

3. ____2.9 m/s____ Assume that your displacement-time graph from this experiment has a vertical scale factor of 0.050 m/block and a horizontal scale factor of 0.025 s/block. What is the slope of the tangent line (the instantaneous velocity) at 0.3 s if the triangle formed with the tangent line to the graph at 0.3 s has a rise (Δd) of 6.1 blocks and a run (Δt) of 4.2 blocks?

    Given: $\Delta d = 6.1$ blocks; $\Delta t = 4.2$ blocks; y-scale factor $= 0.050$ m/block;

    x-scale factor $= 0.025$ s/block; $m_{0.3 \text{ s}} = $?

    Formula: $m_t = \dfrac{\Delta d}{\Delta t}$

    Solution: $m_{0.3 \text{ s}} = \dfrac{\left(6.1 \text{ blocks} \times 0.050 \tfrac{m}{block} \right)}{\left(4.2 \text{ blocks} \times 0.025 \tfrac{s}{block} \right)} = \dfrac{0.305 \text{ m}}{0.105 \text{ s}} \doteq 2.9 \tfrac{m}{s}$

4. How is the average acceleration of a moving object estimated in this exercise?

    Acceleration is estimated by determining the slope of the velocity-time graph.

5. When determining the acceleration due to gravity (g) in this exercise, describe in general terms what kind of results the class must obtain in order to have good *precision?* Good *accuracy?*

    For the class to obtain good *precision,* all of the results for the experiment should

    agree within a few percentage points, but the results need not be close to the ac-

    cepted value of g. To have good *accuracy,* the results need to be close to the

    accepted value of g (9.81 m/s^2).

HORIZONTAL PROJECTION

Purpose

Experimenting with horizontal projection situations provides a good introduction to concepts involving motion in two dimensions. The purpose of this lab is to

- give you experience in determining the range of a projectile under different horizontal velocities.
- give you practice in calculating the initial horizontal velocity when the range and vertical displacement are determined experimentally.
- determine the relationship between horizontal velocity and range by plotting the variables on a graph.

Prelab Discussion

Your text discussed motion in two dimensions as a means of introducing the three equations of motion. One simple form of two-dimensional motion is called **horizontal projection,** which occurs in the vertical plane. An object is given an initial horizontal velocity; then it is allowed to fall under the influence of gravity until it hits the ground or floor. The time of fall and the average horizontal velocity determine how far the projectile travels horizontally (its **range**). Both the time of fall and the range are obtained from the **second equation of motion,**

$$d = v_0\Delta t + \tfrac{1}{2} a(\Delta t)^2, \tag{1}$$

where v_0 is the initial velocity, d is the displacement, and a is the average acceleration during the time interval Δt. To analyze horizontal projections, it is assumed that the horizontal velocity and the vertical acceleration are constant.

In this exercise the projectile will be a large steel ball bearing or a marble, which will be called the *ball* for brevity's sake. You will give the ball an initial horizontal velocity by rolling it down an inclined projectile track attached to either a level plank or the tabletop, which will be called the *rolling surface.* You will then determine the horizontal velocity of the ball, using two methods. First, you will experimentally measure the ball's horizontal velocity as it leaves the surface by timing how long it takes the ball to roll a known horizontal distance. Since the average velocity of the ball is not influenced significantly by friction or position on the rolling surface, you can assume that its instantaneous velocity at the moment it leaves the surface is equal to its average velocity. Second, you will calculate the horizontal velocity of the ball as follows:

    a. After measuring the height of the rolling surface from the floor (the vertical displacement of the ball as it falls), calculate the time of fall, which is the time the ball is in its trajectory, using the second equation of motion.

    b. Once you know the time of fall, measure the horizontal range of the ball along the floor; then calculate the horizontal velocity of the ball when it leaves the rolling surface.

These two methods of determining horizontal velocity can then be compared in order to obtain the percent difference between the two methods.

During this exercise you will also vary the velocity of the ball by changing the distance through which the ball accelerates down the projectile track. After completing five trials, you should be able to determine the relationship between horizontal velocity and range.

The experiment assumes that there is no friction between the ball and the rolling surface. Obviously this is not true, but the amount of friction is small enough that it will not significantly affect your results. The rolling surface must be smooth, flat, and *level.* The preferred surface for this exercise is a **leveling**

Required Equipment

ball bearing, large
carbon paper
carpenter's level
C-clamps, 2
leveling board or a table
masking tape
metric ruler
plumb line and bob
projectile track
stopwatch
unlined paper

Optional Equipment

marble

Prelab Discussion

- Review the prerequisites for Lab 2-5 in the back of this manual.

- This exercise will give your students practice using the second equation of motion, and it will affirm that horizontal velocity is independent of vertical velocity for horizontal projections. Ensure that they review the applicable sections in the textbook prior to performing this lab.

Equipment and Setup

- The leveling board recommended in this lab may be constructed from the same board used in Lab 2-3.

- Following are instructions for constructing a leveling board.

    1. The plank can be a 4 ft section of 1 × 6 lumber or 5/8 in. plywood cut to the desired width of about 6 in. Verify that the plank is perfectly flat.

    2. You will need 3 fine-thread machine bolts about 4 in. long and 3 threaded inserts to accept the bolts (6 nuts can be substituted). Using the appropriate drill size for the inserts, drill two holes about 3/4 in. from the sides and end of the plank. Screw two threaded inserts into these holes. Drill a single hole in the center of the other end of the plank about 3/4 in. from the

edge. Screw the remaining insert into this hole.

3. Screw the 3 bolts into the inserts from the top side of the plank to the same depth. The plank will rest on the threaded ends of the bolts rather than their heads to provide greater stability.

- Some projection ramps have a small swing-out arm attached to the underside of the lower end of the track that must be removed before you can clamp the track to the table.

- Steel balls or large ball bearings are recommended because they are machined to a tighter tolerance for roundness than glass marbles.

Procedure

- Monitor the trials that start low on the projectile track. The balls tend to meander at lower velocities, introducing larger errors.

- Be sure that the students label the first dot formed under the carbon paper during each trial. When the ball bounces, it will make extra dots, and it is easy to lose track of what is data and what is extraneous.

Postlab Exercises

- The graph should be a straight line rising to the right. The data from a well-done lab will produce a line that passes through the origin.

- Consider giving additional credit for percent differences less than 5%.

Prelab Homework

- It is recommended that students use complete sentences when defining terms.

- Answers given in the Teacher's Edition reflect the correct number of SDs.

- Be sure that the students show all of their work.

Home School Notes

- A standard plastic ruler with a pencil rest can be substituted for the projectile track. The ball can roll in the pencil rest. Ideally, a holder could be fashioned to bend the ruler so that the marble leaves the track nearly horizontally.

board, which consists of a plank of wood supported by three machine bolts screwed into threaded inserts. Using a carpenter's level, you can level the board perfectly by adjusting the three bolts. (See Figure 1 for the arrangement of the leveling board.) If you do not have experience reading a carpenter's level, ask someone to show you. If you use a tabletop as the rolling surface, the table must be movable so that it can be leveled. Fold a sheet of paper in half several times and place the paper under the table legs in order to level the table.

This experiment works best on a hard floor surface. If you have carpeted floors, you can use a wide wooden plank or a sheet of plywood along the trajectory of the ball to form a hard surface.

Before proceeding, state a hypothesis regarding the relationship between horizontal velocity and range. Remember that a hypothesis is an "educated" guess. That is, it is based on the facts that you know. You do not necessarily have to agree with your hypothesis. You may actually set out to disprove a hypothesis because you do not believe it to be true. You need to approach the problem logically. What happens to the range if the velocity increases? The answer seems logical. Now apply the equations of motion in order to check out your logic. Does your hypothesis agree with the theoretical principles involved? If so, then your hypothesis provides a good framework for your investigation. If not, your work will not have a clear purpose. Write your hypothesis here.

Answers will vary.

Procedure

Setup

1. Measure the height of the rolling surface above the floor and record it in the appropriate blank above Table 1.

2. Place the edge of a piece of tape on the rolling surface so that it marks 100.0 cm (1.000 m) from the end of the board or from the edge of the table over which the ball will roll (see Figure 1).

3. Clamp or tape the projectile track to the rolling surface so that the lower end of the track is positioned at the 1 m mark. A ball released on the track should roll down the track onto the rolling surface, roll 1 m to the edge, and fall to the floor below (see Figure 2).

4. Level the rolling surface, using a carpenter's level. After threading in the bolts the same distance to roughly level the board, adjust the height of the single bolt to level the board lengthwise; then adjust only one of the pair of bolts at the other end to level the board from side to side. Recheck the level both ways. If you are leveling a table, level it lengthwise first by shimming one end with folded paper; then level it from side to side by shimming the legs on one side, frequently rechecking the level lengthwise.

5. Suspend a plumb bob from the position on the edge of the rolling surface where the ball will roll off. Adjust the string so that the bob swings freely just above the floor (~1 mm). Tape the string to the end of the board or table. Do not place the tape on top of the rolling surface (see Figure 1).

6. From the highest position on your track, release the ball and allow it to roll off the rolling surface. Observe the approximate spot where the ball strikes the floor.

7. Place sheets of paper on the floor end-to-end, beginning under the plumb bob and extending past the point where the ball struck the floor. This may require two or more sheets of paper. Tape the pieces of paper together to form a continuous strip; then tape them to the floor at several spots to keep them from moving.

8. Steady the plumb bob; then mark the position of its point on the paper.

9. When you are ready to begin collecting data, place a sheet of carbon paper carbon-side down over the paper on the floor. When the ball strikes the floor, it will leave a carbon impression on the paper underneath. The distance from the plumb bob mark to the point where the ball strikes the paper is the range.

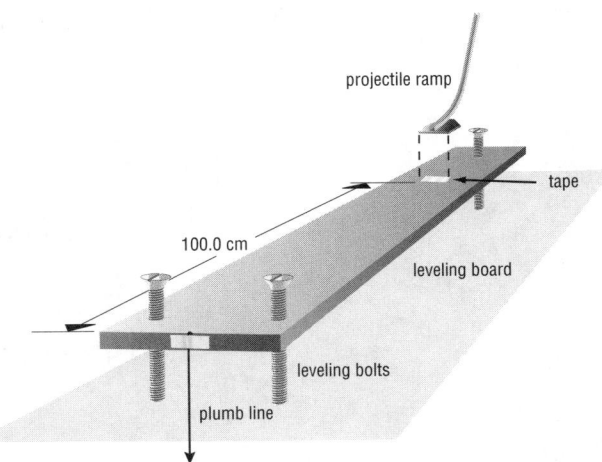

Figure 1

Data Collection

10. Horizontal Velocity Determined by Timing

    a. Hold a book at the end of the rolling surface so that when released, a ball will roll down the track across the surface and strike the book exactly at the point where you expect it to roll off the edge.

    b. Mark a position near the top of the projectile track with a pencil or a piece of tape. Choose a reference point on the ball (front edge, center line, or back edge) to align with the mark on the track (see Figure 2). Release the ball from this position and determine the length of time the ball takes to roll 1 m to the book. You will be able to hear the ball hit the horizontal surface when it leaves the track, and you will hear it again when it hits the book. Start and stop the stopwatch when you hear the corresponding sounds. If the ball is moving too fast to time accurately, release it from a lower position on the track and mark that position.

    c. Perform the timing process five times, using the same reference point on the ball, and record your results in Table 1 for Track Position 1. You will determine horizontal velocity and range later in the lab. If one of your five trials is greatly different from the others, cross out the time in Table 1 and perform another trial. You should have five trials that are close to one another (i.e., the measurements should show good precision).

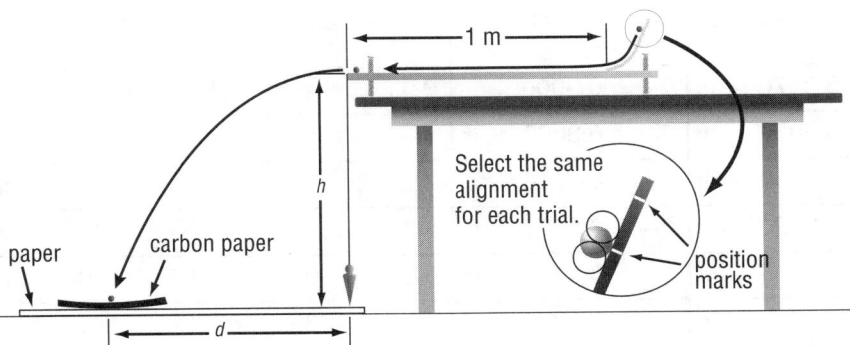

Figure 2

11. Range Determined by Track Position

    In these steps you will allow the ball to roll off the end of the rolling surface onto the floor. Work in teams of two, with one partner observing where the ball strikes the paper and the other partner releasing the ball from the marked position on the ramp.

    a. The observer should hold the carbon paper while the other student conducts a practice run from the track position to be tested. The observer should center the carbon paper over the place where the ball landed.

    b. Perform five trials. Between each trial, the observer should remove the carbon paper and label the newest dot closest to the plumb bob mark (the ball may bounce and make multiple marks) with "1-1" (for Track Position 1, Trial 1), "1-2," etc. The notation should be adjacent to the spot where the ball strikes the paper. Cross out any extra dots before going on to the next trial.

12. Repeat Steps 10–11 for three other positions on the track. Try one position near the bottom of the ramp but high enough that the ball still rolls at a fairly constant speed straight across the 1 m distance. Choose two other positions spaced evenly between the top and bottom positions.

13. After completing the data collection for all four track positions, carefully remove the paper from the floor, keeping the sheets taped together.

14. Measure the distance from the plumb bob mark to the center of each of the labeled ball marks. Record the range (d) for each track position in Table 1.

Data

Table 1

Initial and Experimental Data

Height of rolling surface above paper surface, h _____0.746_____ m

Time of fall of ball through h, t_f _____0.390_____ s

	Trial	Track Position 1		Track Position 2		Track Position 3		Track Position 4	
Table Time, t_t	1		1.01 s		1.31 s		2.12 s		2.81 s
	2		1.12 s		1.32 s		2.06 s		2.70 s
	3		0.99 s		1.40 s		2.07 s		2.82 s
	4		1.01 s		1.29 s		2.03 s		2.81 s
	5		0.98 s		1.34 s		2.00 s		2.74 s
	Average		1.02 s		1.33 s		2.06 s		2.78 s
Table Velocity, v_t	Average		0.980 m/s		0.752 m/s		0.486 m/s		0.360 m/s
Range, d	1	1-1	0.3770 m	2-1	0.3000 m	3-1	0.1940 m	4-1	0.1440 m
	2	1-2	0.3850 m	2-2	0.3002 m	3-2	0.1950 m	4-2	0.1450 m
	3	1-3	0.3780 m	2-3	0.3006 m	3-3	0.1890 m	4-3	0.1490 m
	4	1-4	0.3790 m	2-4	0.2998 m	3-4	0.2000 m	4-4	0.1420 m
	5	1-5	0.3700 m	2-5	0.3003 m	3-5	0.1900 m	4-5	0.1300 m
	Average		0.3780 m		0.3002 m		0.1936 m		0.1420 m
Air velocity, v_a	Average		0.969 m/s		0.770 m/s		0.496 m/s		0.364 m/s
Percent Difference			1.13 %		2.37 %		2.04 %		1.10 %

Data and calculations in Table 1 will vary. Data and calculations are typical.

Postlab Exercises

1. Calculate the time required for the ball to fall from the rolling surface to the floor, using the second equation of motion, Equation (1). This quantity is t_f. Record the time of fall in seconds in the blank above Table 1.

2. Calculate the average table time (t_t) for each track position. Record the value under the appropriate track position in Table 1.

3. Use the average t_t to calculate the horizontal velocity (v_t) of the ball as it traveled 1 m over the rolling surface, where $v_t = (1.000 \text{ m})/t_t$. Record the value for v_t for each track position in Table 1.

4. Calculate the average range (d) for each track position and enter the value in Table 1.

5. Table 1 now contains ordered pairs of horizontal table velocity (v_t) and range (d). Plot these coordinates for the four track positions on Graph 1. Select appropriate scales that include all of the values of velocity, ranging from zero to the maximum value, while making the graph as large as possible. After plotting the points, draw a line of best fit that lies as close as possible to all of the data points.

6. Calculate the horizontal velocity of the ball in the air (v_a) for each track position, using the average range (d) and the time of fall (t_f), where $v_a = d/t_f$. Record the values for v_a in Table 1.

7. Calculate the percent difference between v_t and v_a for each track position and enter the values in Table 1. Recall that

$$\text{percent difference} = \frac{|\text{difference between the two values}|}{} \times 100\%.$$

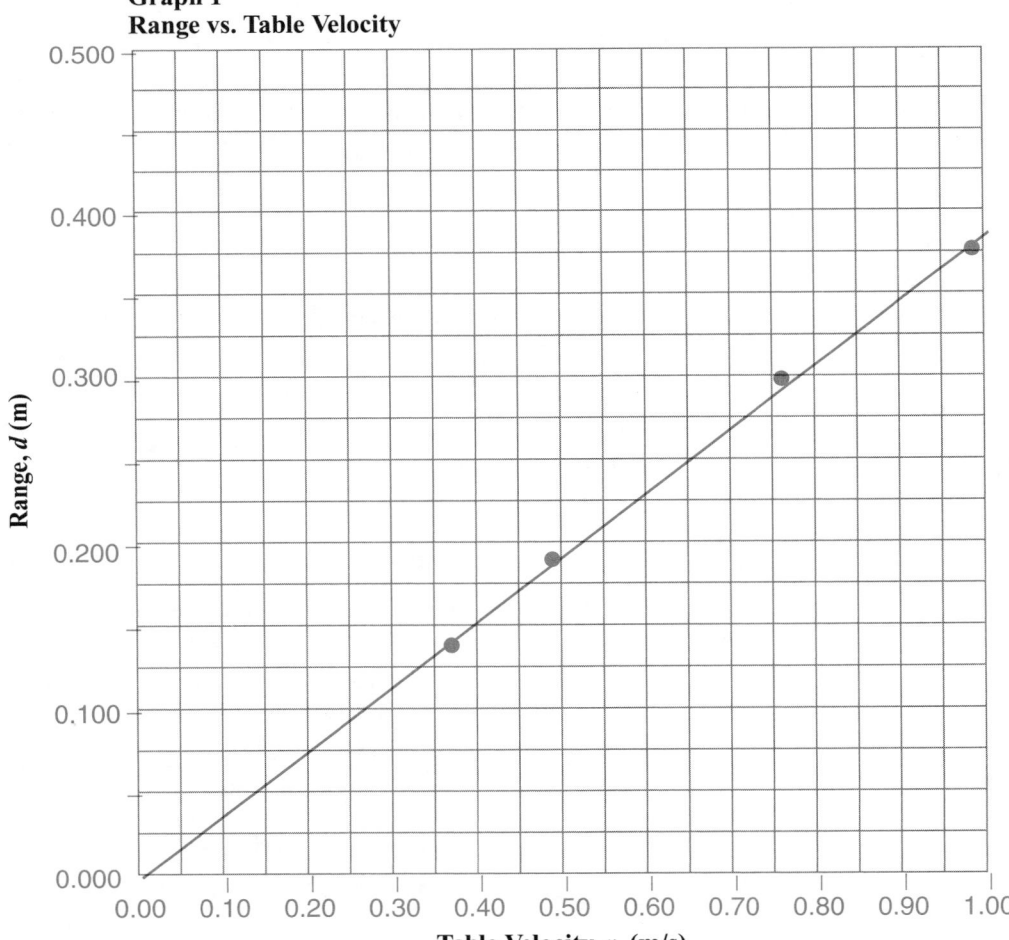

Graph 1
Range vs. Table Velocity

Range, d (m) vs. Table Velocity, v_t (m/s)

Answers will vary. Plotted graph is from typical data.

Postlab Analysis

1. _____b_____ How does the range compare to the horizontal velocity?

   a. It is inversely proportional.

   b. It is directly proportional.

   c. It is proportional to the square of the velocity.

   d. It is proportional to the square root of the velocity.

2. _____yes_____ Does your answer to Question 1 agree with the hypothesis you stated in the Prelab Discussion? A *no* answer is possible if the answer to Question 1 is incorrect.

3. _____b_____ Friction between the rolling surface and the ball is one possible source of error. Increasing friction would likely . . .

   a. increase the range.

   b. decrease the range.

   c. not affect the range.

4. _____a_____ How does increasing the rolling distance of the ball *on the projectile track* affect the average range for each position?

   a. It increases the range.

   b. It decreases the range.

   c. It does not affect the range.

5. _____b_____ How does increasing the rolling distance of the ball *on the projectile track* affect the average time that the ball takes to roll across the horizontal surface?

   a. It increases the time.

   b. It decreases the time.

   c. It does not affect the time.

6. _____yes_____ Does your graph approximate a straight line rising diagonally toward the right? A *no* answer is possible.

7. _____c_____ The range is directly proportional to . . .

   a. the horizontal velocity.

   b. the time that the ball is in the air.

   c. both a and b.

   d. neither a nor b.

8. _____False_____ The horizontal range is directly proportional to the height that the projectile must drop. (True/False)

9. Discuss three *specific* factors that could contribute to differences between the two methods of determining horizontal velocity in this experiment.

   Possible answers include errors measuring the time interval as the

   ball rolls 1 m, friction of the ball on the rolling surface, the ball not

   rolling in a straight line, irregularities in the rolling surface, errors

   measuring the range from the plumb bob, calculation errors, or not

   following the lab instructions.

Name _____

Date _____ Hour _____

PRELAB HOMEWORK

1. Write complete definitions for the following terms.

   a. projectile

   A projectile is an object that is given an initial velocity and then is permitted to
   fall under the influence of only gravity.

   b. horizontal projection

   A horizontal projection is an event in which an object initially possesses only a
   horizontal velocity and then falls under the influence of only gravity.

   c. range

   Range is the horizontal distance traversed by a projectile during its time of
   fall (or through its trajectory).

2. Discuss the two methods for determining the horizontal velocity of the ball in this lab.

   One method involves measuring the time required for the ball to traverse a
   measured distance (1 m) and computing velocity directly. The second method
   requires calculating the time of fall of the ball, using the second equation of
   motion, and measuring the range of the projectile. The horizontal velocity can
   be calculated from these two quantities.

3. ___0.452 s___ How long (in seconds) will it take an object initially at rest to fall a vertical distance of 1.000 m?

   Given: $d = 1.000$ m; $a = g = 9.81 \frac{m}{s^2}$; $t_f = ?$

   Formula: $t_f = \sqrt{\dfrac{2d}{g}}$ (derived from the second equation of motion)

   Solution: $t_f = \sqrt{\dfrac{2(1.000 \text{ m})}{9.81 \frac{m}{s^2}}} \doteq 0.452$ s

4. ___1.43 m/s___ If a ball rolls along a horizontal surface 2.000 m long in 1.40 s, what is its
   average velocity?

   Given: $d = 2.000$ m; $\Delta t = 1.40$ s; $v = ?$

   Formula: $v = \dfrac{d}{\Delta t}$

   Solution: $v = \dfrac{2.000 \text{ m}}{1.40 \text{ s}} \doteq 1.43 \frac{m}{s}$

5. ___1.43 m/s___ If there is no friction, then what is the instantaneous horizontal velocity at
   any point along the 2 m path for the ball in Question 4?

6. ___2.21 m/s___ If a horizontally projected object falls a vertical distance of 1.000 m and
   its range is 1.000 m, what is its initial horizontal velocity?

   From Question 3, the time of fall (t_f) through 1.000 m (time in the air) is 0.452 s.

   $v_x = \dfrac{d_x}{t_f} = \dfrac{1.000 \text{ m}}{0.452 \text{ s}} \doteq 2.21 \frac{m}{s}$

7. ___4.42 m/s___ What would the initial horizontal velocity be if the projectile falls the same vertical distance as in Question 6 but has a range of 2.000 m?

The object is still in the air for 0.452 s; but it travels twice as far.

$$v_x = \frac{d_x}{t_f} = \frac{2.000 \text{ m}}{0.452 \text{ s}} \doteq 4.42 \; \frac{\text{m}}{\text{s}}$$

8. ___1.56 m/s___ What would the velocity be if the projectile falls twice the vertical distance (2.000 m) and has a range of 1.000 m?

Since the vertical distance is greater, the object is in the air longer.

$$t_f = \sqrt{\frac{2d}{g}} = \sqrt{\frac{2(2.000 \text{ m})}{9.81 \; \frac{\text{m}}{\text{s}^2}}} \doteq 0.639 \text{ s}$$

$$v_x = \frac{d_x}{t_f} = \frac{1.000 \text{ m}}{0.639 \text{ s}} \doteq 1.56 \; \frac{\text{m}}{\text{s}} \; (1.57 \; \frac{\text{m}}{\text{s}} \text{ for composite calculation})$$

9. _____a_____ If horizontal velocity and range were plotted on a Cartesian coordinate system, the resulting graph would probably be . . .

a. a straight diagonal line rising to the right.

b. a hyperbola.

c. a straight horizontal line.

d. a straight diagonal line rising to the left.

e. a curve rising to the right.

10. _____b_____ If the vertical distance is increased by a factor of 9, the time required for an object to fall through the distance would be . . .

a. 9 times greater.

b. 3 times greater.

c. 2 times greater.

d. 1/3 as great.

CIRCULAR MOTION

Purpose

This lab will familiarize you with some of the physical properties of circular motion. The purpose is to

- experimentally determine some factors that influence centripetal acceleration.
- provide practice generating graphs from data.
- provide experience interpreting graphic data.
- graphically determine a constant of proportionality.

Prelab Discussion

Before proceeding with the discussion, it is worthwhile to note that many of the physical quantities considered in this lab are vectors (velocity, force, and acceleration) and should normally be treated as such. However, in introductory physics courses it is often acceptable to deal with these quantities as scalars while retaining their vector names in order to keep the concepts from becoming excessively complicated. Labs that deal specifically with the vector nature of such quantities (where direction is important) employ the appropriate vector notation. In this lab you will determine how the velocity of an object in circular motion is related to the centripetal force that maintains the motion.

You know that in general, $F = ma,$ and thus for circular motion

$$a_c = \frac{F_c}{m}.$$

You also learned while studying circular motion that

$$a_c = \frac{v_t^2}{r}, \tag{1}$$

where a_c is the **centripetal acceleration,** v_t is the tangential velocity, and r is the radius of the circular path. Therefore, to determine the relationship between **centripetal force (F_c)** and velocity, F_c/m can be substituted for a_c in Equation (1), giving

$$\frac{F_c}{m} = \frac{v_t^2}{r}. \tag{2}$$

Rearranging Equation (2) to place the constants m and r on the right side yields

$$\frac{F_c}{v_t^2} = \frac{m}{r}. \tag{3}$$

The mass, $m,$ of any given object is constant, so if the radius of circular motion is kept constant, m/r will be constant. Symbolically,

$$\frac{m}{r} = k.$$

Consequently, according to Equation (3), the ratio F_c/v_t^2 should also be constant. Substitute k into Equation (3) and rearrange in order to obtain the following two equations:

$$\frac{F_c}{v_t^2} = k \tag{4}$$

$$F_c = kv_t^2 \tag{5}$$

From your study of algebra, you should recognize that Equation (5) has the form of a quadratic function, $y = kx^2,$ where y and x are the dependent and

---

Required Equipment

balance
glass tubing
masking tape
metal washers, 30
rubber stopper (or other mass)
stopwatch
string, 1 m

Optional Equipment

metric masses

Prelab Discussion

- Review the prerequisites for Lab 2-6 in the back of this manual. Ensure that you have covered the applicable sections before performing this lab.

- The Prelab Discussion reviews the material presented in the textbook. Emphasize which quantities vary and which are constant when performing this experiment.

- Point out that students will be making several graphs of their data in order to verify a particular relationship between force and speed. Scientists often follow such a procedure in order to determine an empirical relationship among variables.

Equipment and Setup

- With the exception of the balance, the recommended equipment is easily and inexpensively obtained locally or from science equipment suppliers.

- Any compact solid object that can be tied to a string may be substituted for the stopper.

- The glass tube should be approximately 15 cm long and 4 mm ID. It may be replaced by the barrel of a ballpoint pen.

- Metal washers are preferred over metric masses because they can be added in smaller increments. Keep the stopper mass and the total washer mass small. The success of this lab depends on maintaining the string and stopper in an essentially horizontal plane.

- Use sewing thread that has been precut into 1 m lengths.

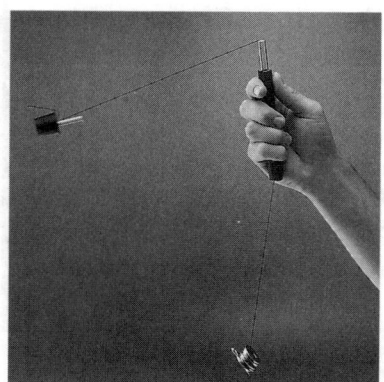

Figure 1

Procedure

- This lab is simple to prepare, but the technique required to obtain good data will take some practice. Instruct the students to set up Trial 1 and practice swinging the stopper until they can consistently keep the stopper swinging horizontally at a constant speed with the tape marker stationary. See the photo for the preferred technique.

- By stipulating constant radius, constant revolving mass, and *constant string tension* for a given trial, the entire system will be in equilibrium only at a certain orbital period. Any other period will cause the tape marker to rise or fall from the position specified in the procedure.

- The student swinging the stopper should count revolutions out loud while another student monitors the position of the marker and notes the elapsed time.

- In order to save time, ensure that students spend the lab period collecting the time and mass data. All calculations and graphing can be done afterward.

Postlab Exercises

- Some students may have difficulty setting up the scales for Graphs 1 and 2. Remind them to set the scales so that they maximize the size of the graph.

- The graphs can be compared more easily by starting the scales at the

independent variables, respectively. The graph of such a function would be a parabola, which is somewhat difficult to evaluate with basic graphic tools.

If the *square* of v_t in Equation (5) were considered the variable instead of v_t, then you would have a function in the form of a **direct variation,** $y = kx$, where k is the **constant of variation.** Direct variations are *linear functions*. If you plotted F_c vs. (v_t^2) on a graph, then you would expect the graph to be a straight line that passes through the origin with a constant positive slope, k. (This is characteristic of a direct variation.) Under what conditions would this be true? From the above discussion, you should see that for any given object, the quantity k (recall that $k = m/r$) is constant *as long as the radius of the circle of motion of the object is constant.*

You will verify this hypothesis by using the simple apparatus shown in Figure 1. You will revolve an object on a string in an approximately horizontal circle. (Ideally, the string and the object should lie in a single plane, but that will not be possible.) The string passes through a glass tubing handle with which you swing the object, and metal washers or other masses are attached to the bottom end of the string. Assuming that the string acts as an ideal string and the object moves in a horizontal path, *the centripetal force holding the object in the circle is equal to the weight of the washers.* You can determine the mass of the washers, and since gravity acts on the washers, you can calculate their weight. The glass tube is required so that your hand does not restrict the movement of the string or affect the tensioning force as you swing the assembly.

You will make a total of seven data collection trials revolving a constant mass. They will be made with a *constant radius,* but you will vary the centripetal force by increasing the number of washers with each trial. This will require you to increase the tangential velocity of the object in order to balance the additional weight. You will be able to determine the velocity for each trial by timing the revolutions of the object. In the Postlab Exercises you will graph F_c vs. v_t, F_c vs. v_t^2, F_c vs. $1/v_t$, and F_c vs. $1/v_t^2$. Since you are trying to find a direct-variation relationship to support your hypothesis, you will look for the graph having the properties of the direct-variation graph discussed above. The particular function that produces such a graph contains a constant of variation and represents the hypothetical relationship.

Procedure

Setup

1. Measure the mass of a medium-sized, two-hole rubber stopper (or other object) to be used in this experiment. Record the mass (m_s) in the blank above Table 1.

2. Place 30 identical washers on a balance and determine their total mass. Divide the mass by 30 to find the average mass per washer. Record this value in the blank above Table 1.

3. Refer to Figure 2 as you construct the apparatus. Tie the stopper to one end of a string that is about 1 m long. Thread the other end of the string through the glass or heavy plastic tube (e.g., ballpoint pen barrel) that will serve as the handle. Tie a large paper clip to the end of the string opposite the rubber stopper. Open the paper clip slightly so that you can hook the washers onto it.

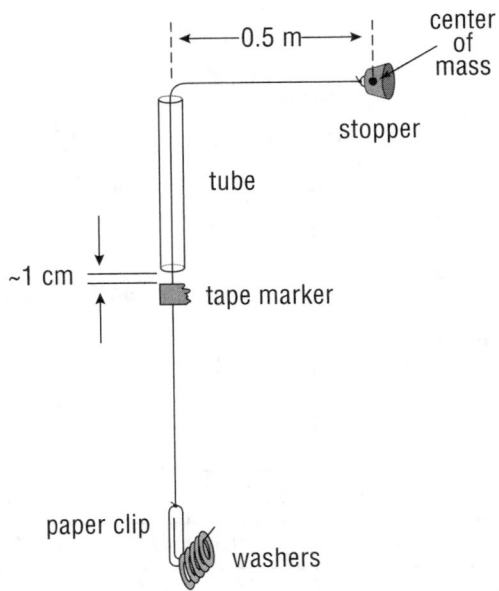

Figure 2

origin (0, 0). The direct variation of F_c vs. v_t^2 should be obvious.

- The quality of the graphs will depend heavily on the quality of the data that was collected. The relationship that exists between the variables may not be obvious from the manually plotted data points. If possible, have students use an advanced graphing calculator to analyze the graphs, using the techniques discussed in Appendix D. Regression analysis using a calculator should reveal the proper relationships.

4. Pull the string through the handle until the distance from the center (of mass) of the stopper to the top of the handle is 0.500 m. Without moving the string, have your partner place a piece of tape on the string 1.0 cm below the bottom end of the handle.

Data Collection

5. Place six washers (or approximately 40 g) on the paper clip hook. Swing the stopper in a circular path above your head as horizontally as possible. Adjust the speed with which you swing the stopper until the tape marker stays steady at 1 cm below the handle. When the marker is steady, you know that the forces along the string are in equilibrium, and you can presume that the velocity of the stopper is also constant.

6. When you feel confident that you can swing the stopper at a constant velocity, have your partner measure the amount of time that it takes to complete 10 revolutions while you maintain the velocity. You should count out loud as the stopper passes a predetermined point while your partner watches a stopwatch or clock (the clock must have a second hand). Record the number of washers used and the elapsed time for Trial 1 in Table 1. (If you are using metric masses, record the mass in Table 1 under m_w.) To save time, leave the other columns in Table 1 blank. You can make those calculations after you finish all of the trials.

7. For the remaining six trials, use the following masses. Use the same 0.5 m radius for all of the trials. Record mass and time data for each trial in Table 1.

Trial	Washers	Mass
2	9	60 g
3	12	80 g
4	15	100 g
5	18	120 g
6	21	140 g
7	24	160 g

Data

Table 1
Data and Calculations

Mass of stopper, m_s ___0.012 40___ kg   Mass per washer ___0.006 67___ kg/washer

Radius of orbit, r ___0.500___ m   Circumference of orbit, C ___3.142___ m

Trial	Time for 10 Orbits, t (s)	Number of Washers, n	Mass of Washers, m_w (kg)	Weight of Washers, $F_w = m_w g$ (N)	Period, T (s)	Tangential Velocity, v_t (m/s)	v_t^2 $\left(\frac{m^2}{s^2}\right)$	$\frac{1}{v_t}$ $\left[\left(\frac{m}{s}\right)^{-1}\right]$	$\frac{1}{v_s^2}$ $\left[\left(\frac{m}{s}\right)^{-2}\right]$	$\frac{m_s}{r}$ $\left(\frac{kg}{m}\right)$	$\frac{F_c}{v_t^2}$ $\left[\frac{N}{\left(\frac{m}{s}\right)^2}\right]$	Percent Difference %
1	7.80	6	0.0402	0.394	0.780	4.03	16.2	0.248	0.0616	0.0248	0.0243	
2	6.39	9	0.0600	0.589	0.639	4.92	24.2	0.203	0.0413	0.0248	0.0243	
3	5.51	12	0.0800	0.785	0.551	5.70	32.5	0.175	0.0308	0.0248	0.0242	
4	5.02	15	0.100	0.981	0.502	6.26	39.2	0.160	0.0255	0.0248	0.0250	
5	4.60	18	0.120	1.18	0.460	6.83	46.6	0.416	0.0214	0.0248	0.0253	
6	4.19	21	0.140	1.37	0.419	7.50	56.3	0.133	0.0178	0.0248	0.0243	
7	3.91	24	0.160	1.57	0.391	8.04	64.6	0.124	0.0155	0.0248	0.0243	
Average										0.0248	0.0245	1.22

Postlab Exercises

1. For each trial, calculate the following and record the values in Table 1.

    a. total mass of the washers, $m_w = (n$ washers$)(m$/washer$)$

    b. weight of the washers, $F_w = m_w g$

    c. period of each orbit, $T = t/10$

    d. tangential velocity, $v_t = C/T$

    e. numerical values for v_t^2, $1/v_t$, and $1/v_t^2$

    f. ratio of the stopper's mass to the radius of its orbit, m_s/r

    g. ratio of centripetal force (same as F_w) to tangential velocity squared, F_c/v_t^2

    h. percent difference between m_s/r and the average of F_c/v_t^2

2. Plot the following sets of data from Table 1 on the graphs.

    a. Graph 1: F_c vs. v_t and F_c vs. v_t^2

    b. Graph 2: F_c vs. $1/v_t$ and F_c vs. $1/v_t^2$

    Use contrasting colors to differentiate the graphs as suggested in the legend for the graphs.

3. As an alternative to Exercise 2, you may enter your data in a spreadsheet program or an advanced graphing calculator and produce the graphs in a digital format. Be sure that the resulting graphs are labeled correctly.

Postlab Analysis

1. _____kg/m_____ Using Equation (4), determine the *simplified* units for k.

$$k = \frac{F_c}{v_t^2} \Rightarrow \frac{N}{\frac{m^2}{s^2}} = \frac{\frac{kg \cdot m}{s^2}}{\frac{m^2}{s^2}} = \frac{kg \cdot m}{m^2} = \frac{kg}{m}$$

2. __0.0248 kg/m__ Record the ratio of the mass of the rubber stopper, m_s, and the radius of the circular path, r, determined in Table 1, This is equivalent to the constant, k.

   Answers will vary. The answer is from the typical data used in the lab.

3. __0.0246 kg/m__ Determine the slope of the line of best fit in the F_c vs. v_t^2 graph. Use the same method as in Lab 2-4. Show your work in the unused space in Graph 1.

   Answers will vary. The answer is based on the plot of the typical data.

4. __0.810%__ Calculate the percent difference between the results from Questions 2 and 3.

   Answers will vary. The result is based on the typical data.

$$\text{percent difference} = \frac{\left| 0.0248 \frac{kg}{m} - 0.0246 \frac{kg}{m} \right|}{\left(\frac{0.0248 \frac{kg}{m} + 0.0246 \frac{kg}{m}}{2} \right)} \times 100\% = 0.810\%$$

5. How do the graphic slope determined in Question 3 and the average of F_c/v_t^2 from Table 1 compare?

   The two values are very close. This is a characteristic of a direct variation.

6. Discuss the error that is introduced if the string is not horizontal as the stopper revolves in a circle (allowing the stopper to sag). Specifically mention how the stopper's weight affects the tension on the string.

   In this experiment it is assumed that the weight of the washers is equal to the tension in the string, which is F_c if the string is horizontal. If the stopper is permitted to sag as it revolves, the tension in the string becomes the resultant of F_c and the weight of the stopper, and the assumption becomes untrue. The tangential velocity is lower in this case than it should be; therefore, the value of k computed from F_c/v_t^2 will be higher than the value computed from m_s/r.

7. If the mass of the rubber stopper were increased, what would happen to the force needed to keep it in orbit if the tangential velocity and radius remained the same? How would the orbital period change?

   The centripetal force would increase.

$$F_c(\uparrow) = m_s(\uparrow)a_c(\leftrightarrow) = m_s(\uparrow)\frac{v_t^2(\leftrightarrow)}{r(\leftrightarrow)}$$

   The orbital period would remain the same. $T(\leftrightarrow) = \frac{C}{v_t} = \frac{2\pi r(\leftrightarrow)}{v_t(\leftrightarrow)}$

8. If the radius of the string were longer while maintaining constant mass and tangential velocity, how would the centripetal force change to compensate? How would the orbital period change?

   The centripetal force would decrease. $F_c(\downarrow) = m_s(\leftrightarrow) \dfrac{[v_t(\leftrightarrow)]^2}{r(\uparrow)}$

   The orbital period increases (takes more time per orbit).

   $T(\uparrow) = \dfrac{2\pi r(\uparrow)}{v_t(\leftrightarrow)}$

9. If the tangential velocity of the stopper increases while maintaining constant mass and constant radius, how does the centripetal force change? The orbital period?

   The centripetal force increases. $F_c(\uparrow) = m_s(\leftrightarrow) \dfrac{[v_t(\uparrow)]^2}{r(\leftrightarrow)}$

   The orbital period decreases (takes less time per orbit).

   $T(\downarrow) = \dfrac{2\pi r(\leftrightarrow)}{v_t(\uparrow)}$

Graph 1
F_c vs. V_t
F_c vs. V_t^2

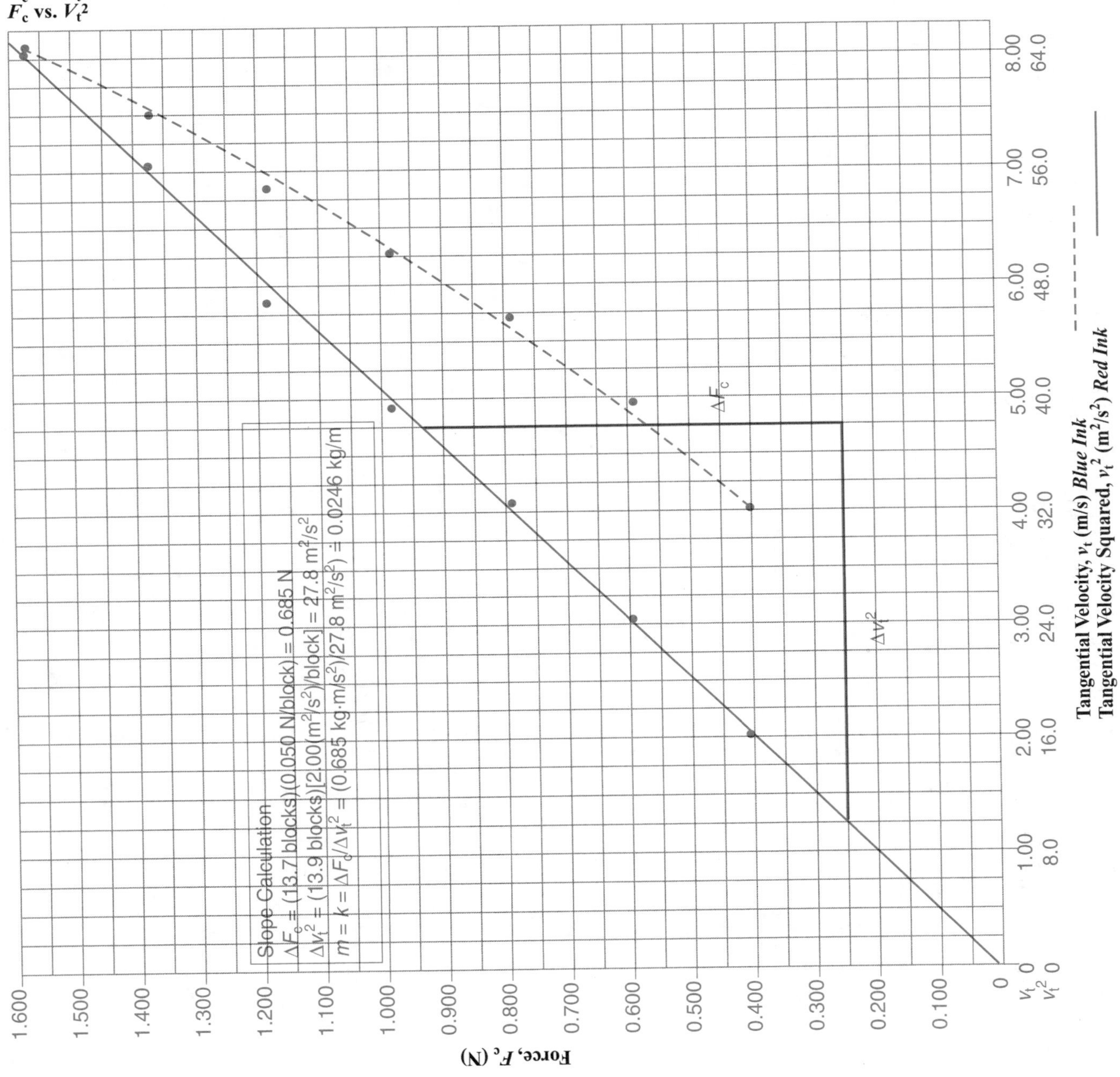

Slope Calculation
$\Delta F_c = (13.7 \text{ blocks})(0.050 \text{ N/block}) = 0.685 \text{ N}$
$\Delta v_t^2 = (13.9 \text{ blocks})[2.00 \text{ (m}^2\text{/s}^2\text{)/block}] = 27.8 \text{ m}^2\text{/s}^2$
$m = k = \Delta F_c/\Delta v_t^2 = (0.685 \text{ kg·m/s}^2)/27.8 \text{ m}^2\text{/s}^2) \doteq 0.0246 \text{ kg/m}$

ΔF_c

Δv_t^2

Force, F_c (N)

1.600 1.500 1.400 1.300 1.200 1.100 1.000 0.900 0.800 0.700 0.600 0.500 0.400 0.300 0.200 0.100 0

v_t 0   1.00   2.00   3.00   4.00   5.00   6.00   7.00   8.00
v_t^2 0   8.0   16.0   24.0   32.0   40.0   48.0   56.0   64.0

Tangential Velocity, v_t (m/s) Blue Ink ----
Tangential Velocity Squared, v_t^2 (m²/s²) Red Ink ——

Graph 2
F_c vs. $1/V_t$
F_c vs. $1/V_t^2$

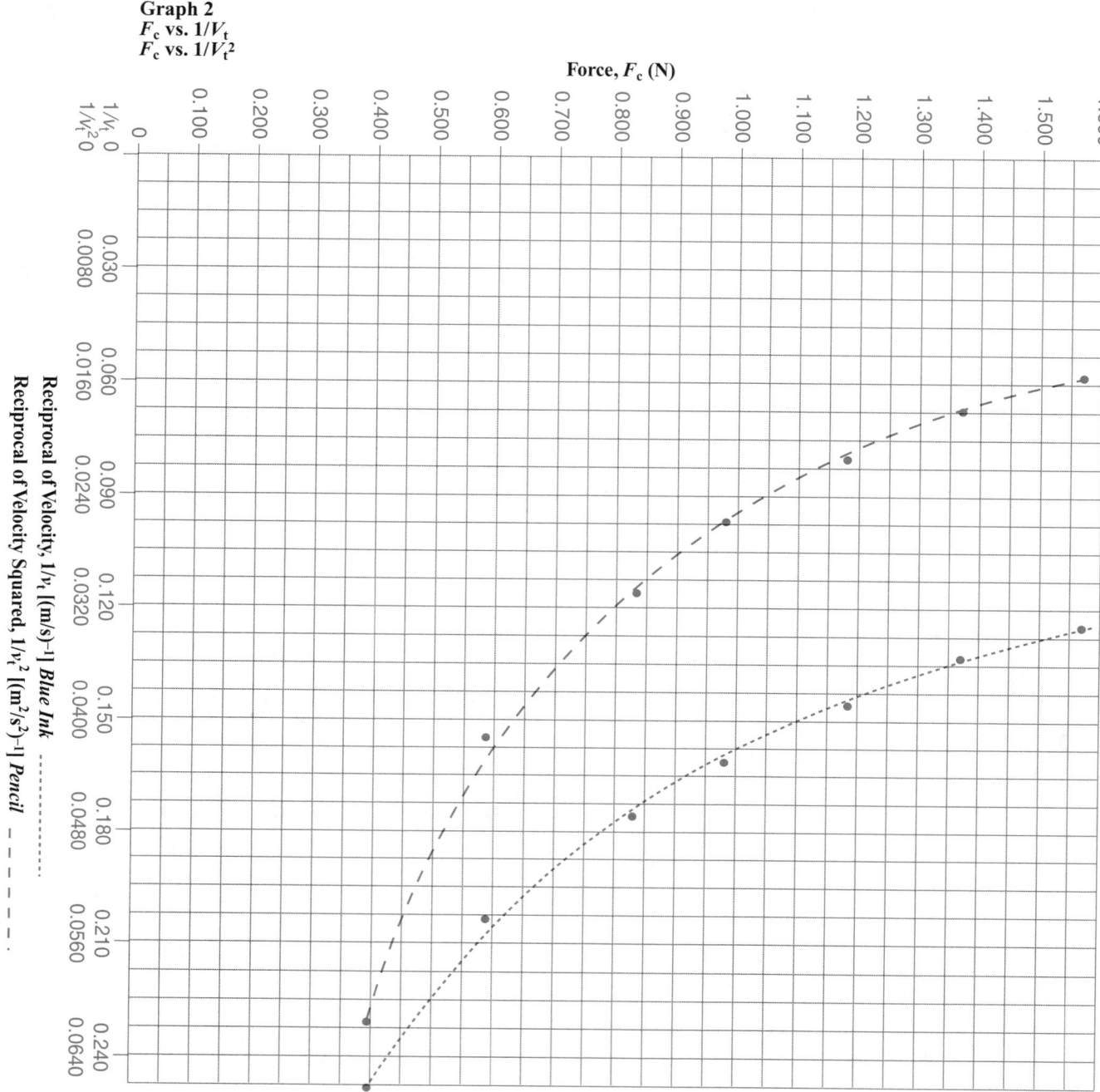

Force, F_c (N)

Reciprocal of Velocity, $1/v_t$ [(m/s)-1] *Blue Ink* --------

Reciprocal of Velocity Squared, $1/v_t^2$ [(m²/s²)-1] *Pencil* – – – – – – .

Name _____

Date _____ Hour ____

PRELAB HOMEWORK

1. Write the formula that you will use to determine the distance that an object will travel in one complete revolution of circular motion.

    $C = 2\pi r$

2. Define the period of an object in circular motion.

    The period is the time required for one complete revolution.

3. ___0.50 s/rev.___ If an object revolves 50 times in 25 s, what is the period of the object?

    Given: total time of revolutions, $t = 25$ s; number of revolutions, $n = 50$; $T = ?$

    Formula: $T = \dfrac{t}{n}$

    Solution: $T = \dfrac{25 \text{ s}}{50 \text{ rev.}} = 0.50 \frac{\text{s}}{\text{rev.}}$ (Revolutions are *counted*, so 2 SDs are allowed based on the *measured* time.)

4. ___9.4 m/s___ What is the tangential speed (v_t) of the object in Question 3 if the radius is 0.75 m?

    Given: $T = 0.50 \frac{\text{s}}{\text{rev}}$; $r = 0.75$ m; $v_t = ?$

    Formulas: $C = 2\pi r$; $v_t = \dfrac{C}{T}$

    Solution: $C = 2\pi(0.75 \text{ m}) \doteq 4.7$ m; $v_t = \dfrac{4.7 \frac{\text{m}}{\text{rev.}}}{0.50 \frac{\text{s}}{\text{rev.}}} = 9.4 \frac{\text{m}}{\text{s}}$

5. Write the formula for determining the magnitude of centripetal acceleration (a_c) for an object in circular motion. (Refer to your textbook if necessary.)

    $a_c = \dfrac{v_t^2}{r}$

6. ___120 m/s²___ Calculate the magnitude of centripetal acceleration for the object in Questions 3 and 4.

    Given: $v_t = 9.4 \frac{\text{m}}{\text{s}}$; $r = 0.75$ m; $a_c = ?$

    Formula: $a_c = \dfrac{v_t^2}{r}$

    Solution: $a_c = \dfrac{\left(9.4 \frac{\text{m}}{\text{s}}\right)^2}{0.75 \text{ m}} = \dfrac{88.36 \frac{\text{m}^2}{\text{s}^2}}{0.75 \text{ m}} \doteq 118 \frac{\text{m}}{\text{s}^2} \approx 120 \frac{\text{m}}{\text{s}^2}$ (2 SDs allowed)

7. ___30. N___ Calculate the centripetal force (F_c) on the object in Question 6 if its mass is 0.25 kg.

    Given: $m = 0.25$ kg; $a_c = 120 \frac{\text{m}}{\text{s}^2}$; $F_c = ?$

    Formula: $F_c = ma_c$

    Solution: $F_c = (0.25 \text{ kg})(120 \frac{\text{m}}{\text{s}^2}) = 30.$ N (2 SDs allowed)

8. Based on your knowledge of centripetal acceleration, you would expect that doubling the tangential speed of an object revolving in a circular orbit would ___quadruple___ the centripetal force on the object. (Be specific.)

9. List the two quantities in this experiment that you will attempt to maintain constant for every trial.

    a. the mass of the object

    b. the radius of the circular motion

10. Based on the relationship shown for the constant k in Equation (4) in the Prelab Discussion, what would you expect to be the units associated with this constant?

    The units for the constant k should be $\dfrac{N}{\left(\frac{m}{s}\right)^2}$, $\dfrac{N}{\frac{m^2}{s^2}}$, or $\dfrac{kg}{m}$.

11. Which two variables would you have to graph to obtain a straight line with a slope having the units given in your answer to Question 10? (Remember that slope is the ratio of the change in the dependent variable to the change in the independent variable.)

    Graphing force vs. velocity squared will yield a straight line having a slope with units of $\dfrac{N}{\left(\frac{m}{s}\right)^2}$ or $\dfrac{kg}{m}$.

Name _____

Date _____ Hour _____

MECHANICAL ADVANTAGE—EFFICIENCY

Purpose

This laboratory exercise will help you better understand the concept of mechanical advantage and efficiency. The purpose is to

- distinguish between effort and resistance forces.
- calculate the theoretical mechanical advantage of a simple machine.
- calculate the efficiency of a simple machine.

Required Equipment
dual-tandem pulleys, 2
masking tape
meter stick
metric masses, 3
pulley support
spring scale
string or cord, 3 m

Prelab Discussion

In this activity you will use pulleys to demonstrate **mechanical advantage (MA)**. A pulley is a simple machine functionally similar to a lever in that it consists of an effort arm and a resistance arm pivoting on a fulcrum. In a pulley, the effort and resistance arms are of equal length (why?), and the fulcrum is the pulley axle. The advantage of a pulley over a lever is that a pulley's movement is not constrained—the angle through which it can rotate is unlimited in response to the efforts and loads applied to it.

There are two basic types of pulleys that serve different purposes. A **fixed pulley,** one that is attached to an unmovable point, does nothing more than change the direction of the force applied to it. Since its effort and resistance arms are equal, the MA of a fixed pulley will always be 1. A pulley that is attached directly or indirectly to the load so that it can move with the load will always have two lines (e.g., ropes, strings) supporting it. This **movable pulley** will have an MA greater than 1 because the effort force is applied to only one of the supporting lines.

Some special terms that are associated with pulleys are useful in describing the procedures in this lab. A **pulley block** consists of a rotating wheel called a **sheave,** which is supported by a framework called the **cheeks.** The sheave rotates on a **pin** that passes through the cheeks of the block. Pulley blocks are named according to the number of sheaves they contain. Single-, double-, and triple-sheave blocks are common in lab experiments. If the pulley sheaves are *not* mounted on the *same* pin, the block is called a **tandem** block. The end of the line that supports the load is called the **standing part,** and the line that is pulled through the block is called the **running part.** If a block has a ring where a line can be connected to the bottom of the block, the point of attachment is called a **becket.** A pulley system consisting of two or more pulley blocks and the associated lines and hooks that are connected together to lift a load is called a **block and tackle.**

The mechanical advantage usually associated with simple machines is the **theoretical mechanical advantage (TMA).** The word "theoretical" implies that TMA is not realistic. In real life, friction operates at all points in a process, ensuring that no machine produces the same amount of work that is put into it. This is the measure of efficiency—the ratio of work out to work in. There are several ways to measure efficiency. Recall that the concept of the conservation of work allows us to say

$$W_{in} = W_{out},$$

and therefore,

$$F_{in}d_{in} = F_{out}d_{out}.$$

Prelab Discussion

- Review the prerequisites for Lab 2-7 in the back of this manual.

- Emphasize that the theoretical mechanical advantage (TMA) cannot be attained in real systems because of the presence of nonconservative effects, such as friction. Note that d_{in}/d_{out} yields the TMA. Because of the concept of the conservation of work, this quantity should be equal to the other side of the proportion, F_{out}/F_{in}. The presence of friction, however, opposes the output force, so the ratio of the real forces gives the AMA for the system.

- The symbol for mechanical efficiency, η (Greek letter eta), may be new to your students.

Equipment and Setup

- Multiple sheave pulleys can be obtained inexpensively from science equipment supply companies. Tandem pulleys are recommended over standard gang blocks because students can follow the path of the cord through the block more easily.

- The support should be substantial— use a heavy-duty lab support stand or a support rod set into a lab-bench socket. You may also use two ring stands with a crossbar clamped to them. A stick of wood laid across the backs of two chairs is serviceable.

- Using large metric masses for the test objects is preferable, but any objects that can be weighed may be used.

- The meter stick may be clamped using a buret clamp or a right-angle clamp. It can also be taped to the horizontal support arm next to the block and tackle.

Procedure

- The procedure is simple and self-explanatory. Remind students to read their measurements to the limits of precision allowed by their instruments.

- Remind students to zero the spring scale for the position in which it will be used. The zero setting when weighing the objects will be different from the zero setting when the scale is used upside down to measure the effort force.

By rearranging terms, we see that

$$\frac{F_{out}}{F_{in}} = \frac{d_{in}}{d_{out}}.$$

From the discussion of TMA in your text, you should remember that d_{in}/d_{out} equals TMA. This implies that F_{out}/F_{in} is also equal to TMA. However, this assumption is never true in the real world. The quantity F_{out}/F_{in} is called the **actual mechanical advantage (AMA).** The ratio of AMA to TMA is the **efficiency** of a machine, represented by η (Greek letter eta). The force that is put into a machine to do work (F_{in}) is usually called the **effort.** The force that the machine puts out (F_{out}), which is the reaction force equal to the load, is called the **resistance.**

Keep in mind that machines are generally designed to multiply force, which makes work appear "easier." Machines cannot change the amount of work required. If they did, a fundamental law of conservation would be violated. Work is "easier" in that it requires less force, but you have to apply that force over a greater distance.

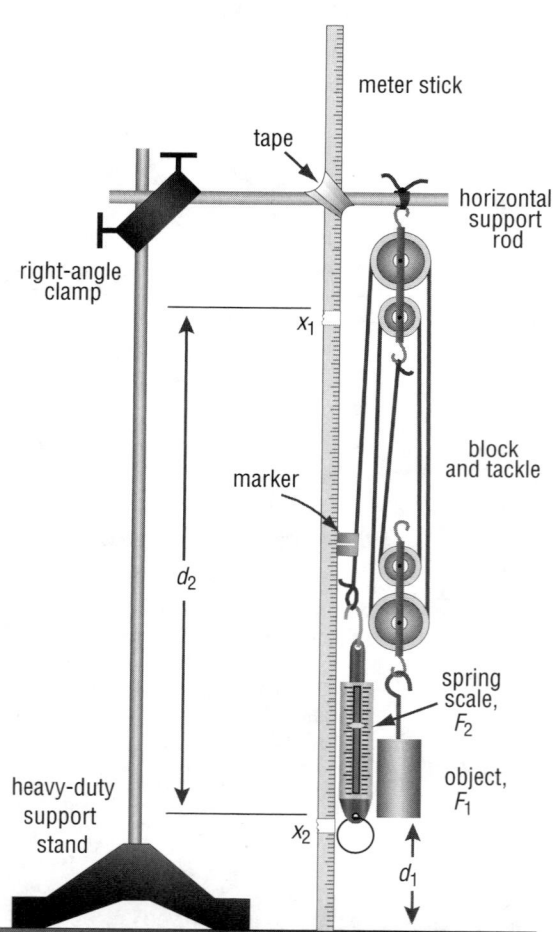

Figure 1

- Check during the lab to ensure that the running parts of the lines are essentially vertical when students measure the upper and lower positions (x_1 and x_2). If the lines are not vertical, then the calculated change in position will be incorrect.

Procedure

Setup

1. Assemble the block and tackle apparatus according to Figure 1. (Your pulley blocks may not be tandem as shown.) When loading the line into the blocks, tie or hook the upper block to the support first; then tie the standing part of the line to the becket on the bottom of the fixed block. Ask an assistant to hold the movable block while you run the line through the remaining sheaves. When the block and tackle is assembled, hook the first 1 kg mass into the lower block and tie off the running part on the support stand until you are ready to begin recording data. Always keep tension on the lines through the blocks in order to prevent the lines from slipping out of the sheaves.

2. Clamp or tape the meter stick to the support stand next to the block and tackle so that the running part of the line lies against the meter stick. Hold the running part taut and carefully wrap a piece of masking tape around the line about 10 cm from the upper pulley. Draw a thin horizontal mark on the tape. This will be the reference mark for the measurement of effort distance. Tie a loop in the line just below the tape.

Data Collection

3. Hold the running part of the line taut and against the meter stick. The mass should be barely touching the table. Place a piece of tape on the meter stick corresponding to the position of the mark drawn on the tape in Step 2. The upper edge of the tape should be used to indicate the marker position (x_1).

4. Pull down on the running part until the marker is near the tabletop. Place a piece of tape corresponding to this position (x_2) on the meter stick. At the same time, without moving the line, measure the distance that the mass was raised off of the table (d_{out}).

5. Check that the spring scale is zeroed for upside down use. Hook it into the loop and measure the force (F_{in}) required to suspend the 1 kg mass. The mass should not be moving when you make the measurement. Record this value in Table 1.

6. Lower the mass to the table and tie the running part to the support stand.

7. Record the positions of x_1 and x_2 in Table 1 for Trial 1. Zero the spring scale for use in the normal upright position and record the weight of the load (F_{out}). Remove the pieces of tape from the meter stick.

(F_{out}). Remove the pieces of tape from the meter stick.

8. Perform Steps 1—5 twice more, once with a heavier mass than you used in Trial 1 and once with a lighter mass. Record your data in Table 1.

- An optional step may be performed in order to clearly demonstrate the effects of friction on efficiency. Have students measure the force required to raise the object at a slow

Table 1
Experimental Data

Trial	Resistance Distance, d_{out}		Effort Start Position, x_1		Effort End Position, x_2		Effort Distance, d_{in} $|x_2 - x_1|$		Resistance, F_{out}		Effort, F_{in}	
1	0.1500	m	0.7000	m	0.1000	m	0.6000	m	9.8	N	2.5	N
2	0.1500	m	0.7000	m	0.1000	m	0.6000	m	19.6	N	5.0	N
3	0.1500	m	0.7000	m	0.1000	m	0.6000	m	4.9	N	1.3	N

Data shown in Table 1 is typical. Actual data will vary.

Data

Postlab Exercises

1. Calculate TMA (two ways), AMA, W_{out}, W_{in}, and η (two ways).

2. Calculate the percent difference between the two efficiencies.

but constant speed using the pulley system. Students will observe that dynamic F_{in} is larger than static F_{in}. The presence of rolling friction in the pins of the pulleys causes this reduction in efficiency. Question 7 in the Postlab Analysis deals with this situation.

Table 2
Calculations

Trial	TMA (number of supporting strands)	TMA $\left(\dfrac{d_{in}}{d_{out}}\right)$	AMA $\left(\dfrac{F_{out}}{F_{in}}\right)$	Work Out, W_{out} ($F_{out}d_{out}$)	Work In, W_{in} ($F_{in}d_{in}$)	η_1 $\left(\dfrac{AMA}{TMA}\right)$	η_2 $\left(\dfrac{W_{out}}{W_{in}}\right)$	Percent Difference between η_1 and η_2
1	4	4	3.9	1.47 J	1.5 J	98 %	98 %	0 %
2	4	4	3.9	2.94 J	3.0 J	98 %	98 %	0 %
3	4	4	3.8	0.74 J	0.78 J	95 %	95 %	0 %
Average						97 %	97 %	0 %

Answers shown in Table 2 are typical. Actual answers will vary.

3. Record your results in Table 2. Neatly show your work in the space provided.

Calculations

Prelab Homework

- As always, insist on observing correct SDs in calculations.

- The questions are designed to exercise students in all of the calculations that they will have to perform for the lab.

Postlab Analysis

All questions refer to a block and tackle pulley system similar to the one used in this lab.

1. How does the TMA determined from counting the number of supporting lines compare to the TMA calculated from the ratio of the effort distance to the resistance distance?

   The two TMAs should be essentially the same.

2. What effect does increasing the *mass* of the load have on the *amount of line* pulled through the pulleys in lifting the mass a given distance?

   The mass of the load has no effect on the amount of line pulled through the pulleys.

3. How is the *theoretical force* needed to lift the load related to the *weight* of the load?

   The theoretical force is equal to the weight of the load divided by the TMA.

4. How will the actual force required to move a load compare to the theoretical force determined by the method in Question 3? Explain your answer.

   The actual force required will be greater than the theoretical force because of the presence of friction.

5. What effect does increasing the mass of the load have on the amount of work put into the system in order to lift the load a given distance?

   The amount of work will increase in proportion to the increase in mass.

6. If you found the efficiency to be 100% or greater, what source of error would be likely?

   Accept any of the following: malfunction of the spring scale, error zeroing the spring scale, error reading instruments, not following the procedure, or calculation error.

7. Explain why you may have to exert 10.5 N of effort to lift a 10 N object but only 10.1 N to hold it suspended above the table. What consequences will this observation have on determining the efficiency of the system?

   The friction of the system when moving an object is greater than when holding the object in one position. The calculated efficiency would be greater when the object is stationary. Therefore, the condition of the system must be specified.

Name _____

Date _____ Hour _____

PRELAB HOMEWORK

1. _____b_____ The TMA of a single fixed pulley is . . .

   a. <1.

   b. 1.

   c. >1.

   d. undeterminable from the given information.

2. _____5_____ What is the TMA of the block and tackle in Figure 2?

3. _____200. N_____ What force would be required to lift an object weighing 1000. N with the block and tackle shown in Figure 2? Provide the *theoretical* answer in newtons, assuming 100% efficiency. Use the appropriate number of SDs.

   $\text{TMA} = \dfrac{F_{out}}{F_{in}}; F_{in} = \dfrac{F_{out}}{\text{TMA}} = \dfrac{1000.\,\text{N}}{5} = 200.\,\text{N}$ Note: The answer can be precise only to 1 N. Since the 5 in the denominator is a *counted* number; the final result cannot be more precise than the original measurement.

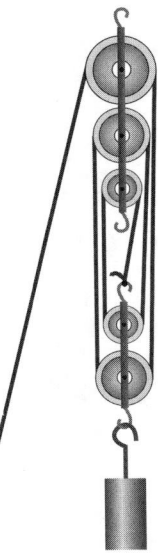

Figure 2

4. _____8 lines_____ Suppose that you need to lift a 6000. N object and you are able to exert no more than 800. N of force. What is the minimum number of supporting lines in a block and tackle system that would allow you to accomplish this job? (Assume no friction in the system.)

   $\text{TMA} = \dfrac{F_{out}}{F_{in}} = \dfrac{6000.\,\text{N}}{800.\,\text{N}} = 7.50 \Rightarrow 8 \text{ lines (minimum)}$
   The system would have to have at least 8 supporting lines.

5. _____5_____ Suppose that you pull a rope attached to a block and tackle in order to lift a 20. N object. After pulling 5 m of line through the pulleys, the load has risen only 1 m. What is the TMA of the pulley system?

   $\text{TMA} = \dfrac{d_{in}}{d_{out}} = \dfrac{5\,\text{m}}{1\,\text{m}} = 5$

6. _____5_____ Suppose that you use a block and tackle system with 5 supporting lines to lift a 1.00×10^3 N object. You measure your effort to be 2.10×10^2 N. What is the TMA of the system?

   The number of supporting lines is 5; therefore TMA = 5. Calculating the answer from $\dfrac{F_{out}}{F_{in}}$ would give the AMA, which would not be the correct answer to this question. See Question 7.

7. _____4.76_____ What is the actual mechanical advantage of the system in Question 6?

   $\text{AMA} = \dfrac{F_{out}}{F_{in}} = \dfrac{1.00 \times 10^3\,\text{N}}{2.10 \times 10^2\,\text{N}} \doteq 4.76$

8. _____95.2%_____ What is the efficiency of the system in Question 6, expressed as a percentage?

   $\eta = \dfrac{\text{AMA}}{\text{TMA}} = \dfrac{4.76}{5} \times 100\% = 95.2\%$ (3 SDs allowed)

9. _____1050 J_____ In Question 6, if you pulled 5.00 m of line through the pulleys, the object would be lifted 1.00 m. How much work (in joules) would be done by your hand on the pulley system? (Report your answer in standard notation.)

   $W_{in} = F_{in}d_{in} = (2.10 \times 10^2\,\text{N})(5.00\,\text{m}) = 1050\,\text{J}$

10. _____False_____ You can assume the pulley system did the same amount of work on the object as your answer to Question 9. (True/False) Support your answer.

$$W_{out} = F_{out}d_{out} = (1.00 \times 10^3 \text{ N})(1.00 \text{ m}) = 1.00 \times 10^3 \text{ J}$$

Name _____

Date _____ Hour ____

CONSERVATION OF ENERGY— SPRING CONSTANT

Purpose

This laboratory exercise is designed to reinforce concepts regarding springs and the conservation of energy. The purpose is to

¥ determine a spring constant.
¥ calculate the potential energy of a falling mass.
¥ calculate the potential energy stored in a spring.
¥ observe that the potential energy lost by a falling mass equals the potential energy gained by a spring that is stretched by that mass.

┌─────────────────────────────────┐
│ **Required Equipment** │
│ masking tape │
│ meter stick │
│ metric masses │
│ spring │
│ string │
│ support stand and hardware │
└─────────────────────────────────┘

Prelab Discussion

Energy is often described as the ability to do work. Potential energy, as the name implies, is energy that has the potential to do work if it is released in some way. Mechanical potential energy is possessed by mechanical systems either in a particular physical condition or in a certain position with respect to an outside force. You will be investigating the transfer (and conservation) of energy when one form of potential energy is converted to kinetic energy and then stored again as another form of potential energy.

The potential energy of an object suspended in a gravitational field will be at a minimum when its height above a reference point is at a minimum. As the object s height increases, its gravitational potential energy (U_g) increases. Similarly, a spring possesses minimum potential energy when it is relaxed in an unstretched condition. It has increasing spring potential energy (U_s) as it is stretched as long as its stretch is less than its elastic limit (the point at which permanent deformation of the metal takes place).

Examine Figure 1. A mass, when hung from a spring, will be at equilibrium when the weight of the mass is equal to the tension in the spring. If the mass is pulled downward a short distance from the equilibrium position and then released, it will oscillate up and down. It will be momentarily motionless at both the highest and lowest positions in its cycle. The potential energy of the system is the sum of the gravitational potential energy and the potential energy of the spring. When the mass is at the highest position, the potential energy due to gravity is at its maximum value, while the potential energy due to the energy stored in the stretched spring is at its minimum value. When the mass is at the lowest position, the opposite is true the potential energy due to gravity is at its minimum value, and the potential energy due to the spring is at its maximum value.

In an ideal system, all work is conserved. Thus, in an ideal oscillating system, you would expect the work done *by* gravity *against* the force of the spring to equal the work done *by* the spring *against* the force of gravity. You know that the change in potential energy is equal to the work, so by measuring the change in either the potential energy of the mass due to gravity or the potential energy of the spring, you can determine the work

Prelab Discussion

• Review the prerequisites for Lab 2-8 in the back of this manual.

• The background information for this lab is extensive. Be sure that your students are familiar with determining mechanical, gravitational, and elastic work and potential energies, as well as conservation of energy principles.

• Consider using the Prelab Discussion as a lesson in order to prepare your students.

• There are a lot of variable symbols in this lab. Thoroughly review their meanings until your students are comfortable using them.

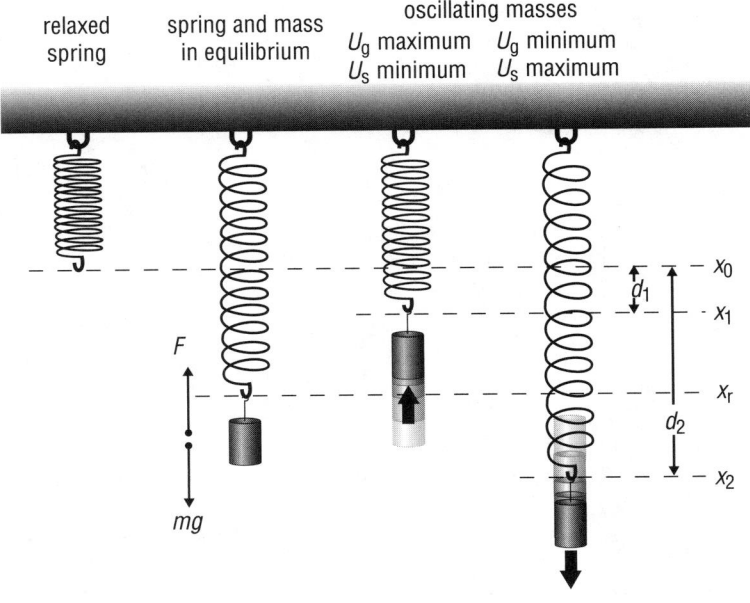

Figure 1

- Here are some basic facts to keep in mind when evaluating the sign of work and change in potential energy:

  1. If the work is done in the same direction as the force that is causing it, work is positive. If work occurs against the force being considered, the work is negative.

  2. If a spring is stretched or compressed from its rest position, it *gains* potential energy and positive work was done *on* the spring. If it returns to its rest position, it *loses* potential energy (*positive* work by the spring).

  3. If an object rises against gravity, it *gains* potential energy because work is done *on* it. If the object drops, it *loses* gravitational potential energy (*positive* work by gravity).

- For advanced classes, you may want to consider one or both of the following activities:

  1. Use the regression analysis feature of an advanced graphing calculator such as the TI-83 Plus to determine the slope of the spring constant data points as well as the variance of the data from a true line. See Appendix E.

  2. Graphically determine the work required to displace the masses by computing the area under the curve of the graph or determine the integral of the work function over the interval of interest.

Equipment and Setup

- A rigid support stand is essential for success. The recommended support is a heavy-duty lab stand or a support rod inserted into the tabletop. Clamp a horizontal rod to the support with a right-angle clamp. Acceptable alternatives are two tall ring stands with a metal rod clamped between them or even a 2 × 4 set across the backs of two rigid chairs.

- Springs may be obtained from science equipment suppliers in a variety of tensions that require relatively small masses to stretch. Screen door springs can be used,

done in moving the mass up and down. The gravitational potential energy of the mass is

$$U_g = mgh, \tag{1}$$

where m is the mass of the object, g is the acceleration due to gravity, and h is the distance of the mass above the position considered to have zero gravitational potential energy. In this experiment you will stipulate that $U_g = 0$ at the lower oscillating rest position (x_2). The potential energy of the spring at any point is found by

$$U_s = \tfrac{1}{2} k (d)^2, \tag{2}$$

where k is the spring constant and d is the stretch of the spring from the spring's rest position.

The change in potential energy that occurs in moving from one position to the other and thus the work required to accomplish the change is found by determining the difference in potential energies at the higher and lower positions.

$$W = -\Delta U = -(U_2 - U_1)$$

Calculating the **work done against gravity** is quite simple. The change in position is easily measured. Thus, the work done against gravity by the spring force is

$$W_s = \Delta U_g = U_{g_2} - U_{g_1}.$$

Substituting Equation (1) for U_g, you have

$$W_s = \Delta U_g = mgh_2 - mgh_1,$$

where h_2 is *higher* than h_1, or

$$W_s = mg(h_2 - h_1) = mg\Delta h. \tag{3}$$

When determining the **work done against the spring**, d_1 will represent the *stretch* of the spring when the oscillating mass is at its *highest* position, and d_2 will represent the *stretch* of the spring when the oscillating mass is at its *lowest* position. Remember that the stretch, d, is the change in position from the spring's *relaxed* position (x_0), not the difference between the upper and lower oscillating positions (see Figure 1). Thus, the work done in stretching the spring by gravity from position x_1 to position x_2 is

$$W_g = \Delta U_s = U_{s_2} - U_{s_1}.$$

Substituting Equation (2) for U_s, you have

$$W_g = \Delta U_s = \tfrac{1}{2}k(d_2)^2 - \tfrac{1}{2}k(d_1)^2$$

or

$$W_g = \tfrac{1}{2}k[(d_2)^2 - (d_1)^2]. \tag{4}$$

You would expect the gravitational potential energy lost by the falling mass to be equal to the potential energy gained by the spring and vice versa. To find out whether or not this is true, you must determine k, m, Δh, d_1, and d_2. The work done *on* the mass *against* gravity by the spring in moving the mass from its lowest position to its highest position is equal to the gravitational potential energy of the mass gained at its highest position. Likewise, the work done by gravity *on* the mass *against* the spring in moving the mass from its highest position to its lowest position is equal to the difference in elastic potential energy for the spring between its highest and lowest positions.

This experiment has two parts—determining the spring constant of your spring and investigating the conservation of energy.

Determining the Spring Constant

Hooke's law states that the magnitude of the spring constant for an ideal spring is equal to the force required to stretch the spring divided by the distance that it is stretched.

$$k = \frac{F}{d}$$

However, calculating the spring constant by using only one measurement of force and displacement will not yield a reliable value. Real springs may require a great deal of force to produce any degree of initial displacement. A more reliable value for the spring constant is found by taking multiple force and stretch measurements, plotting them on a graph, and then determining the slope of the graph. Keep in mind that the internal resistance of the spring will affect your results because you are using a real spring. Also, if you exceed the elastic limit of the spring, you will ruin the spring, and measurements will not be valid. Careful experimental design takes both internal resistance and elastic limit into account.

In the Procedure section, it is suggested that you use five masses to stretch the spring. Your measurement for d is the distance from position x_0 to the rest position x_r. The mass, starting with the lightest mass, is increased by whatever amount you find to be convenient for the range of your particular spring. To determine the range of your spring, suspend a mass that will extend the spring enough to oscillate freely when stretched without causing the mass to bounce around haphazardly. Then carefully add more mass to the spring until it stretches at least another 10 to 15 cm. Again, the spring should be able to oscillate freely without being permanently deformed. You will then need to choose three masses between these two. For example, if 500 g will permit the spring to oscillate freely and 1500 g will safely stretch the spring, then add three 200 g masses to the 500 g mass (one at a time) in order to obtain the three intermediate points. When you have graphed the five points representing force vs. stretch on Graph 1, you will draw a straight line (line of best fit) through them. The slope of this line is the spring constant. See Figure 2 for an example of this graph.

After drawing the line on Graph 1, you should note that when d equals zero, the extrapolated line crosses the y-axis above the origin. What force is being applied when the stretch is zero? It approximates the force required to overcome the **internal resistance** of the spring. For example, if you apply 9 N of force to a spring that requires 5 N to overcome the internal resistance, then only 4 N is being used to stretch the spring.

To verify your value of k determined by the graphic method, you will also calculate the magnitude of the spring constant for each of the five trials and find the average of these five measurements. Use a modified form of Hooke's law:

$$k = \frac{F_t \, F_i}{d} \tag{5}$$

where F_t is the tensional force applied to the spring by the mass (equal to the weight, mg) and F_i is the internal resistance of the spring obtained from Graph 1. Thus, $(F_t - F_i)$ is the net force that actually stretches the spring. The average value of k should agree closely with the slope of the graph. Expect some experimental error because Hooke's law applies only to ideal springs. If you make careful observations, your results should be reasonably close.

Conservation of Energy

The second part of the experiment involves your determination and comparison of the changes in the elastic and gravitational potential energies. During each

but they require heavy masses. Lighter-duty springs may be obtained from home improvement or auto parts stores.

- The equipment setup is simple (see Figure 3). Ensure that the meter stick is fixed close to but not touching the mass as it oscillates.

- The lab is written assuming the meter stick scale increases upward. If it is installed the other way, the Postlab Exercise instructions will not make sense.

Procedure

- Prior to the lab period, you should determine the approximate maximum mass needed to successfully complete the exercise for each spring. Monitor the experiments to ensure the springs are not overstretched.

- Students may mistakenly assume that they must determine the spring constant first and then go back and repeat the trials to obtain conservation of energy data. If this is the

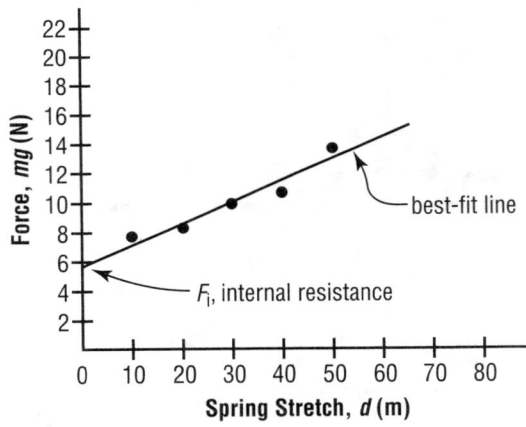

Figure 2

case, clarify the procedure.

- The basis for a successful lab is obtaining spring constant data over a sufficiently wide range of forces so that the nonconservative effects of friction will be minimized. Have the teams practice obtaining oscillation data before beginning to record trial data.

Prelab Homework

- Discuss the homework thoroughly

prior to the lab.

- Review the characteristics of a good data graph. Some students may still have difficulty determining

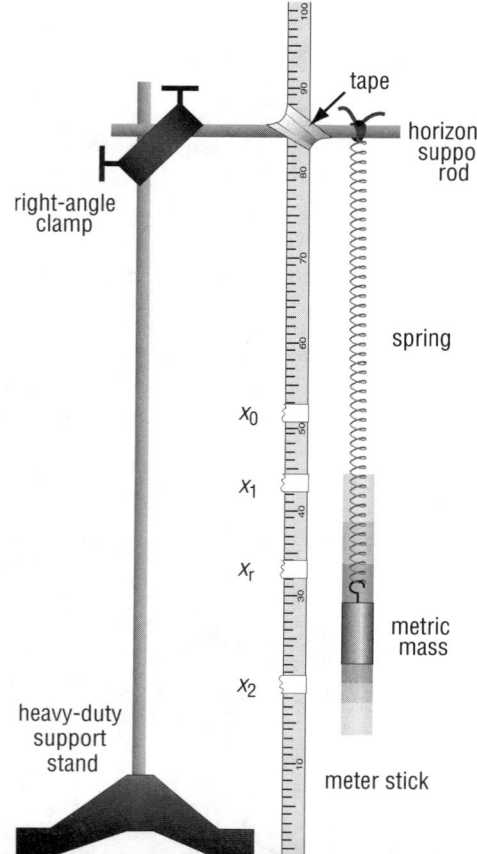

Figure 3

the slope of a line.

- Point out that the work done to stretch a spring is graphically represented by the area on the graph bounded by the curve on top, the *x*-axis below, and the vertical lines bounding the displacement interval on the *x*-axis.

- After this lab, students should understand that energy can be conserved between two different but related processes.

trial, you will pull the mass downward from its equilibrium position. When you release the mass, it will oscillate between an upper position x_1 and a lower position x_2 for a short time. This will allow you to obtain the data necessary for your calculations. Your Prelab Homework will further your understanding of the procedures for this lab. Complete it before proceeding.

Procedure

Setup

1. Assemble the apparatus according to Figure 3. Do not hook any masses to the spring yet. Make sure that you attach the meter stick to the support next to the spring so that the numerical scale *increases upward.* Your setup may not be exactly like the diagram. Your teacher will give you specific instructions if necessary.

2. Determine which masses you will be using. Read the Prelab Discussion for guidance in choosing five masses that will give you a good data spread for finding the spring constant.

Determining the Spring Constant

3. Examine your spring as it hangs from the support. Identify a point on the spring where measurements can be made consistently, such as the rim of the last twist of the spring or the bottom of the loop or hook. This will be called the spring's **reference point.** Place a piece of tape on the meter stick so that its edge marks the level of the spring's reference point, being careful to avoid parallax. Label this position x_0. This will be the zero point for all spring stretch measurements. Record this value in the blank above Table 1.

4. Hook the lightest mass on the spring. Review the suggestions in the Prelab Discussion. Ensure that the spring oscillates freely by pulling down slightly on the mass and releasing it. If it bounces unpredictably or if the spring collapses in such a way that it interferes with the free movement of the mass, select a larger mass until you obtain free movement.

5. Stop the mass and note the position of the spring's reference point against the meter stick. This measurement is the rest position of the mass-spring system when all forces are in equilibrium. Record x_r in Table 1.

6. Perform Steps 7–9 with the first mass before continuing with the additional masses.

Conservation of Energy

7. Pull the mass downward a few centimeters from the rest position; then release it.

8. Using the spring's reference point, your lab partner should note the upper limit of travel of the mass (x_1) while you note the lower limit (x_2) on the meter stick. Avoid parallax! Both measurements must be noted in the same cycle of movement. The two positions should be nearly equidistant from the rest position (x_r). You may have to repeat the process several times before you are able to obtain accurate readings.

9. Record x_1 and x_2 in Table 1 for Trial 1.

10. Repeat Steps 3–9 with masses 2–5. Work carefully and quickly so that you obtain all of your measurements before the end of the lab period.

Data

Table 1
Spring Constant and Oscillation Data

Spring relaxed position, x_0 _____ 0.5800 m

Trial	Mass, m	Tensioning Force, F_t	Spring Rest Position, x_r	Stretch, d $(x_0 - x_r)$	Upper Spring Position,	Lower Spring Position,
	0.200 00	1.96	0.5410	0.0390	0.5610	0.5210
1	0.400 00 kg	3.92 N	0.4970 m	0.0830 m	0.5170 m	0.4770 m
2	0.600 00 kg	5.89 N	0.4500 m	0.1300 m	0.4700 m	0.4300 m
3	0.800 00 kg	7.85 N	0.4060 m	0.1740 m	0.4260 m	0.3860 m
4	1.000 00 kg	9.81 N	0.3600 m	0.2200 m	0.3800 m	0.3400 m
5	kg	N	m	m	m	m

Data and results in Table 1 are typical. Student data will vary.

Postlab Exercises

Determining the Spring Constant

1. Calculate the tensioning force ($F_t = F_w = mg$) and stretch ($d = x_0 - x_r$) from the data for all trials and record the values in Table 1.

2. Plot F_t vs. d on Graph 1, using the data from Table 1. The origin is zero for both axes. Scale your graph so that you use as much of the graphing area as possible.

3. Draw a straight line of best fit through the plotted points on the graph. Extend the line to the left through the y-axis. The y-intercept is the internal resistance of the spring (F_i). Enter this value in all rows of the F_i column of Table 2.

4. Determine the slope of the line on the graph, using the same method as in Lab 2-4. Show your calculations next to the graph.

5. Calculate the average spring constant, using Equation (5).

   a. Fill in the values for F_t in Table 2, using the values calculated in Table 1. Find the difference between F_t and F_i for each trial and write these values in the F column of Table 2. F is the force needed to actually stretch the spring.

   b. Determine the spring constant (k) for each trial by dividing F by d (obtained in Table 1). Enter each value of k in Table 2.

   c. Average the five values of k and enter the result in Table 2. This number should be close to the value obtained graphically in Step 4 from the slope of the line.

   d. Determine the percent difference between the graphic and calculated values of k and enter the result next to Graph 1.

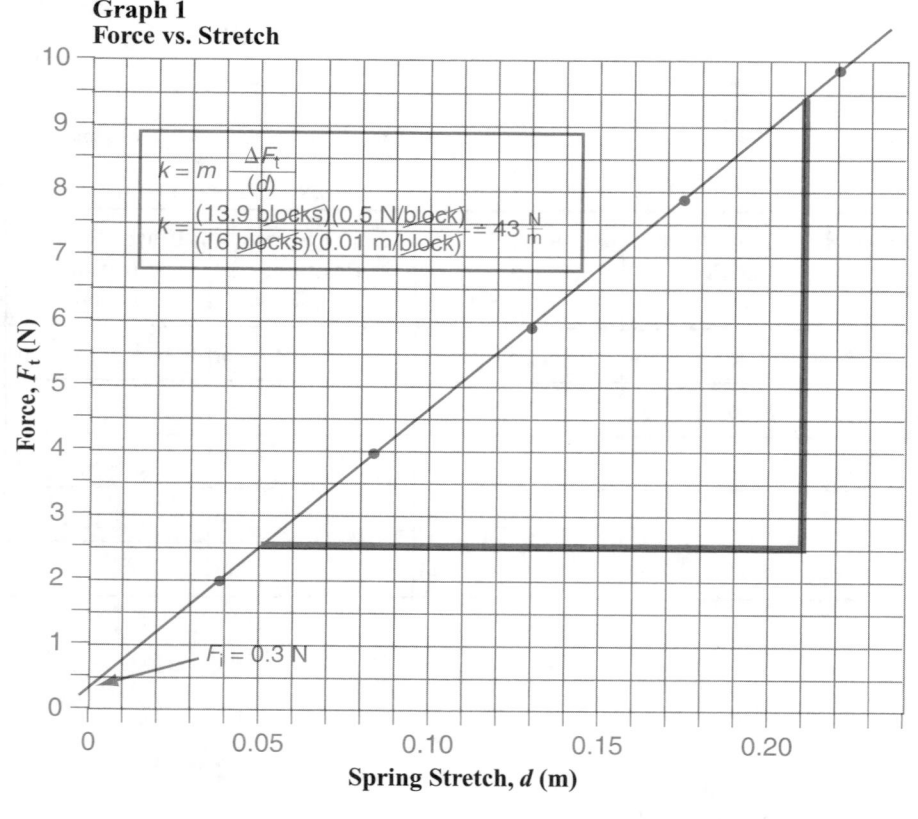

Graph 1
Force vs. Stretch

$$k = m \frac{\Delta F_t}{(d)}$$

$$k = \frac{(13.9 \text{ blocks})(0.5 \text{ N/block})}{(16 \text{ blocks})(0.01 \text{ m/block})} = 43 \frac{N}{m}$$

$F_i = 0.3$ N

$k =$ _____43_____ N/m

percent difference in $k =$ _____0_____ %

Table 2
Spring Constant Calculations

Trial	F_t (from Table 1)		F_i (from Graph 1)		F ($F_t - F_i$)		k (F/d)	
1	1.96	N	0.3	N	1.7	N	44	N/m
2	3.92	N	0.3	N	3.6	N	43	N/m
3	5.89	N	0.3	N	5.6	N	43	N/m
4	7.85	N	0.3	N	7.6	N	44	N/m
5	9.81	N	0.3	N	9.5	N	43	N/m
Average							43	N/m

Results in Table 2 are typical. Student results will vary.

Conservation of Energy

6. Calculate the change in potential energy of the spring (ΔU_s) as it oscillates from minimum to maximum stretch.

   a. Calculate d_1 and d_2, using the values from Table 1 ($d_1 = x_0 - x_1$; $d_2 = x_0 - x_2$). Enter d_1 and d_2 in Table 3 for each trial.

   b. For each trial, calculate $\Delta U_s = \frac{1}{2}k[(d_2)^2 - (d_1)^2]$, using the average value of k from Table 2 and enter the results in Table 3.

Table 3
Conservation of Work Calculations

Trial	Stretch to Upper Position, d_1		Stretch to Lower Position, d_2		Change in Spring P.E., ΔU_s		Change in Height, Δh		Change in Gravitational P.E., ΔU_g		Percent Difference*	
1	0.0190	m	0.0590	m	0.067	J	0.0400	m	0.0785	J	15.8	%
2	0.0630	m	0.1030	m	0.14	J	0.0400	m	0.157	J	11.4	%
3	0.1100	m	0.1500	m	0.22	J	0.0400	m	0.235	J	6.59	%
4	0.1540	m	0.1940	m	0.30	J	0.0400	m	0.314	J	4.56	%
5	0.2000	m	0.2400	m	0.38	J	0.0400	m	0.392	J	3.11	%

Results in Table 3 are typical. Student results will vary.

*percent difference = $\dfrac{|\text{difference of the two values}|}{} \times 100\%$

7. Calculate the change in gravitational potential energy (ΔU_g) for the masses as they oscillate from minimum to maximum height.

   a. Calculate Δh for each trial ($\Delta h = x_1 - x_2$) and record the results in Table 3.

   b. Calculate $\Delta U_g = mg\Delta h$ for each trial and enter the results in Table 3.

8. Calculate the percent difference between ΔU_s and ΔU_g for each trial and enter the results in Table 3.

Postlab Analysis

1. Why would you expect the change in gravitational potential energy of the mass at the top of the cycle to be equal to the change in potential energy of the stretched spring at the bottom of the cycle if the system were ideal?

   The principle of the conservation of energy ensures that this is true.

2. Your experiment did not involve an ideal system. Why does the oscillation of the spring stop after a period of time?

   Friction within the spring and air resistance remove energy from the system until motion stops.

3. What unusable form of energy is produced by the oscillation of the mass-spring system?

   Thermal energy is produced within the spring and from air resistance.

4. ___a or b___ One possible source of error in the experiment is the measuring equipment. Which of the following would most likely cause the biggest error?

   a. The meter stick might be calibrated incorrectly, or it may have expanded or contracted. If so, all of the measured distances would be wrong.

   b. The measurement of a nonstandard mass could be in error because of a balance not being adjusted properly. A standard mass could have a mass different from its marking due to a manufacturing defect.

   c. The barometric pressure might change from the beginning of the experiment to the end.

5. _____C_____ Another possible source of error in the experiment is human error. Which of the following would most likely contribute to the largest measurement error?

   a. difficulty reading the marking on a standard mass or difficulty reading the mass balance correctly

   b. students not reading the lab instructions thoroughly before the lab period

   c. difficulty measuring the exact position of either x_1 or x_2

   d. difficulty plotting the dots on the graph consistently

6. Suppose the percent difference in the spring constants was greater than 10%. Which method for determining the spring constant do you think would be more in error—the graphic method or the mathematical method? Explain your answer.

   The graphic method would probably be more in error because of

   the uncertainty of fitting the line to the data points, especially if the

   slope was determined manually instead of using a graphing calcula-

   tor. This would be particularly true if there was some data scatter.

7. What does the area under the line on Graph 1 represent?

   The area under the line graphically represents the work done to

   stretch the spring a certain distance.

Name _____

Date _____ Hour ____

PRELAB HOMEWORK

1. Write the formula for the potential energy possessed by a spring due to its stretch.

$U_s = \frac{1}{2}k(d)^2$

2. Write the formula for the potential energy imparted to an object by gravity.

$U_g = mgh$

3. How is work done on a system related to the system's potential energy? Write this relationship in symbols.

The work done on a system by a conservative force is equal to the negative of the change in the system's potential energy due to that force.

$W = -\Delta U = -(U_2 - U_1)$

4. Write the formula for the work done *by* gravity on an object with mass m as the object's height *increases*.

Work done by gravity when an object is lifted is negative work. Therefore,

$W_g = -\Delta U_g = -m|g|\Delta h = -m|g|(h_2 - h_1)$.

5. Write the formula for the work done *on* a spring as its length is stretched.

$W = \frac{1}{2}k[(d_2)^2 - (d_1)^2]$

6. In the formula for Question 5, what does the term d represent? What does the term *not* represent in this experiment?

The term d represents the amount of stretch of the spring from its relaxed or unstretched position. It does not represent the distance between d_1 and d_2 as the spring oscillates.

7. What do real springs possess that ideal springs do not? How does this affect their performance?

Real springs have internal resistance. More force is required to stretch a real spring a given distance than you would need to stretch an ideal spring the same distance.

8. Write the formula that you will use to calculate the magnitude of the spring constant (k) in this experiment.

$k = \dfrac{mg - F_i}{d}$ or $k = \dfrac{F_t\ F_i}{d}$

Solve problems 9–11 using MKS units and correct significant digits. Assume that ideal springs are used.

9. $\underline{9.03 \times 10^{-3}\,J}$ A spring is stretched 9.50 cm from its rest position. The magnitude of the spring constant is 2.00 N/m. How much work was done *on* the spring?

Given: $k = 2.00\ \frac{N}{m}$; $d = 9.50$ cm $= 0.0950$ m; $W_s = ?$

Formula: $W_s = \frac{1}{2}k(d)^2$

Solution: $W_s = \frac{1}{2}(2.00\ \frac{N}{m})(0.0950\text{ m})^2 = 0.009\ 025$ J $\approx 0.009\ 03$ J (3 SDs allowed)

10. <u>9.20 × 10⁻³ J</u> What would be the work required to stretch the spring in Question 10 an *additional* 4.00 cm?

Given: $k = 2.00 \frac{N}{m}$; $d_1 = 0.0950$ m; $d_2 = 13.5$ cm $= 0.135$ m; $W = ?$

Formula: $W = \frac{1}{2}k[(d_2)^2 - (d_1)^2]$

Solution: $W = \frac{1}{2}(2.00 \frac{N}{m})[(0.135 \text{ m})^2 - (0.0950 \text{ m})^2] = 0.0092$ J (3 SDs allowed)

Work is done *on* the spring, so the result is positive.

11. Assume the apparatus in Figure 3 of this lab has been assembled. The spring without a mass hooked to it rests at the 60.0 cm mark. A 0.500 kg mass is hooked to it, and the spring stretches to the 20.0 cm mark. When the mass is set in motion, it oscillates between 16.0 cm and 24.0 cm. Assume that the spring is ideal. Be sure to indicate whether work is positive or negative (refer to your text for a discussion of negative work).

a. <u>12.3 N/m</u> What is the magnitude of the spring constant of this spring?

Given: $m = 0.500$ kg; $g = 9.81 \frac{m}{s^2}$; $F = ?$; $d = 60.0$ cm $- 20.0$ cm $= 40.0$ cm $= 0.400$ m; $k = ?$

Formulas: $F = mg$; $k = \frac{F}{d}$

Solution: $F = (0.500 \text{ kg})(9.81 \frac{m}{s^2}) = 4.905$ N ≈ 4.91 N (3 SDs allowed)

$k = \frac{4.91 \text{ N}}{0.400 \text{ m}} = 12.275 \frac{N}{m} \approx 12.3 \frac{N}{m}$ (3 SDs allowed)

b. <u>0.392 J</u> During the oscillation, what is the change in the gravitational potential energy of the mass from its *lowest* height to its *greatest* height?

Given: $m = 0.500$ kg; $x_1 = 24.0$ cm $= 0.240$ m; $x_2 = 16.0$ cm $= 0.160$ m; $\Delta U_g = ?$

Formula: $\Delta U_g = mg\Delta h = mg(h_2 - h_1) = mg(x_1 - x_2)$, where $h_2 = x_1$ and $h_1 = x_2$

Solution: $\Delta U_g = (0.500 \text{ kg})(9.81 \frac{m}{s^2})(0.240 \text{ m} - 0.160 \text{ m}) = 0.3924$ J ≈ 0.392 J
(3 SDs allowed)

c. <u>0.394 J</u> How much work was done *on* the spring to stretch it from its *shortest* length to its *longest* length?

Given: $k = 12.3 \frac{N}{m}$; $x_0 = 60.0$ cm $= 0.600$ m; $x_1 = 0.240$ m; $x_2 = 0.160$ m; $W = ?$

Formula: $W = \Delta U = \frac{1}{2}k[(d_2)^2 - (d_1)^2] = \frac{1}{2}k[(x_0 - x_2)^2 - (x_0 - x_1)^2]$

Solution: $W = \frac{1}{2}(12.3 \frac{N}{m})[(0.440 \text{ m})^2 - (0.360 \text{ m})^2] = 0.3936$ J ≈ 0.394 J
(3 SDs allowed)

d. <u>−0.394 J</u> Determine the work done *by* gravity *on* the spring/mass system as it oscillates upward from maximum extension to minimum extension.

$W_g = -\Delta U_g = -0.392$ J (The magnitude of the answer is the same as in Question 11b. However, in this case, the work done by gravity is negative because the spring/mass system is moving in the opposite direction to the applied gravitational force. This is negative work by definition.)

Name _____

Date _____ Hour ____

CONSERVATION OF MOMENTUM

Purpose

This laboratory exercise is designed to give you a better understanding of momentum and the principle of conservation. The purpose is to

- determine the momentum of two objects accelerated by a force and its reaction.
- compare the momentum of the two objects.
- verify the law of the conservation of momentum for a system of objects (within the limits of the experiment).

Prelab Discussion

When a rifle is fired, the force of the exploding cartridge propellant imparts momentum to the bullet. However, the propellant gases also impart an equal amount of momentum to the rifle. To simplify this system, you can assume that the bullet and the rifle exert forces directly on each other, neglecting the propellant gases. Newton's third law states that if the rifle exerts a force on the bullet, the bullet must exert an equal but opposite force on the rifle. The result of this force is called the kick or recoil of the rifle. The principle of the conservation of momentum states that the sum of the changes of momentums of the rifle and bullet during the firing event must equal zero. Mathematically,

$$\Delta \mathbf{p}_1 + \Delta \mathbf{p}_2 = 0,$$

or

$$\Delta \mathbf{p}_1 = -\Delta \mathbf{p}_2. \tag{1}$$

It is possible to observe the same phenomenon by using dynamics carts that are connected together with a compressed spring between them. When the release mechanism is triggered, each cart exerts a force on the other. These forces are equal in magnitude but opposite in direction, and they cause the carts, which were originally at rest, to accelerate apart. If you can measure the velocity of both carts at some instant after they separate, and if you know the mass of each cart, you should be able to determine the *momentum* of the two carts at that instant ($p = mv$).

The key to this experiment is determining the velocities of both carts at the same instant. You can accomplish this by using just one recording timer (see Figure 1). Each cart will pull a tape through the timer in opposite directions as the timer imprints dots at the same time on both tapes. Then, by counting the same number of dots from the starting points on each tape, you will be able to find where each cart was at a particular instant. You can estimate the instantaneous velocity at that point by using the procedure employed in Lab 2-4, which is summarized for you here. The procedure discusses one tape, but it applies to both.

Select a dot near the middle of the series of dots on a tape. This dot will be the point for which the instantaneous velocity will be estimated. The two adjacent dots will define the time interval and displacement for determining average velocity. Velocity is the ratio of the displacement to the elapsed time. The displacement is the

Required Equipment
balance
carpenter's level
dynamics carts with bumpers, 2
masking tape
meter stick
metric masses
paper clips
recording timer and accessories
scissors
string
wooden sticks (or pencils)

Optional Equipment
leveling board

Prelab Discussion

- Review the prerequisites for Lab 2-9 in the back of this manual. The students should be familiar with conservation principles and momentum determinations before attempting this lab.

- The Prelab Discussion reviews the principles of this lab and the procedure for estimating velocity from a timing tape (similar to the process in Lab 2-4).

Figure 1

Equipment and Setup

- The recommended equipment can be obtained from most science equipment suppliers. Some dynamics carts come with the metal spring strips. Other models have a spring-and-plunger assembly that is adequate for this lab. Use only one plunger to impart momentum to the carts.

- Check the apparatus before the lab period to ensure that the recording timer will mark through both tapes and that there will not be excessive drag caused by two tapes running through the guides.

- If your classroom does not have a smooth, hard, level floor, you may want to use the leveling boards from Lab 2-5 for the working surface.

- You may find it more efficient to attach the spring strips, stick supports, and paper clips to the carts prior to the lab in order to save time.

Procedure

- Review how to thread the tapes through the recording timer. Emphasize that the carbon disks must be face down on top of the tapes in order to work properly.

- The carts must separate cleanly in order for the data to be meaningful. Cutting the string with a razor blade or burning it with a match may cause a ragged start as the thread frays.

- The tapes do not have to be longer than half of the length of the work area.

- The data will be most useful just after the springs on the carts separate and before the carts begin to slow down significantly. Depending on your equipment, you may want to modify the instructions regarding the number of dots to count beyond the reference mark (see Step 2 in the Postlab Exercises).

Prelab Homework

- Review the answer key for the homework so that you can provide the appropriate emphasis to the students regarding notation conventions for vector quantities versus

measured distance between the first and third dots in the interval (Δd). Assume for this example that $\Delta d = 3.00$ cm. Assume also that your timer imprints 53.0 dots per second. The calibration (dots per second) for the recording timer should be clearly labeled (or you can determine it before beginning the experiment). Since two dots were imprinted after the start of the measured interval (the first dot is not counted), the time (Δt) required to travel the 3.00 centimeters is

$$\Delta t = \frac{2 \text{ dots}}{} \left| \frac{1 \text{ s}}{53.0 \text{ dots}} \right. \doteq 0.0377 \text{ s.}$$

The average velocity for the interval then would be

$$v_{av} = \frac{\Delta d}{\Delta t} = \frac{3.00 \text{ cm}}{0.0377 \text{ s}} \doteq 79.6 \text{ cm/s} = 0.796 \text{ m/s.}$$

Since the point at which you are determining the instantaneous speed is in the middle of the chosen *time* interval, you can assume that the average velocity and the instantaneous velocity at this point are nearly the same. The shorter the interval, the more likely this assumption is to be true.

After determining the velocity at the same instant for each cart, you can calculate the momentum of each cart at that point in time. Since momentum is conserved, you can expect the momentum of the carts to be equal in magnitude but opposite in direction.

Procedure

Setup

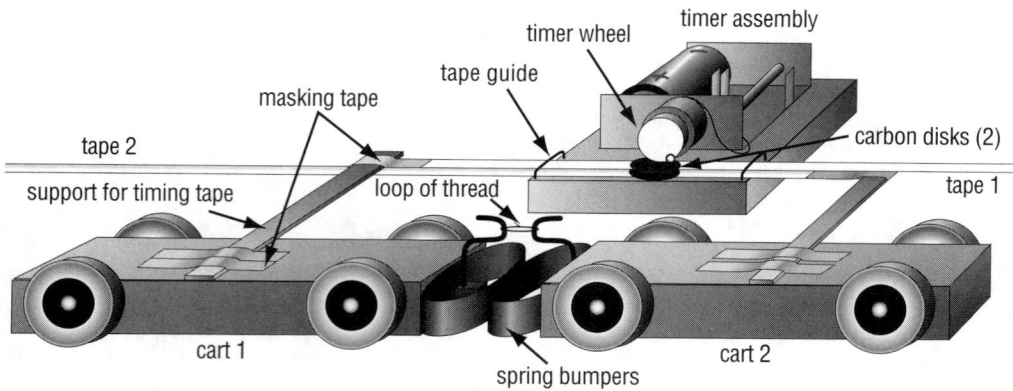

Figure 2

1. Your carts should roll freely but should not roll on their own. (Make sure that you have a level working area with a hard surface.) For the greatest accuracy, use a carpenter's level to verify that the working area is essentially level. You will need at least 4 ft of working space. You may be instructed to use the leveling board suggested for Lab 2-5. If you are working on a table, you will also need to prevent the carts from falling to the floor.

2. Each of your carts will need a support to which the timing tape can be attached. See Figure 2 for an appropriate setup. You may use Popsicle sticks or even long pencils for the supports. Use masking tape to tape them securely onto the carts so that they are both on the side toward the timer when the carts are in position for the experiment.

3. Each cart needs to be equipped with a flexible spring metal strip (see Figure 2). These will probably already be attached. If not, they usually clip on or fasten with screws. Some carts have a spring-and-plunger device. Your teacher will show you how to prepare these carts.

4. Attach a paper clip to the same end of the cart that has the spring strip. Depending on the design of the cart, the paper clip can be hooked to a bumper, tacked to the wood, wrapped around an axle, or hooked through a hole in the end of the cart. Bend the clip in the shape of a hook as in Figure 2. This will give you a hook to which you can attach the thread loop you will use in a later step.

5. Label the carts 1 and 2 so that you can identify them later. Determine the mass of each cart to the nearest gram and record the values (in kilograms) in Table 1.

Data Collection

6. Place the timer in the center of your work area with the two carts directly in front of it (see Figure 2).

7. Use masking tape to attach a strip of timing tape to each of the stick supports. Thread the timing tape from the first cart through your timer as you have done in previous labs. Place the carbon disk over it, but do not insert the pin yet (if your timer requires one).

8. Insert the timing tape from the second cart into the timer from the *opposite* direction and *on top of* the carbon disk. Place a second carbon disk on top of the second timing tape. Insert the pin to retain the carbon disks, if required. One carbon disk will mark the tape being pulled to the left, while the other will mark the tape being pulled to the right (see Figure 2).

9. Tie three pieces of thread into loops 5 to 7 cm in diameter. The loops must hold the carts together so that the springs are compressed well. You will use one loop of thread for each of the trials.

10. Have your lab partner push the spring ends of the two carts together, compressing the spring strips, so that you can hook one loop of thread over both of the paper clip hooks. Slowly release the carts until the thread is under tension, holding the carts in position. Your carts are now loaded and ready for "firing" (see Figure 2).

11. Pull all of the slack out of the two pieces of timing tape. Label each tape with the cart and trial number (for example, Cart 1, Trial 1 or 1-1).

12. The recording timer has wire or metal guides for the timing tape. Mark both tapes at exactly the same point at *both the right-hand and left-hand guides*. You will use these *reference marks* to line up the tapes during the Postlab Exercises.

13. Start the timer.

14. Use a sharp pair of scissors to cut the thread loop that is holding the two carts together. Be careful not to let the scissors touch either of the carts as they separate. If the thread frays and the carts do not separate cleanly, start over.

15. When the carts stop, turn off the timer.

16. Perform Steps 6–15 two more times with the following changes: for Trial 2 add a 1 kg mass to cart 1; for Trial 3 add another 1 kg mass to cart 1. Do not add any masses to cart 2.

17. Record the masses of the carts, including any added masses, in Table 1 as you complete each trial.

scalar quantities. The questions specify the kind of quantity being considered. The best approach is to assume that the vector solution is required unless the question specifically asks for magnitude.

- Remind students to follow the significant digit rules in their solutions. If you are not observing these rules, instruct the students to round their answers to 3 SDs.

Home School Notes

- Standard roller skates may be substituted for the dynamics carts.

- The spring strips can be replaced by flexible hacksaw blades.

Data

Table 1
Cart Momentum Data and Calculations

Calibration of your recording timer _____49.3_____ dots/s

Trial	Cart 1				Cart 2				Percent Difference between p_1 and p_2
	Mass, m_1	Distance, d_1	Velocity at P, v_1	$p_1 = m_1 v_1$ (kg·m/s)	Mass, m_2	Distance, d_2	Velocity at P, v_2	$p_2 = m_2 v_2$ (kg·m/s)	
1	0.596 kg	0.0215 m	0.530 m/s	0.316	0.606 kg	0.0220 m	0.542 m/s	0.328	3.73 %
2	1.596 kg	0.0090 m	0.22 m/s	0.35	0.606 kg	0.0230 m	0.567 m/s	0.344	1.73 %
3	2.596 kg	0.0056 m	0.14 m/s	0.36	0.606 kg	0.0250 m	0.616 m/s	0.373	3.55 %

Data shown in Table 1 is typical. Actual data will vary.

Postlab Exercises

1. Start your data analysis with the tapes from Trial 1. Place the tapes side by side with the pairs of reference marks at the left and the dots on both tapes leading to the right (see Figure 3).

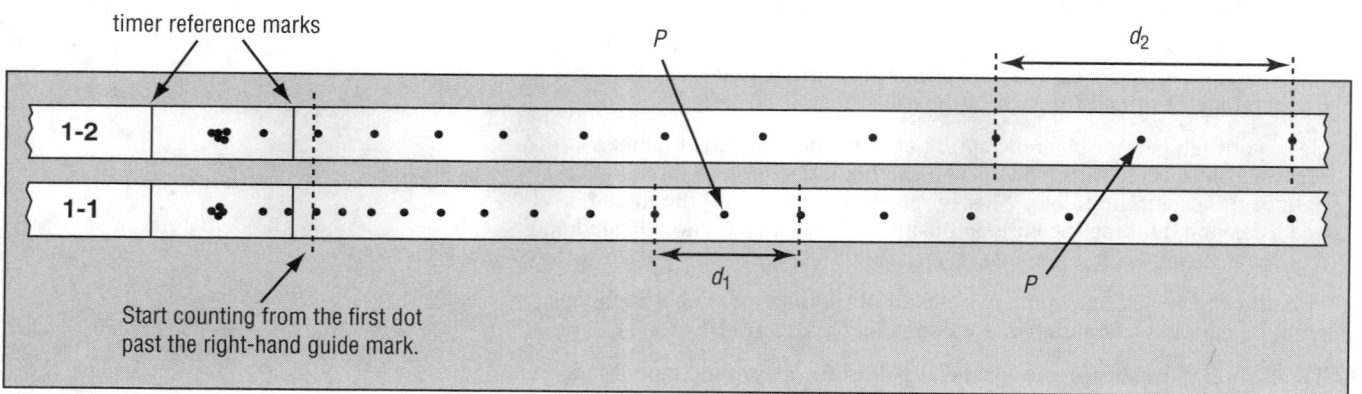

timer reference marks

1-2

1-1

P

d_2

d_1

P

Start counting from the first dot past the right-hand guide mark.

Figure 3

2. Starting at the right-hand reference mark on the tape labeled 1-1, circle the first dot to the right of the reference mark. Count approximately 10 dots past the first dot. (Do not count the first dot.) Label this dot P. Mark the dots on both sides of P and then measure the distance between those two dots. Enter the distance (d_1) in meters in Table 1 under Cart 1.

3. Repeat Step 2 for the tape labeled 1-2, counting the same number of dots as you did on tape 1-1. Record d_2 in Table 1 under Cart 2.

4. Repeat Steps 1–3 for Trial 2 and Trial 3. Record the results in Table 1.

5. Calculate the estimated instantaneous velocities for both carts at P (see Prelab Discussion). Record the values in Table 1.

6. Calculate the magnitude of the momentum of each cart, p_1 and p_2. Record the values for all three trials in Table 1.

7. Determine the percent difference between p_1 and p_2 for each trial. Record the percent differences in Table 1.

Postlab Analysis

Unless otherwise indicated, all questions relate to the conservation of momentum experiment as performed in this lab.

1. If both carts have the same mass, what would you expect to be true about their velocities?

   The velocities of both carts should be equal in magnitude but opposite in direction.

2. When you cut the string and the two carts push apart, how do the forces exerted on each cart by the two spring strips compare?

   The forces are equal in magnitude but opposite in direction.

3. How does the *speed* of the cart with the greater mass compare to the less massive cart?

   The speed of the more massive cart is lower than the speed of the less massive cart.

4. What would happen to the momentums of the two carts if the spring strips were stiffer—that is, the force being exerted were greater? Explain your answer.

   Both momentums would be greater. Greater force produces greater accelerations while the springs are in contact, resulting in higher cart velocities. The products of larger velocities and the same masses of the carts produce higher momentums.

5. Why were the magnitudes of the momentums of the two carts not exactly the same?

   Students could account for the differences by discussing various measurement errors, differences in the carts, or varying frictional conditions.

6. Name the two most likely sources of friction that could produce errors in this experiment.

   The two most likely sources of friction are wheel and axle friction and the friction of the tape slipping through the timer.

7. Discuss the consequences of the table not being perfectly level.

   The slope of the table could produce gravitational accelerations not associated with the springs. This would affect the accuracy of the data collected and the resulting momentum calculations.

8. In the case of a rifle firing, the bullet attains a high velocity, but the rifle does not. Explain the reason for this.

   The total change of momentum of the bullet-rifle system must be
   zero. The high velocity of the low-mass bullet is compensated by the
   low velocity of the relatively high-mass rifle.

9. What is a *nonconservative* force? Give an example.

   A nonconservative force is one that does not conserve total mechanical energy and momentum. Friction is an example that students
   should be familiar with.

Name _____

Date _____ Hour _____

PRELAB HOMEWORK

Use vector or scalar notation when appropriate.

1. Write the formula that expresses the law of conservation of momentum.

   $\Delta \mathbf{p}_1 + \Delta \mathbf{p}_2 = 0$ or $\Delta \mathbf{p}_1 = -\Delta \mathbf{p}_2$

2. ____25.0 kg·m/s____ What is the *magnitude* of the momentum of a 5.000 kg object moving at 5.00 m/s?

   Given: $m = 5.000$ kg; $v = 5.00 \frac{m}{s}$; $p = ?$

   Formula: $p = mv$

   Solution: $p = (5.000 \text{ kg})(5.00 \frac{m}{s}) = 25.0 \frac{kg \cdot m}{s}$

3. ____4.00 kg·m/s____ A 5.00 g bullet leaves the muzzle of a 2.50 kg rifle with a muzzle velocity of 800. m/s. What is the *magnitude* of the bullet's momentum (p_b)?

   Given: $m_b = 5.00$ g $= 0.005\ 00$ kg; $v_b = 800. \frac{m}{s}$; $p_b = ?$

   Formula: $p_b = m_b v_b$

   Solution: $p_b = (0.005\ 00 \text{ kg})(800. \frac{m}{s}) = 4.00 \frac{kg \cdot m}{s}$ (3 SDs allowed)

4. ____−4.00 kg·m/s____ What is the change in momentum that the bullet in Question 3 imparts to the rifle ($\Delta \mathbf{p}_r$) at the given instant? Consider the direction of the bullet to be positive.

   Since momentum must be conserved in a recoil situation, the change in momentum of the rifle must be equal to the change in momentum of the bullet but opposite in direction. Assuming that both started from rest, $\Delta \mathbf{p}_r = -\Delta \mathbf{p}_b = -4.00$ kg·m/s.

5. ____−1.60 m/s____ What is the recoil velocity ($\mathbf{v}_r$) of the rifle in Question 3?

   Given: $\mathbf{p}_r = -4.00 \frac{kg \cdot m}{s}$; $m_r = 2.50$ kg; $\mathbf{v}_r = ?$

   Formula: $\mathbf{p}_r = m_r \mathbf{v}_r$

   Solution: $\mathbf{v}_r = \dfrac{\mathbf{p}_r}{m_r} = \dfrac{-4.00 \frac{kg \cdot m}{s}}{2.50 \text{ kg}} = -1.60 \frac{m}{s}$

6. A conservation of momentum experiment is performed as described in the Procedure section. Cart 1 with additional weights has a total mass of 1.500 kg, and cart 2 has a mass of 0.500 kg. The two marked tapes are shown in Figure 3. Given $d_1 = 4.40$ cm, $d_2 = 12.65$ cm, and a timer calibration of 58.0 dots/s, answer the following questions. Use MKS units for all solutions.

   a. ____1.28 m/s____ Estimate the instantaneous *speed* at point P for cart 1.

   Given: $d = 4.40$ cm $= 0.0440$ m; timer calibration $= 58.0 \frac{dots}{s}$; number of dots $=$ 2 dots

   Formulas: $\Delta t = \text{number of dots} \div \frac{dots}{s}$; $v_1 = \dfrac{d_1}{\Delta t}$

   Solution: $\Delta t = \dfrac{2 \text{ dots}}{58.0 \frac{dots}{s}} \doteq 0.0345$ s; $v_1 = \dfrac{0.0440 \text{ m}}{0.0345 \text{ s}} \approx 1.28 \frac{m}{s}$ (3 SDs allowed)

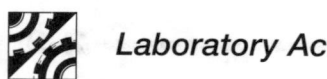

b. ___+1.92 kg·m/s___ Determine the momentum of cart 1 at *P*. Consider cart 1 to be traveling in the positive direction.

Given: $m_1 = 1.500$ kg; $v_1 = +1.28 \frac{m}{s}$; $p_1 = ?$

Formula: $p_1 = m_1 v_1$

Solution: $p_1 = (1.500 \text{ kg})(+1.28 \frac{m}{s}) = +1.92 \frac{kg \cdot m}{s}$

c. ___3.67 m/s___ Estimate the instantaneous *speed* for cart 2 at *P*.

Given: $d_2 = 12.65$ cm $= 0.1265$ m; timer calibration $= 58.0 \frac{dots}{s}$; number of dots $= 2$ dots

Formulas: $\Delta t = $ number of dots $\div \frac{dots}{s}$; $v_2 = \frac{d_2}{\Delta t}$

Solution: $\Delta t = \dfrac{2 \text{ dots}}{58.0 \frac{dots}{s}} \doteq 0.0345 \text{ s}$; $v_2 = \dfrac{0.1265 \text{ m}}{0.0345 \text{ s}} \doteq 3.67 \frac{m}{s}$

d. ___−3.67 m/s___ What is the *velocity* of cart 2 at *P?*

Since cart 2 moves in the opposite direction from cart 1 (positive direction), $v_2 = -3.67 \frac{m}{s}$.

e. ___−1.84 kg·m/s___ Determine the momentum of cart 2 at *P*.

Given: $m_2 = 0.500$ kg; $v_2 = -3.67 \frac{m}{s}$; $p_2 = ?$

Formula: $p_2 = m_2 v_2$

Solution: $p_2 = (0.500 \text{ kg})(-3.67 \frac{m}{s}) = -1.835 \frac{kg \cdot m}{s} \approx -1.84 \frac{kg \cdot m}{s}$

(3 SDs allowed)

f. ___4.26%___ What is the percent difference between the *magnitudes* of the momentum values in b and e?

$$\text{percent difference} = \frac{|\text{difference of the two values}|}{\text{average of the two values}} \times 100\%$$

$$\text{percent difference} = \frac{\left|1.92 \frac{kg \cdot m}{s} - 1.84 \frac{kg \cdot m}{s}\right|}{\left(\dfrac{1.92 \frac{kg \cdot m}{s} + 1.84 \frac{kg \cdot m}{s}}{2}\right)} \times 100\% \doteq 4.26\%$$

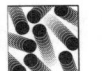
Name _____

Date _____ Hour _____

LENGTH OF A MOLECULE

Purpose

The development of the particle model of matter fundamentally altered the way in which man views God's creation. All matter consists of atoms and molecules. The purpose of this activity is to

- estimate the length of a molecule.
- provide practice using scientific notation in calculations.
- demonstrate how models are developed from conservative assumptions.

Prelab Discussion

The study of matter and its interactions with other matter is principally the concern of chemistry and its allied sciences. However, the physical properties of matter often must be understood in order to accurately predict the behavior of natural and man-made structures and phenomena. The variation of just a few percentage points in the concentration of the components of an alloy, for example, can significantly alter the properties of the metal and consequently its usefulness for, say, constructing the shell of a space probe. The "doping" of semiconductors in the manufacturing of microprocessors is accomplished by the introduction of relatively few atoms with a different size or electrical property from the base material in order to obtain the desired electronic characteristics. The physicist and engineer are as interested in the physical characteristics of atoms and molecules as the chemist is.

Individual atoms and molecules are extraordinarily small. Even the largest biological macromolecules are too small to be seen directly with a light microscope. Many techniques have been developed in recent decades that permit the imaging of individual molecules with electron microscopy. Certain techniques can even produce pseudo images of atoms in crystalline arrays. Your classroom probably does not have the sophisticated and expensive equipment required for these investigations. However, it is possible to measure the average dimensions of an individual molecule indirectly in your school's laboratory.

In your study of geometry, you likely solved a problem in which you were given the volume of a cylinder and the radius or diameter of its base and then had to determine its height. This task was easy if you knew the formula for the volume of a cylinder:

$$V = Bh, \tag{1}$$

where B is the area of the base and h is the height of the cylinder. For a circular cylinder, the base is a circle, so the formula can be rewritten as

$$V = \pi r^2 h. \tag{2}$$

You can use this principle to estimate the average size of a molecule of a given substance by allowing a known volume of the substance to spread out into a circular layer with the thickness of a single molecule. If you measure the diameter of the resulting layer, you can calculate the height of the cylinder. This is equivalent to the *average* size of a molecule. Note that molecules are in constant motion and that the size predicted by this method is potentially less than the actual size because the molecule tends to bend and fold upon itself as it vibrates.

In this lab you will determine the average length of a molecule of oleic acid ($C_{18}H_{34}O_2$). Figure 1 shows a space-filling model of oleic acid. If one drop of pure oleic acid were placed on the surface of water, it could spread out to cover an area greater than that of a large swimming pool. Consequently, in order to fit the layer within a standard pan, you will use a very small amount of the acid diluted in an alcohol solution. When a drop of the solution is placed in the pan of

Required Equipment

beaker, 50 mL
eyedropper
graduated cylinder, 10 mL
lycopodium powder
 (or chalk dust)
meter stick
oleic acid solution, 0.50%
pan, large, shallow
rubbing alcohol
water

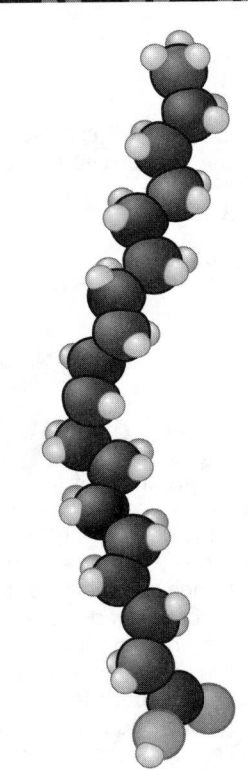

Figure 1

Prelab Discussion

- Review the prerequisites for Lab 3-1 in the back of this manual. Ensure that the students have been introduced to the particle theory of matter and that they are familiar with calculations involving scientific notation.

- This lab is technically much simpler than the majority of the other exercises in this manual, but the results are indicative of how difficult-to-measure quantities may be inferred indirectly by simple means.

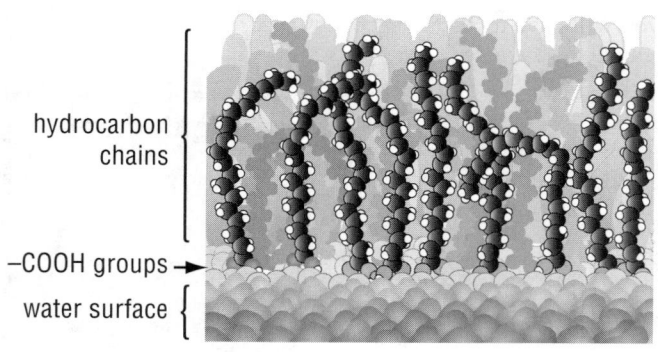

hydrocarbon chains

–COOH groups →

water surface

Figure 2

water, the alcohol will dissolve into the water, and the insoluble acid will spread out on the water's surface. Note that the molecule has a polar end (the –COOH group), which is attracted to water molecules through hydrogen bonding. The remainder of the chain is repelled by water. Oleic acid forms a monolayer (a layer one molecule thick) in which the long dimension of the molecule tends to arrange itself perpendicular to the water's surface (see Figure 2). This property enables you to make a close estimate of the length of the molecule by determining the thickness of the oleic acid layer.

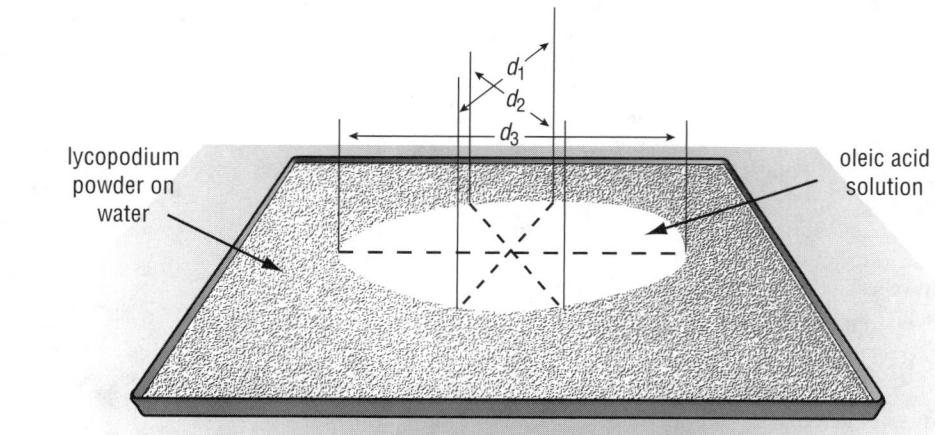

Figure 3

lycopodium powder on water

d_1
d_2
d_3

oleic acid solution

- Discuss the structure of the oleic acid molecule. It is a hydrocarbon consisting of a string of 18 single-bonded carbons (with the exception of a double bond between the ninth and tenth carbons) and a carboxyl group on one end. The long hydrocarbon chain is essentially nonpolar and hydrophobic, but the carboxyl group makes one end polar and hydrophilic. Oleic acid tends to act like an oily soap. This characteristic ensures that the substance forms a monolayer on the surface of water.

Equipment and Setup

- Oleic acid is a safe chemical when handled appropriately. Hazard ratings are Health—0, Flammability—1, Reactivity—0, and Contact—1. Use protective clothing when handling the pure material.

- Prepare the oleic acid solution by diluting 0.5 mL of pure oleic acid with enough rubbing alcohol to make 100.0 mL of solution. You need to make this much in order to measure the acid accurately. This

Procedure

1. Determine the volume of a single drop of oleic acid solution.

    a. Carefully add the oleic acid solution one drop at a time to a 10 mL graduated cylinder to a level of 2.0 mL. Count the number of drops needed to obtain 2.0 mL.

    b. Pour the contents of the graduated cylinder back into the original beaker and rinse out the cylinder with alcohol. Shake the graduated cylinder to remove any drops of alcohol.

    c. Perform Steps 1a and 1b three more times. For each trial, record the number of drops in Table 1.

    d. For each trial, divide the volume by the number of drops to determine the number of milliliters per drop. Record these values in Table 1.

    e. Determine the average volume per drop for the four trials and record this value in Table 1.

2. Set the pan on a level surface near a sink and pour tap water into the pan to a depth of about 1 cm.

3. Allow the water eddies to subside so that there is no swirling movement on the surface. Sprinkle a uniform layer of lycopodium powder (the spores of a form of club moss), chalk dust, or talcum powder over the entire surface of the water.

4. Hold a full eyedropper of the oleic acid solution approximately 1 cm above the surface of the water. Carefully allow a single drop to fall onto the center of the water's surface. Note how the drop spreads out, displacing the powder (see Figure 3).

5. The layer of oleic acid will not likely be a perfect circle, so you will have to measure the diameter in at least three directions and then calculate the average of these measurements. If the margin of the layer is scalloped, visually estimate the position of the edge. Record the measurements to the nearest 0.1 cm in Table 2 and determine the average diameter (d_{av}).

6. (Optional) If time permits, perform Steps 2–5 two more times to obtain an average of several trials. Record these measurements in Table 2.

7. Dispose of the liquid in the sink. Clean all utensils with soap and water.

quantity will be adequate for most classes.

• Provide 10 mL of solution per lab team.

• The pan may be any container that is 30 to 50 cm across in the smallest dimension. A large, shallow baking pan is suggested.

Data

Table 1
Volume of One Drop of Oleic Acid Solution

Trial	Volume	Number of Drops	Volume per Drop
1	2.0 mL	105	0.019 $\frac{mL}{drop}$
2	2.0 mL	110	0.018 $\frac{mL}{drop}$
3	2.0 mL	107	0.019 $\frac{mL}{drop}$
4	2.0 mL	111	0.018 $\frac{mL}{drop}$
Average			0.019 $\frac{mL}{drop}$

Table 2
Diameter of Oleic Acid Layer

Trial	d_1	d_2	d_3	Average, d_{av}
1	15.0 cm	17.0 cm	13.0 cm	15.0 cm
2	16.5 cm	15.0 cm	14.0 cm	15.2 cm
3	16.0 cm	14.5 cm	17.0 cm	15.8 cm
4	cm	cm	cm	cm

Data in Tables 1 and 2 will vary. Data shown is typical.

Postlab Exercises Answers will vary. Solutions use the typical data.

1. __9.5 × 10⁻⁵ cm³/drop__ Most of the drop of oleic acid solution was alcohol, which dissolved into the pan of water, leaving the immiscible oleic acid floating on the surface. The solution is 0.50% oleic acid by volume (5.0 parts per thousand, or 5.0 ppt). This means that the volumetric concentration is 5.0×10^{-3} mL oleic acid/mL solution. Calculate the volume of oleic acid in one drop in cubic centimeters.

$1 \text{ mL} = 1 \text{ cm}^3$

$$\frac{0.019 \text{ mL solution}}{\text{drop}} \left| \frac{5.0 \times 10^{-3} \text{ cm}^3 \text{ oleic acid}}{\text{mL solution}} \right. = 9.5 \times 10^{-5} \frac{\text{cm}^3 \text{ oleic acid}}{\text{drop}}$$

2. __5400 pm__ The result of the calculation in Question 1 is the volume of the layer of oleic acid that was floating on the water. Assuming that the layer is a cylinder having the average diameter recorded for Trial 1 in Table 2, calculate the height of the layer of oleic acid (in pm, or 10^{-12} m). This is the average *length* of an oleic acid molecule.

Given: $V = 9.5 \times 10^{-5} \frac{\text{cm}^3 \text{ oleic acid}}{\text{drop}}$; $r = \frac{d_{av}}{2} = \frac{15.0 \text{ cm}}{2} = 7.5 \text{ cm}$; $h = ?$

Formula: $V = \pi r^2 h \Rightarrow h = \frac{V}{\pi r^2}$

Solution: $h = \frac{9.5 \times 10^{-5} \frac{\text{cm}^3 \text{ oleic acid}}{\text{drop}}}{\pi (7.5 \text{ cm})^2} \doteq 5.4 \times 10^{-7} \text{ cm} = 5400 \text{ pm}$

• If your school has chemical delivery pipets, you can improve your precision by measuring one drop of solution to the hundredth or even thousandth milliliter. If you use these, you may omit the steps for determining the volume per drop in the Procedure section. (Note: Delivery pipets can also be used to improve the precision of the concentration of oleic acid solution.)

• Lycopodium powder is the preferred material to indicate the extent of the oleic acid layer. The dust is microscopic and should give a well-defined layer boundary. Chalk dust or talcum powder may be used, but the grains are much larger and tend to interfere more with the spreading of the oil layer. The typical data was obtained using chalk dust. Save the dust from the chalkboard erasers over several weeks or scrape a piece of chalk with a kitchen knife over the pan during the experiment.

• Place containers of rubbing alcohol and large beakers in several places around the room so that the students can rinse out the graduated cylinders.

Procedure

- Monitor students when they are determining the value for volume per drop. Counting out over 100 drops can be tedious and can lead to errors.

- When a drop is being produced, the dropper should be held *vertically*.

- If the layer of oleic acid touches the edge of the container, the results will be skewed because the layer will no longer approximate a cylinder.

- Students should make all measurements to the limit of precision for the instruments they are using. The only exception is estimating the diameter of the oleic acid layer, which should be measured to the nearest 0.1 cm.

Postlab Analysis

- The exercises give students practice in some practical calculations involving very large and very small numbers in scientific notation.

- The assumed dimensions for intercarbon bond length and molecular diameter are good approximations based on current information.

Home School Notes

- All equipment except graduated cylinders is available locally.

- Since the unique structure of oleic acid is important for success in this lab, there are no convenient substitutions. There is no known local source for this chemical. It must be ordered from a science supply company.

Postlab Analysis Answers will vary. Solutions use the typical data.

1. ___5.4 nm___ Convert your experimental length of an oleic acid molecule to nanometers.

$$\frac{5400 \text{ pm} \quad | \quad 1 \text{ nm}}{\qquad | \quad 1000 \text{ pm}} = 5.4 \text{ nm}$$

2. ___2.7 nm___ Note from Figure 1 that there are 18 carbons in a continuous chain. Assuming that the centers of the carbon atoms in the chain are about 150 pm (0.15 nm) apart, what is the approximate length of the carbon chain in oleic acid in nanometers? Round your answer to 2 SDs.

There are 18 carbon atoms in the chain. The distance between each pair of atoms (bond length) is approximately 150 pm. There are 17 bonds between the first and the last atom in the chain. Ignoring the —COOH group on one end, the radii of the two end carbons count for an additional bond length. The approximate calculated length is 18(150 pm) = 2700 pm = 2.7 nm.

3. ___62%___ Calculate the percent difference between the values for molecular length obtained from experimental data and bond length.

$$\text{percent difference} = \frac{|\text{difference of the two values}|}{\text{average of the two values}} \times 100\%$$

$$= \frac{|5.1 \text{ nm} - 2.7 \text{ nm}|}{\dfrac{5.1 \text{ nm} + 2.7 \text{ nm}}{2}} \times 100\% \doteq 62\%$$

Note: Do not let your students become discouraged at the apparently low accuracy. Considering the relatively crude methodology used in this experiment and the extremely small dimensions involved, results within one order of magnitude are acceptable.

4. ___9.5×10^{-23} cm³___ Assuming the oleic acid molecule is a cylinder with a diameter of 150. pm (1.50×10^{-8} cm), what is the volume of the molecule in cubic centimeters? Use your experimental value for the length of the molecule.

Given: $h = 5.4 \times 10^{-7}$ cm; $r = \dfrac{d}{2} = \dfrac{1.50 \times 10^{-8} \text{ cm}}{2} = 7.5 \times 10^{-9}$ cm; $V = ?$

Formula: $V = \pi r^2 h$

Solution: $V = \pi (7.5 \times 10^{-9} \text{ cm})^2 (5.4 \times 10^{-7} \text{ cm}) \doteq 9.5 \times 10^{-23}$ cm³

5. ___1.0×10^{18} molecules/drop___ Using the volume you calculated in Question 4, estimate the number of oleic acid molecules in one drop of the solution. Remember that the drop is *not* pure oleic acid (see Question 1 in the Postlab Exercises).

volume of oleic acid in one drop = 9.5×10^{-5} cm³;

volume of one molecule = 9.5×10^{-23} cm³

$$\text{number of molecules per drop} = \frac{9.5 \times 10^{-5} \frac{\text{cm}^3}{\text{drop}}}{9.5 \times 10^{-23} \frac{\text{cm}^3}{\text{molecule}}}$$

$$\doteq 1.0 \times 10^{18} \frac{\text{molecules}}{\text{drop}}$$

6. ___Ans. vary.___ (Optional) If you performed the additional trials, compare the precision of your results. Refer to Appendix A for the procedure used to determine precision.

See Appendix A, Section III B 4.

Name _____

Date _____ Hour ____

PRELAB HOMEWORK

1. From your reading in the textbook and the Prelab Discussion, discuss why a physicist would be interested in knowing the dimensions of molecular or atomic particles.

   The dimensions of particles, particularly in crystal lattices, often determine the

   physical properties of the substance, such as the mechanical strength of an alloy

   or the electrical characteristics of a semiconductor. These are areas of professional

   concern to a physicist.

2. Note the shapes of the oleic acid molecules in Figure 2. Explain why you will be determining the *average* length of the molecule.

   The length of the molecule is highly variable because it can twist at most carbon-

   carbon bonds. Therefore, the thickness of the oleic acid layer is the average of the

   combinations of the various dimensions of the molecules as they vibrate.

3. A molecule that has distinct charged regions on its surface is called a ____polar____ molecule.

4. What characteristic of oleic acid makes it ideal for use in the technique discussed in this lab?

   Oleic acid is a polar molecule that will naturally arrange itself on the surface of

   water so that it stands on end, practically perpendicular to the water's surface.

5. Describe the process by which the volume of one drop of the oleic acid solution is determined.

   Count the drops of solution needed to fill a graduated cylinder to a predetermined

   level (2.0 mL). Divide the volume by the number of drops in order to obtain the

   volume per drop.

6. ____9.1×10^{-5} mL/drop____ One student found that it required 110 drops of solution to fill a graduated cylinder to 2.0 mL. A 0.50% solution of oleic acid contains 5.0×10^{-3} mL oleic acid/mL solution. What is the volume of oleic acid per drop of solution for that dropper?

   number of drops = 110; V = 2.0 mL;

   oleic acid concentration = $5.0 \times 10^{-3} \frac{\text{mL oleic acid}}{\text{drop}}$

   mL oleic acid/drop = $\dfrac{2.0 \text{ mL solution}}{110 \text{ drops}} \Big| \dfrac{5.0 \times 10^{-3} \text{ mL oleic acid}}{\text{mL solution}}$

   $\doteq 9.1 \times 10^{-5} \ \frac{\text{mL oleic acid}}{\text{drop}}$

7. ____180 cm²____ The same student determined that the average diameter of the oleic acid layer on the water was 15.0 cm. Assuming a circular shape, what is the area of this layer?

   Given: d_{av} = 15.0 cm; A = ?

   Formulas: $A = \pi r^2$; $r = \dfrac{d_{av}}{2}$

   Solution: $A = \pi \left(\dfrac{15.0 \text{ cm}}{2}\right)^2 = \pi(7.5 \text{ cm})^2 \doteq 177 \text{ cm}^2 \approx 180 \text{ cm}^2$ (2 SDs allowed)

8. _____ 5.1 × 10⁻⁷ cm _____ Using the information from Questions 6 and 7, determine the length of the oleic acid molecule in centimeters. Refer to Equation (2) from the Prelab Discussion.

Given: $V = 9.1 \times 10^{-5}$ mL (cm³); $A = 180$ cm²; $h = ?$

Formula: $h = \dfrac{V}{\pi r^2} = \dfrac{V}{A}$

Solution: $h = \dfrac{9.1 \times 10^{-5} \text{ cm}^3}{180 \text{ cm}^2} \doteq 5.1 \times 10^{-7}$ cm

Name ━━━━━━━━━━━━━━

Date ━━━━━━━━ Hour ━━━

LATENT HEAT OF FUSION

Purpose

The flow of thermal energy is a vital aspect of many natural and artificial processes. The purpose of this lab is to

- familiarize you with the use of a calorimeter.
- introduce the concept of equipment calibration as part of the experimental process.
- experimentally determine the latent heat of fusion of ice.
- compare an experimentally determined value with the accepted value.

Prelab Discussion

When thermal energy is transferred to or from an object, its temperature usually changes as the particles of the object gain or lose kinetic energy. This change in temperature responding to changes in thermal energy is predictable. The amount of heat required to increase the temperature of a unit mass of a substance one degree is a basic physical property of substances called **specific heat (c_{sp}).**

Thermal energy changes in an object, however, do not always result in temperature changes in the object. Before a solid can melt, the particles must absorb sufficient energy to break the bonds or intermolecular forces that hold them in their solid-phase positions. At the melting point, there is no measurable change in average temperature of the melting substance as energy is added to it. The excess energy seems to disappear in the process. Physicists call the energy required to bring about a phase change of a given amount of a substance from the solid to the liquid state (as well as the reverse process) the **latent heat of fusion.** The term *latent* comes from the Latin word *latens,* meaning hidden or concealed.

The investigation of the flow of thermal energy (heat) in a laboratory requires a special apparatus called a *calorimeter.* This device is essentially an insulated chamber that thermally isolates the process that is being investigated from its surroundings. A calorimeter may be a sophisticated, multijacketed insulated container or just two polystyrene cups nested together (see Figures 1 and 2). The temperature changes of an object or a substance placed within a calorimeter can be precisely measured.

When scientists perform experiments, they must often account for the effects of the instrument on the data. The following example illustrates the reason that this must be done. Suppose you add 20.0 g of cold water to a calorimeter and allow it to stand for several minutes to permit the water and the calorimeter to come to thermal equilibrium. You then measure the temperature of the water and find it to be 10.0 °C. You add 20.0 g of hot water at 50.0 °C to the water in the calorimeter. You note after a few minutes that the temperature stabilizes at 28.0 °C. Now examine the data. The hot water's temperature changed from 50.0 to 28.0 °C, losing 22.0 C°. Using the formula

$$Q = mc_{sp}\Delta T, \tag{1}$$

you determine that the hot water lost 1840 J of thermal energy (see the box in the margin). On the other hand, the cool water's temperature changed from 10.0 to 28.0 °C, increasing 18.0 C°, so it gained 1500 J. Notice that the heat gained was less than the heat lost. What happened to the other 340 J? Since no chemical or phase change took place, the explanation must involve the calorimeter itself. The calorimeter evidently absorbed 340 J and experienced an 18 C° rise in temperature. How can these quantities be related? Recall that **heat capacity (C)** is dependent on the *quantity of matter*

Required Equipment
balance
beaker, 50 mL
calorimeter
graduated cylinder, 100 mL
ice, crushed
lab thermometer
paper towels
water, hot and cold

Optional Equipment
insulated cover for cups
polystyrene cups, 2

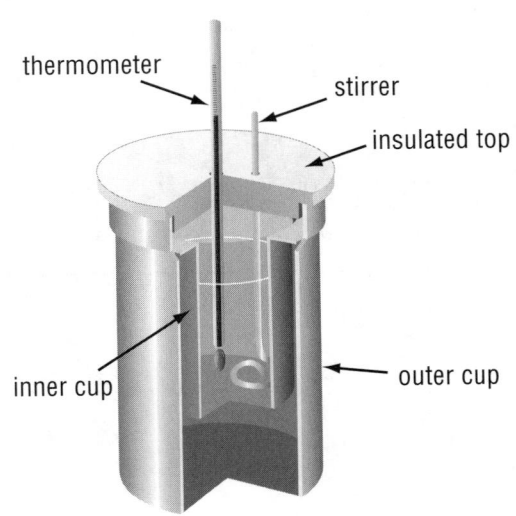

thermometer
stirrer
insulated top
inner cup
outer cup

Figure 1

Prelab Discussion

- Review the prerequisites for Lab 3-2 in the back of this manual.

- This manual uses the symbol c_{sp} to represent specific heat rather than the usual c in order to avoid confusion with other physical quantities that have the same symbol.

- The discussion is a detailed presentation of the calorimetric procedure. Review the Prelab Homework in conjunction with the discussion.

$$Q_{hw} = (20.0 \text{ g})(4.18 \tfrac{J}{g \cdot C°})(-22.0 \text{ C°}) \doteq -1840 \text{ J}$$

$$Q_{cw} = (20.0 \text{ g})(4.18 \tfrac{J}{g \cdot C°})(+18.0 \text{ C°}) \doteq +1500 \text{ J}$$

Definitions for Subscripts

cal—calorimeter
cw—cold water
f—fusion
hw—hot water
ice—before the phase change
iw—ice water, the water from melted ice
w—generic water
ww—warm water

- Some textbooks define specific heat, heat capacity, and heats of fusion and vaporization in terms of calories. This practice has been generally supplanted by the use of joules for nearly all forms of energy.

- In this manual, the symbol °C is associated with a specific temperature

$Q_{hw} = (50.0 \text{ g})(4.18 \frac{\text{J}}{\text{g·C°}})(-28.3 \text{ C°}) \doteq -5910 \text{ J}$

$Q_{cal} = (18 \frac{\text{J}}{\text{C°}})(-28.3 \text{ C°}) \doteq -520 \text{ J}$

$Q_{ice} = (15.0 \text{ g})(2.09 \frac{\text{J}}{\text{g·C°}})(+3.0 \text{ C°}) \doteq 94 \text{ J}$

$Q_{iw} = (15.0 \text{ g})(4.18 \frac{\text{J}}{\text{g·C°}})(+21.7 \text{ C°}) \doteq 1360 \text{ J}$

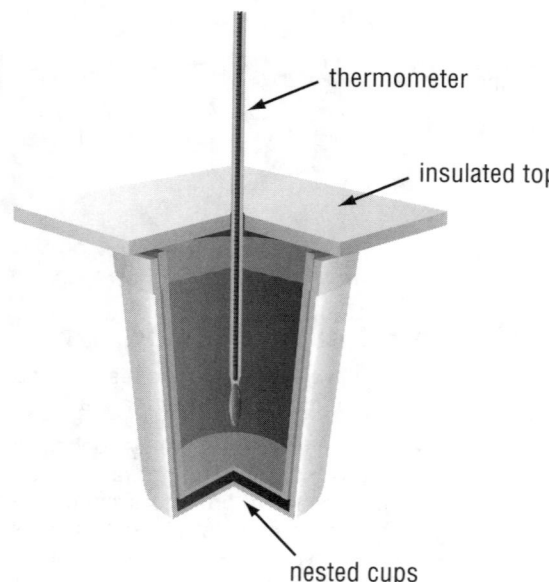

thermometer

insulated top

nested cups

Figure 2

on the Celsius scale, while the symbol C° represents a temperature band or range of Celsius degrees at any temperature. The latter is most often used in association with changes of temperature.

present and therefore is unique to a given object or quantity of a substance. Heat capacity is defined as the quantity of heat gained or lost by an *object* per Celsius degree change and can be expressed by the formula

$$C = \frac{Q}{\Delta T}. \tag{2}$$

The heat capacity of the calorimeter in the example is 340 J ÷ 18 C° ≐ 19 J/C°. Once the heat capacity of a particular calorimeter is known, it can be considered a constant for that calorimeter, regardless of what is placed inside it. Any temperature changes that take place within the calorimeter will be affected by the calorimeter itself, and this heat capacity must be taken into account when you perform calorimetric experiments. In summary, the heat balance equation for calibrating the calorimeter is

$$(mc_{sp}\Delta T)_{hw} + (mc_{sp}\Delta T)_{cw} + (C\Delta T)_{cal} = 0. \tag{3}$$

After the calorimeter is *calibrated,* it can be used to carefully measure heat transfers that occur during a phase change of a substance. Suppose you add 15.0 g of ice at −3.0 °C to 50.0 g of water at 50.0 °C. If the ice melts and the mixture of hot water and ice water reaches equilibrium at 21.7 °C, then the hot water changed −28.3 C°. The specific heat of water is 4.18 J/(g·C°) near room temperature, so you know that the hot water lost 5910 J of energy (see the box in the margin). The calorimeter was the same temperature as the water in it, so its temperature change was also −28.3 C°. Since $Q_{cal} = C_{cal}\Delta T$, the calorimeter gave up 520 J of heat. Together, the water and calorimeter lost about 6430 J to the melting ice. It seems logical that the ice would gain that amount of energy. You can consider the ice to be gaining energy in three steps: before the phase change, during the phase change, and after the phase change. Before the ice can melt, it has to warm 3.0 C° to 0.0 °C. The specific heat of ice is 2.09 J/(g·C°). It must therefore absorb 94 J of heat from the warm water and calorimeter. Once the ice melted, it became water. The temperature change from 0.0 to 21.7 °C for 15.0 g of ice water would require 1360 J. The total heat gain for the ice and ice water would be about 1450 J. Notice that there is a difference of nearly 5000 J between the heat lost by the water-calorimeter system and the heat gained by the ice. Evidently, the ice required about 333 J/g to change from a solid to a liquid. This "lost" energy is the latent heat of fusion for ice (h_f).

The *conservation of thermal energy,* or *heat balance* equations will help you in understanding the exchange of thermal energy in this experiment.

$$Q_{lost} + Q_{gained} = 0$$

or

$$Q_{gained} = -Q_{lost}, \tag{4}$$

where

$$Q_{gained} = Q_{ice} + Q_f + Q_{iw} \tag{5}$$

and

$$Q_{lost} = Q_{hw} + Q_{cal}. \tag{6}$$

Substituting Equations (5) and (6) into Equation (4) yields

$$Q_{ice} + Q_f + Q_{iw} = -[Q_{hw} + Q_{cal}].$$

Solving for the total heat absorbed to melt the ice gives

$$Q_f = -[Q_{hw} + Q_{cal} + Q_{ice} + Q_{iw}].$$

Given that $Q_f = h_f m_{ice}$, $Q_w = m_w c_{sp} \Delta T$, and $Q_{cal} = (C \Delta T)_{cal}$, substituting these values produces

$$h_f = \frac{-[(mc_{sp}\Delta T)_{hw} + (C\Delta T)_{cal} + (mc_{sp}\Delta T)_{ice} + (mc_{sp}\Delta T)_{iw}]}{m_{ice}}. \qquad (7)$$

Solving problems of this type requires care in using the proper sign (+ or −) for temperature changes. Always express ΔT as $T_2 - T_1$.

Procedure

Instructions to record data refer to blanks in the Data section.

Calorimeter Heat Capacity

1. Remove the inner cup from the calorimeter and determine its mass. Record the mass in 1a. Also record the mass in 3a.

2. Add approximately 50 mL of *cold* tap water to the inner cup of the calorimeter. Determine the combined mass of the calorimeter's inner cup and the water. Record the mass in 1b.

3. Assemble the calorimeter as shown in Figure 1 if you are using a standard calorimeter, or as shown in Figure 2 if you are using polystyrene cups. Verify that the thermometer is immersed in the water without touching the bottom of the cup.

   Caution: Avoid punching a hole through the bottom of the polystyrene cup!

4. While you are waiting for the temperature of the calorimeter, the thermometer, and the cold water to come to equilibrium, measure out 50 mL of *hot* water into a separate container.

5. Record the temperature of the cold water in the calorimeter in 2a.

   Note: Steps 6–8 must be performed quickly so that the temperature of the water is not significantly affected by room temperature.

   Keep the cover on the calorimeter except when adding a substance to the calorimeter.

6. Determine the temperature of the hot water and record the temperature in 2b.

7. Add the hot water to the cold water already in the calorimeter. Replace the cover and insert the thermometer back into the calorimeter. Carefully swirl the calorimeter constantly for about 30 seconds (until the temperature stabilizes at a maximum value) to mix the contents. If your calorimeter has a built-in stirrer, you can use that instead. Record the temperature at which the system attains equilibrium in 2c.

8. Remove the thermometer and lid from the calorimeter. Determine the mass of the inner cup of the calorimeter and combined samples of water. Record the mass in 1c.

Latent Heat of Fusion for Ice

9. Empty the calorimeter, dry it, and add 100 mL of hot water to the cup. Determine the mass of the inner cup of the calorimeter and the water. Record the mass in 3b.

10. Reassemble the calorimeter and the thermometer and allow the system to reach equilibrium.

- Make sure that the students understand all of the subscripts used in this lab.

- It is advisable that you work through the algebraic derivation of the heat of fusion formula.

Equipment and Setup

- The recommended apparatus is the double-walled aluminum calorimeter offered through BJUP and other scientific equipment suppliers.

- An adequate substitute calorimeter is pictured in Figure 2, employing two 12 oz polystyrene cups. To make an insulated top, cut two pieces of 1/2 in. foam board so that the smaller piece fits snugly inside the lip of the inner cup and the other piece covers the top. Glue these pieces together and bore a hole slightly smaller than the diameter of a thermometer through the center of the lid.

- Crush the ice at least 1 hour before class and return it to the freezer or a cooler containing dry ice. This experiment works best with large changes in temperature, so make (and keep) the ice as cold as possible until just prior to use.

Procedure

- Students must ensure that the thermometer bulb is immersed in the water inside the calorimeter by adjusting its position in the lid. If the thermometer touches the bottom of the cup, it may give an erroneous reading.

Note: Steps 11–15 must be performed quickly so that the temperatures of the ice and water are not significantly affected by room temperature.

11. Obtain a 50 mL beaker full of crushed ice from the freezer. Pour the ice out onto a doubled paper towel.

12. Record the temperature of the hot water in 4a.

13. Remove the thermometer from the hot water, keeping the lid on the calorimeter. Measure the temperature of the ice by tightly wrapping a mound of ice in a paper towel around the bulb of the thermometer for about 30 seconds or until the temperature stabilizes. After determining the ice temperature, have your lab partner record the temperature in 4b. *Immediately* add the ice to the hot water in the calorimeter. Replace the cover and thermometer.

14. Carefully swirl the calorimeter continuously (or use the stirrer) while monitoring the temperature until the system comes to thermal equilibrium. This is determined *after* the ice has completely melted. The lowest temperature achieved is the equilibrium temperature. If the temperature begins to rise, you have passed the equilibrium point, and the water is gaining heat from the surroundings. Record the lowest temperature achieved by the system in 4c.

15. Determine the combined mass of the inner cup and water and record the mass in 3c.

Data Actual data will vary. Data shown is typical.

Calorimeter Heat Capacity

1. Mass Measurements

    a. Mass of empty calorimeter cup   1.85 g

    b. Mass of calorimeter cup and cold water   51.60 g

    c. Mass of calorimeter cup and mixture of hot and cold water   103.20 g

2. Temperature Measurements

    a. Temperature of cold water   19.6 °C

    b. Temperature of hot water   95.3 °C

    c. Temperature of mixture of hot and cold water   54.5 °C

Latent Heat of Fusion for Ice

3. Mass Measurements

    a. Mass of empty calorimeter cup   1.85 g

    b. Mass of calorimeter cup and hot water   53.70 g

    c. Mass of calorimeter cup, melted ice, and water   71.10 g

4. Temperature Measurements

    a. Temperature of hot water   66.5 °C

    b. Temperature of ice pack   −7.4 °C

    c. Temperature of melted ice and water mixture at equilibrium   33.0 °C

Postlab Exercises

Answers shown use typical data. Solutions refer to steps in the Data section.

Calorimeter Heat Capacity

1. Determine the mass of the cold water.

   1b − 1a = 51.60 g − 1.85 g =   _____49.75_____ g

2. Determine the change in temperature of the cold water.

   2c − 2a = 54.5 °C − 19.6 °C =   _____34.9_____ C°

3. Determine the heat gained by the cold water, using Equation (1).

   Q_{cw} = (49.75 g)(4.18 $\frac{J}{g \cdot C°}$)(34.9 C°) ≈   _____7260_____ J   (3 SDs allowed)

4. Determine the mass of the hot water.

   1c − 1b = 103.20 g − 51.60 g =   _____51.60_____ g

5. Determine the change in temperature of the hot water.

   2c − 2b = 54.5 °C − 95.3 °C =   _____−40.8_____ C°

6. Determine the heat lost by the hot water, using Equation (1).

   Q_{hw} = (51.60 g)(4.18 $\frac{J}{g \cdot C°}$)(−40.8 C°) ≐ −8800 J ≈   _____-8.80×10^3_____ J   (3 SDs allowed)

7. Determine the change in temperature of the calorimeter.

   2c − 2a = 54.5 °C − 19.6 °C =   _____34.9_____ C°

8. Determine the heat capacity of the calorimeter, using Equation (3).

   $$C_{cal} = \frac{-[(mc_{sp}\Delta T)_{hw} + (mc_{sp}\Delta T)_{cw}]}{\Delta T_{cal}}$$

   $$= \frac{-[(-8800 \text{ J}) + (+7260 \text{ J})]}{34.9 \text{ C°}} \doteq \quad \underline{\quad 44.1 \quad} \text{ J/C°}$$

Latent Heat of Fusion for Ice

9. Determine the mass of the hot water.

   3b − 3a = 53.70 g − 1.85 g =   _____51.85_____ g

10. Determine the change in temperature of the hot water.

    4c − 4a = 33.0 °C − 66.5 °C =   _____−33.5_____ C°

11. Determine the heat lost by the hot water, using Equation (1).

    Q_{hw} = (51.85 g)(4.18 $\frac{J}{g \cdot C°}$)(−33.5 C°) ≈   _____−7260_____ J   (3 SDs allowed)

12. Determine the mass of the ice.

    3c − 3b = 71.10 g − 53.70 g =   _____17.40_____ g

13. Determine the change in temperature of the ice before it melted.

    0.0 °C − 4b = 0.0 °C − (−7.4 °C) =   _____7.4_____ C°

14. Determine the heat gained by the solid ice, using Equation (1).

    Q_{ice} = (17.40 g)(2.09 $\frac{J}{g \cdot C°}$)(7.4 C°) ≐ 269 J ≈   _____270_____ J   (2 SDs allowed)

15. Determine the temperature change of the ice water after melting.

    4c − 0.0 °C = 33.0 °C − 0.0 °C =   _____33.0_____ C°

16. Determine the heat gained by the ice water after melting, using Equation (1).

(3 SDs allowed)
$$Q_{iw} = (17.40 \text{ g})(4.18 \tfrac{J}{g \cdot C°})(33.0 \text{ C°}) \doteq 2400 \text{ J} \approx \underline{\quad 2.40 \times 10^3 \quad} \text{ J}$$

17. Determine the change in temperature of the calorimeter.

$$4c - 4a = 33.0 \text{ °C} - 66.5 \text{ °C} = \underline{\quad -33.5 \quad} \text{ C°}$$

18. Determine the heat lost by the calorimeter, using Equation (2).

$$Q_{cal} = (44.1 \tfrac{J}{C°})(-33.5 \text{ C°}) \doteq -1477 \text{ J} \approx \underline{\quad -1480 \quad} \text{ J}$$

19. Determine the heat of fusion of the ice, using Equation (7).

$$h_f = \frac{-[(mc_{sp}\Delta T)_{hw} + (C\Delta T)_{cal} + (mc_{sp}\Delta T)_{ice} + (mc_{sp}\Delta T)_{iw}]}{m_{ice}}$$

$$h_f = \frac{-[(-7260 \text{ J}) + (-1480 \text{ J}) + (+270 \text{ J}) + (+2400 \text{ J})]}{17.40 \text{ g}}$$

(3 SDs allowed)
$$= \frac{-(-6070 \text{ J})}{17.40 \text{ g}} \approx \underline{\quad 349 \quad} \text{ J/g}$$

20. The accepted value for the heat of fusion for ice is 333 J/g. Determine your percent error.

$$\text{percent error} = \frac{(\text{experimental value} - \text{accepted value})}{\text{accepted value}} \times 100\%$$

(3 SDs allowed)
$$\text{percent error} = \frac{(349 \tfrac{J}{g} - 333 \tfrac{J}{g})}{333 \tfrac{J}{g}} \times 100\% \approx \underline{\quad 4.80 \quad} \%$$

Postlab Analysis

1. After adding the ice to the calorimeter, compare the temperature change of the hot water to the temperature change of the calorimeter.

   The two temperature changes are the same.

2. When you compare the total thermal energy lost by the hot water and calorimeter to the total thermal energy gained by the ice and ice water, there is a significant difference between the two values when considering temperature changes alone. What happened to the "missing" heat?

   The "missing" heat was absorbed by the ice in order to break the ice

   crystal bonds as it changed from a solid to a liquid.

For Questions 3–5, circle the correct answer.

3. (True/**False**) During the melting process, the mixture of ice and water experiences a continuous temperature change.

4. (True/**False**) An ice cube at equilibrium in a container of water at 0.0 °C will melt even if no additional heat is added to the container.

5. (True/**False**) Heat of fusion can be measured directly with a thermometer.

6. *Calibrating* an instrument often means adjusting it so that it reads accurately. Discuss another meaning of the word as it pertains to experiments.

   Calibrating an instrument is necessary in order to understand how it

   affects the data during the experiment.

Name _____

Date _____ Hour _____

PRELAB HOMEWORK

1. __4.18 J__ How much thermal energy is required to change the temperature of 1 g of water 1 C°? Express your answer in joules to 3 SDs.

2. __2.09 J__ How much thermal energy is required to change the temperature of 1 g of ice 1 C°. Express your answer in joules to 3 SDs.

3. Define *heat capacity*.
   Heat capacity is the total amount of thermal energy transfer (or heat) required to change the temperature of an object or a known quantity of matter one degree.

4. Define *specific heat*.
   Specific heat is the amount of thermal energy gain (or heat) required to raise the temperature of a unit mass of a substance one degree (units depend on the system of measurement).

5. Define *latent heat of fusion*.
   The latent heat of fusion (or enthalpy of fusion) is the amount of thermal energy change required to change 1 g of a substance from the solid to the liquid state (or vice versa).

6. __29.3 J/C°__ Suppose that you add 50.0 g of hot water to a calorimeter and allow the system to reach its equilibrium temperature. At equilibrium, the temperature measures 55.0 °C. You then add an equal amount of cold water measuring 25.0 °C and mix. You find that the mixture attains thermal equilibrium at 41.0 °C. What is the heat capacity of the calorimeter? Express your answer in joules per Celsius degree to 3 SDs.

   Given: $m_{hw} = 50.0$ g; $\Delta T_{hw} = 41.0\ °C - 55.0\ °C = -14.0\ C°$; $m_{cw} = 50.0$ g; $\Delta T_{cw} = 41.0\ °C - 25.0\ °C = 16.0\ C°$; $\Delta T_{cal} = \Delta T_{hw}$; $C_{cal} = ?$

   Formula: $(mc_{sp}\Delta T)_{hw} + (mc_{sp}\Delta T)_{cw} + (C\Delta T)_{cal} = 0$

   Solution:

   $(50.0\ \text{g})(4.18\ \frac{J}{g \cdot C°})(-14.0\ C°) + (50.0\ \text{g})(4.18\ \frac{J}{g \cdot C°})(16.0\ C°) + C_{cal}(-14.0\ C°) = 0$

   $(-2930\ J) + (+3340\ J) + C_{cal}(-14.0\ C°) = 0$

   $C_{cal} = \dfrac{-[(-2930\ J) + (+3340\ J)]}{-14.0\ C°} \doteq 29.3\ \frac{J}{C°}$

7. ___331 J/g___ If you add 20.0 g of ice at a temperature of $-5.0\ °C$ to 100.0 g of warm water at 39.0 °C and the ice-water mixture comes to equilibrium at 20.0 °C, what is the heat of fusion of the ice if the heat capacity of the calorimeter is 29.5 J/C°? Express your answer in joules per gram to 3 SDs.

Given: m_{ice} = 20.0 g; ΔT_{ice} = 0.0 °C $-$ (-5.0 °C) = $+5.0$ C°;

ΔT_{iw} = 20.0 °C $-$ 0.0 °C = $+20.0$ C°; m_{ww} = 100.0 g; ΔT_{ww} = 20.0 °C $-$ 39.0 °C = -19.0 C°; ΔT_{cal} = ΔT_{ww}; C_{cal} = 29.5 $\frac{J}{C°}$; h_f = ?

Formula: $h_f = \dfrac{-(Q_{ww} + Q_{cal} + Q_{ice} + Q_{iw})}{m_{ice}}$

$\qquad\quad = \dfrac{-[(mc_{sp}\Delta T)_{ww} + (C\Delta T)_{cal} + (mc_{sp}\Delta T)_{ice} + (mc_{sp}\Delta T)_{iw}]}{m_{ice}}$

Solution: Q_{ww} = (100.0 g)(4.18 $\frac{J}{g\cdot C°}$)(-19.0 C°) $\doteq$ -7942 J $\approx$ -7940 J;

Q_{cal} = (29.5 $\frac{J}{C°}$)(-19.0 C°) $\doteq$ -561 J;

Q_{ice} = (20.0 g)(2.09 $\frac{J}{g\cdot C°}$)($+5.0$ C°) = $+209$ J $\approx$ 210 J (2 SDs allowed);

Q_{iw} = (20.0 g)(4.18 $\frac{J}{g\cdot C°}$)($+20.0$ C°) $\doteq$ 1672 J $\approx$ $+1670$ J (3 SDs allowed);

$h_f = \dfrac{-[(-7940\ J) + (-561\ J) + (+210\ J) + (+1670\ J)]}{20.0\ g} \doteq \dfrac{-(-6620\ J)}{20.0\ g}$ = 331 $\frac{J}{g}$

8. ___-0.900%___ The accepted value for the heat of fusion of ice is 333 J/g. If you attain a value of 330. J/g as an experimental value, what is your percent error?

percent error = $\dfrac{\text{(experimental value} - \text{accepted value)}}{\text{accepted value}} \times 100\%$

percent error = $\dfrac{(330.\frac{J}{g} - 333\frac{J}{g})}{333\frac{J}{g}} \times 100\%$ $\doteq$ -0.900%

9. Based on your reading of the Prelab Discussion and the Procedure section, give two specific problems that could contribute to errors in this experiment.

Acceptable answers include incorrect calibration of the calorimeter (temperatures were not permitted to attain equilibrium); too much delay between measuring the temperature of the warm water and adding the ice; too much delay between measuring the temperature of the ice and adding it to the calorimeter; final measured temperature of the calorimeter not being the equilibrium temperature; errors measuring the masses of the cup, water, and ice; splashing or spilling the water or ice during the procedure.

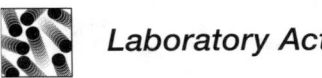
Name _____

Date _____ Hour _____

COEFFICIENT OF THERMAL EXPANSION

Purpose

Thermal expansion and contraction of materials determines their usefulness for many applications. The purpose of this lab is to

- determine the linear coefficient of thermal expansion for several metals.
- gain experience with unfamiliar measuring instruments.

Prelab Discussion

Nearly all materials expand when heated. As you learned from your textbook, the change in length or dimension of a solid is, for all practical purposes, directly proportional to the change in temperature over a broad temperature range. The change in length is also proportional to the original length of the object. The longer the object, the greater the change in length per degree of temperature change. This property of solid materials can be characterized by a physical constant called the **coefficient of linear thermal expansion,** denoted α (Greek letter alpha).

Because α is not always constant for a material over a wide range of temperatures, scientists have calculated α for many materials based on an initial temperature (T_0) of 25 °C. For the purpose of calculation, the length of any sample of material at the reference temperature of 25 °C is called L_0. If you know α, you can predict the change in length of the sample after heating by using the formula

$$\Delta L = L_0 \alpha \Delta T, \tag{1}$$

where $\Delta L = L_2 - L_1$ and $\Delta T = T_2 - T_1$. This expression may be solved for α to yield

$$\alpha = \frac{\Delta L}{L_0 \Delta T} = \frac{L_2 - L_1}{L_0(T_2 - T_1)}. \tag{2}$$

Since room temperature is so close to the reference temperature of 25 °C, we will ignore the difference and use L_1, the length of the sample at room temperature, in place of L_0 in Equation (2). Therefore, Equation (2) may be rewritten as

$$\alpha = \frac{L_2 - L_1}{L_1(T_2 - T_1)} = \frac{\Delta L}{L_1 \Delta T}. \tag{3}$$

If you solve Equation (3) for L_2, the final length at T_2, you obtain the expression

$$L_2 = L_1 + L_1 \alpha \Delta T. \tag{4}$$

Why would you want to know the length of an object at a particular temperature (i.e., why would you want to know the coefficient of linear thermal expansion)? Engineers, builders, scientists, and most manufacturers of materials need to know the coefficients of linear expansion so that they can predict how the materials they use will change with various temperature changes. If expansion is not taken into account, these changes can cause sidewalks and railroad tracks to buckle, steel rivets to pop, and pistons and shaft bearings to seize. For many objects, expansion and contraction may change their shape so much that they no longer function as designed. Users, as well as manufacturers, must have an awareness of these effects, and this requires knowledge about coefficients of expansion.

Required Equipment

beaker, 250 mL
hoses
lab thermometer or thermocouple
 and multimeter
linear expansion apparatus
metal tubes or rods
meter stick
steam generator and heat source
water

Optional Equipment

Bunsen burner and lighter
buzzer, DC
glycerin or soap
lab battery, 6 V
rubber stoppers, one-hole, 3
wire leads

Prelab Discussion

- Review the prerequisites for Lab 3-3 in the back of this manual.

- The theoretical information required for this lab is fairly basic, and it is presented clearly in the discussion.

- Provide some typical values for the variables in Equation (3) when introducing the lab so that the students will know what to expect. Emphasize that the accurate measurement of the change of length is far more critical than the measurement of the original length in this experiment.

- Demonstrate the type of equipment that your class will use and point out which steps in the Procedure section apply.

- If your apparatus uses an external indicator, such as a buzzer or ohmmeter, to show contact between the micrometer and the sample, be sure to demonstrate its use.

Equipment and Setup

- The recommended apparatus is the tube type shown in Figure 1. It is the least expensive model offered by science suppliers, and it can be easily built (see the Home School Notes).

- The temperature of the tube apparatus should be measured with a thermocouple probe attached to a multimeter designed to indicate temperature. These multimeters cost about $80 per unit, but the total cost of a tube apparatus and multimeter is less than one steam-jacket apparatus with a dial indicator. One multimeter can be used for several lab teams, and it is useful for many other activities in the physical sciences. The procedure provides alternative instructions if a temperature-reading multimeter is not available.

- If you have the steam-jacket apparatus, ensure that the required number of one-hole rubber stoppers of the right size are available. Stoppers that are too small can be pulled into the steam-jacket cylinder when disassembling the apparatus.

- Specially designed steam generators are available, but they can be inexpensively substituted (see the Home School Notes).

Procedure

- Perform this lab yourself before conducting it in class.

- The components of the apparatus tend to move around when the hoses are being attached because of the handling required. Ensure that the hoses are connected before zeroing the instrument indicators. Also, the hose connections

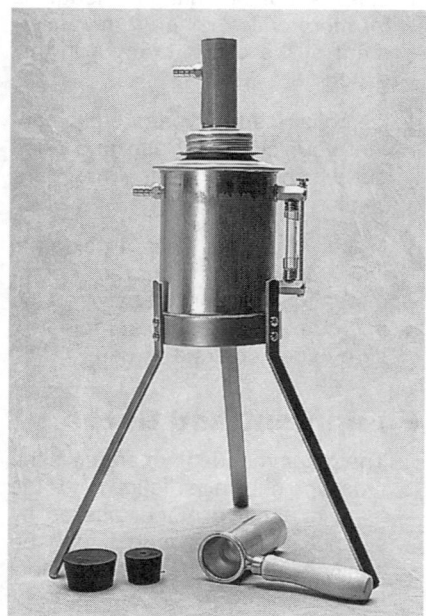

Figure 2 Steam Generator

When a new plastic or alloy is developed, one of the important properties that must be determined is how the material responds to heating or cooling. You can imagine that a plastic that expands significantly when heated to 140 °F would not be appropriate for the interior of an automobile. On a hot summer day, the interior of a car exposed to the sun can easily reach this temperature, and components made of this plastic would be severely distorted. Material suppliers can measure this thermal expansion property by exposing a long rod of the material to a temperature change and measuring its change in length. The coefficient of expansion may then be computed. This is the procedure you will use in this lab.

For this experiment you will probably use one of the two types of apparatus shown in Figures 1 and 3. In the **tube apparatus** (Figure 1), a rigid metal sample tube is mounted on a base so that one end of the tube is fixed and the other end rests on a roller connected to a pointer. A steam generator or boiler (Figure 2) is connected to the metal tube with a rubber hose. Steam flows *through* the sample tube to be tested, and as the tube expands, the movement of the tube rotates the roller. The pointer magnifies the movement, which is indicated on a scale. Temperature changes are best measured with a thermocouple connected to a multimeter. (A thermocouple is a device that produces a variable electrical output as its electrical resistance changes in response to temperature changes.)

The **steam-jacket apparatus** (Figure 3) also uses steam but requires a solid metal rod sample. The rod is sealed inside a tube, which forms a container (or steam jacket) around the sample rod. One end of the rod is clamped in a fixed position, and the other end makes contact with an instrument designed to measure the change in length. Steam flows inside the steam jacket *around* the metal rod, and the change in length of the rod is determined at the end of the instrument. This measuring instrument may be either a **dial indicator** (Figure 3A) or a **micrometer** (Figure 3B). A dial indicator consists of a spring-loaded contact pin attached to a circular dial that automatically measures very small changes in length. A micrometer is a device that measures changes in length by manually adjusting a scale on a threaded knob. Temperature changes are measured using a thermometer inserted into the steam jacket.

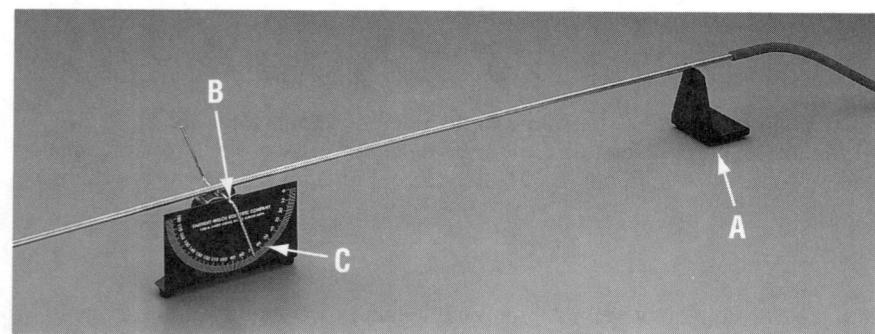

Figure 1 Tube Apparatus

Procedure

Tube Apparatus

1. Fill the steam generator (see Figure 2) about half full of water and begin heating it. This may consist of turning on an electric heater built into the boiler, lighting a burner, or placing the container on a hot plate or electric stove. Do not connect the hose to the apparatus yet.

2. Record the kind of material for each tube to be tested (called the sample) in Table 1. Obtain the accepted value for the coefficient of linear thermal expansion (α_a) from your teacher for each metal and record it in Table 1.

3. Set up the tube apparatus (see Figure 1).

   a. Clamp or otherwise secure the tube onto the fixed end of the base (A). Place the support for the roller indicator (B) under the opposite end of the tube.

   b. Measure the length of the tube between the two points of support to 0.1 mm precision and record it as L_1 in Table 1.

   c. Measure the temperature of the metal tube at its midpoint, using a thermocouple probe attached to a multimeter. If you do not have such an instrument, measure the room ambient temperature with a lab thermometer. Record this value as T_1 in Table 1.

   d. Attach the hose from the steam generator to the fixed end of the tube.

   e. Adjust the roller pointer to the zero mark on the scale.

4. When the apparatus begins to emit steam, start monitoring the temperature at the midpoint of the sample. When the temperature stabilizes at a maximum, allow the system to steam for 4 to 5 minutes more in order to permit the sample to achieve thermal equilibrium. Record this temperature as T_2 in Table 1.

   If you do not have a thermocouple-multimeter instrument, you may place the bulb of a lab thermometer into the steam jet exiting the end of the tube. When the temperature has been stable for 3 to 4 minutes, record the temperature here.

   exit temperature _____

5. Note the position of the pointer on the scale (C). Record this value as ΔL in Table 1.

   Caution: The tube, steam jacket, and steam generator surfaces are hot.

6. Turn off the heat supply to the steam generator. Using hot mitts or towels to protect your hands, disconnect the steam supply hose from the tube. Unclamp the tube and pour out the remaining hot condensate into a container. Take the tube to a sink and pour cool water through it until it is again near room temperature.

7. If additional samples are to be tested, repeat Steps 3–6. Perform two trials on one of the samples for the purpose of evaluating the precision of the experimental technique.

8. When you have finished collecting data, carefully pour the hot water remaining in the steam generator into the sink and completely disassemble the apparatus according to your teacher's instructions.

must be made before steam begins to flow so that the instruments can be zeroed with the tube or rod at the initial temperature.

- At the end of a trial, caution your students about the presence of steam and hot water when disconnecting hoses and dumping out the condensate inside the tube or steam jacket. Unwary students could receive a burn.

- Make sure that the students understand the proper use of the micrometer. When using a micrometer, they must take several readings and calculate the average. Once they have found the average and calculated ΔL, have them record ΔL in Table 1.

Postlab Analysis

- **Accepted Values of α for Typical Metal Samples[1]**

These values of α apply to metals near room temperature. They are representative of the listed metals, but actual values will vary based on the alloy formulation and processing. Units are $10^{-6}\ C^{\circ -1}$. Some references use $(10^6\ K)^{-1}$, which is equivalent.

Aluminum, alloy 360	21.0
Aluminum, rolled	23.2
Brass, yellow	20.3
Copper	16.5
Steel, stainless	17.3
Steel, carbon	11.7

[1]David Lide, ed., *CRC Handbook of Chemistry and Physics,* 75th ed. (Boca Raton: CRC Press, 1995).

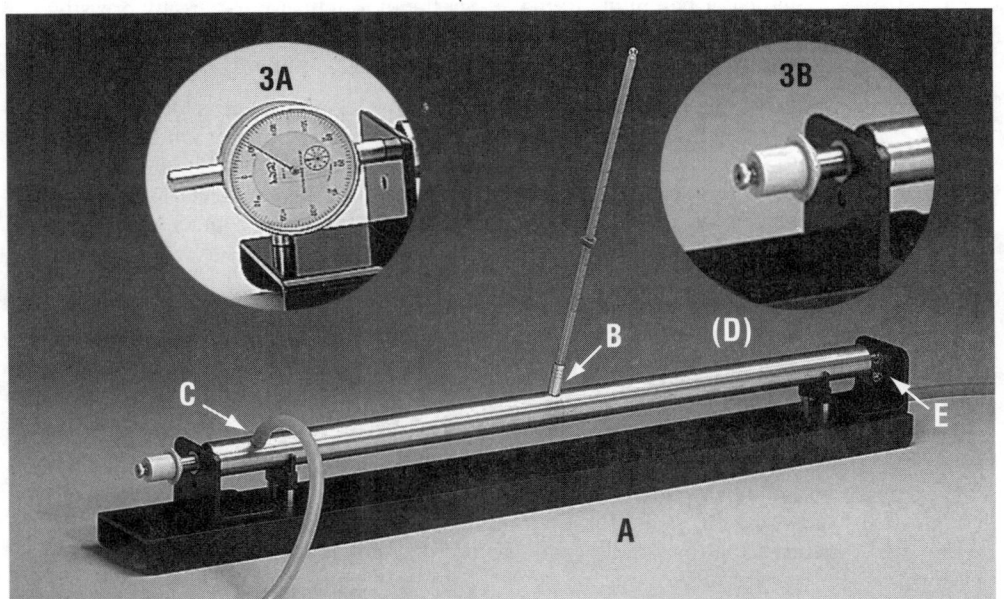

Figure 3 Steam-Jacket Apparatus showing Dial Indicator (3A) and Micrometer (3B)

- The exercises include several thought-provoking questions. Do not deprive your students of the opportunity to apply what they have learned.

Prelab Homework

- The unit of $10^{-6}\ C^{\circ -1}$ may be hard for the students to understand. Its basic meaning is millionths of a linear unit per Celsius degree.

Home School Notes

- **Construction of a Tube-Type Thermal Expansion Apparatus**

  1. A variety of 1/4 in. (6 mm) diameter metal tubes of several materials may be purchased at hobby shops dealing in radio-controlled models. Steel, aluminum, and copper tubes may be purchased at some home improvement stores. Cut the tubes into 60 cm lengths.

  2. Build a base from a piece of 1 × 2 or 1 × 4 lumber about 70 cm long.

  3. Make a fixed support about 10 cm high from the same material as the base. Attach the support at one end of the base, using screws and glue. On top of the fixed support, install a clamp that will hold the tube rigid. This could be a piece of wood attached to the top of the support by a hinge. Install a screw or nail through the free end of the piece of wood to keep the rod from slipping off the top of the support.

  4. The indicator support can be made from a strip of aluminum flashing or any other stiff sheet metal bent into a U-shape. Before bending, cut a rounded V-notch in each end of the metal strip. Bend the strip into a U so that the bottom of the notches will be the same height above the base as the top of the fixed support. These notches will hold the roller and pointer. Attach the U-support to the base about 55 cm from the fixed support.

Steam-Jacket Apparatus

1. Fill the steam generator (see Figure 2) about half full of water and begin heating it. This may consist of turning on an electric heater built into the boiler, lighting a burner, or placing the container on a hot plate or electric stove. Do not connect the hose to the apparatus yet.

2. Record the kind of material for each rod to be tested (called the sample) in Table 1. Obtain the accepted value for the coefficient of linear thermal expansion (α_a) from your teacher for each metal and record it in the α_a column in Table 1.

3. Set up the steam-jacket apparatus (see Figure 3).

   a. Measure the length of the rod to 0.1 mm precision and record the measurement as L_1 in Table 1.

   b. Press a one-hole rubber stopper onto the rod so that the end of the rod is flush with the large end of the stopper. Insert the rod into the steam-jacket cylinder and seat the stopper in the end opening. Press another stopper onto the other end of the rod and twist it onto the rod until it is firmly seated in the other end of the steam jacket.

   c. Insert the steam-jacket assembly into the base (A) so that the end of the rod that is flush with the stopper is at the end opposite the measuring device.

   d. Insert a lab thermometer into the hole (B) in the side of the steam jacket (if a stopper is required, glycerin or soap will help the stopper slide onto the thermometer more easily). Seat the stopper, if required, and gently push the thermometer in until it just touches the metal rod inside. Note the temperature and record the value as T_1 in Table 1 for the applicable sample.

   e. Connect the supply hose from the steam generator to the upward-pointing hose fitting (C) on the steam jacket before it begins to emit steam. Connect another hose to the downward-pointing hose fitting (D). This hose should be directed to a container to catch the waste steam and condensate as it drains from the steam jacket.

4. Adjust the measuring device according to the type of instrument.

   a. For a dial indicator (see Figure 3A), verify that the pin just touches the rod, then clamp the steam jacket in place with the clamp screw (if provided with one). Turn the setscrew (E) clockwise until you note the dial indicator beginning to move. Set the dial indicator to zero by pressing a zeroing knob on the dial case or rotating a watchlike stem in the appropriate direction so that all needles on the dial point to zero.

   b. For a micrometer (see Figure 3B), turn the micrometer clockwise until it just touches the end of the rod; then continue turning it until it is aligned to the zero mark. Turn the setscrew (E) clockwise until it just touches the rod. Depending on your apparatus, you may have an electric lamp, buzzer, or meter to assist you in determining when contact has been made, but these are not essential. Tighten the clamp screw, if provided with one, in order to clamp the steam jacket into the base frame. Back up the micrometer half a turn (counterclockwise); then carefully turn it in to verify that the contact point is at zero. Adjust the setscrew and micrometer as necessary until the rod and micrometer barely make contact when the micrometer is at zero. Turn the micrometer out 2.00 mm before the apparatus begins to emit steam.

5. When the apparatus begins to emit steam, start monitoring the temperature with the thermometer. When the temperature stabilizes at a maximum, allow the system to steam for 4 to 5 minutes more in order to permit the sample to achieve thermal equilibrium. Record this temperature as T_2 in Table 1.

6. Measure ΔL according to the type of measuring device.

   a. For a dial indicator, read the sum of all of the dials. The small inner dial usually indicates whole millimeters, and the outer dial indicates hundredths of a millimeter. Record this value as ΔL in Table 1.

   b. For a micrometer, gently turn the micrometer clockwise until it just touches the rod. This may be indicated by an electric light, buzzer, or meter. In order to determine ΔL, you must note not just the micrometer indication, but how far the micrometer must be rotated in order to make contact. Recall that you backed out the micrometer 2.00 mm. The micrometer normally makes one full turn per millimeter, so if you had to rotate the micrometer 1.44 turns in order to make contact, ΔL will be $+2.00$ mm $- 1.44$ mm $= +0.56$ mm. Record the turns of the micrometer in the margin of the Data section. Back the micrometer out until it no longer touches the rod and repeat this step three more times, recording the turns from the original $+2.00$ mm position in the margin as before.

   Caution: The tube, steam jacket, and steam generator surfaces are hot.

7. Turn off the heat supply to the steam generator. Using hot mitts or towels to protect your hands, disconnect the steam supply hose from the steam jacket. Unclamp the apparatus and pour out the remaining hot condensate into a container. Take the apparatus to a sink and pour cool water through it until it is again near room temperature. Cool the sample rod also.

8. If additional samples are to be tested, repeat Steps 3–6. Perform two trials on one of the samples for the purpose of evaluating the precision of the experimental technique.

9. When you have finished collecting data, carefully pour the hot water remaining in the steam generator into the sink and completely disassemble the apparatus according to your teacher's instructions.

5. Cut a piece of 1/8 or 3/16 in. wood dowel so that it will fit between the legs of the U-support. This will be the roller for the indicator. Obtain some thick wire (or thin rod) for the pointer. Drill holes slightly smaller than the wire in both ends of the roller. The holes must be centered in the ends and aligned with the axis of the roller.

```
            1.360 mm
            1.355 mm
            1.365 mm
          + 1.385 mm
          ─────────
            5.465 mm

Average:   1.366 mm

          + 2.00 mm
          − 1.37 mm
          ─────────
          + 0.63 mm
```

Data

Table 1
Thermal Expansion Data and Calculations

Sample	Initial Length, L_1	Change in Length, ΔL	Initial Temp., T_1	Final Temp., T_2	Change in Temp., ΔT	α_e ($\times 10^{-6}$ C$^{\circ -1}$)	α_a ($\times 10^{-6}$ C$^{\circ -1}$)	Percent Error
copper	698.9 mm	0.63 mm	26.1°C	97.6 °C	71.5 C°	13	16.5	−21 %
	mm	mm	°C	°C	C°			%
	mm	mm	°C	°C	C°			%
	mm	mm	°C	°C	C°			%
							Average	%

Actual data in Table 1 will vary. Data and calculations shown are typical for a micrometer apparatus.

Postlab Exercises

1. If you used the tube apparatus and measured the temperature with a thermometer rather than a thermocouple and multimeter, you need to find the average of the steam temperature as it enters the tube and the steam temperature as it exits the tube. Use an assumed steam generator temperature of 100.0 °C and the temperature recorded in Step 5. Enter your average as T_2 in Table 1. (Using this assumption may not produce results as accurate as an actual measurement, but it will allow you to complete the exercise.)

6. Cut two pieces of wire about the same length. Bend one end of each piece at a right angle such that the long parts are *exactly* the same length. File a point on the end of the long parts of the wires. You must leave the short end long

enough that after it is inserted into the end of the roller it will extend past the support before it bends. Insert the short end of the wire into the hole drilled into each end of the roller. Place the roller into the V-notches of the U-support. The short section of the indicator wires should be resting in the notches. Note that the two wires must point in opposite directions so that the wires counterbalance each other.

7. Measure the diameter of the roller as accurately as possible. A set of calipers will help. Compute the circumference of the roller. (1 in. = 25.40 mm)

8. Create a protractor scale that equates degrees of rotation of the roller to linear movement along its circumference. A roller with a diameter of 0.250 in. will have a circumference of 19.9 mm. A needle deflection of 1° is equivalent to 1/360 of this distance, or 0.055 mm/degree.

9. Note that the smaller you can make the diameter of the roller, the larger the angle of deflection for a given change in length of the sample tube. Commercial apparatuses use only the thick wire (see Figure 1).

10. You may have to hang some weights from the tubing with thread to provide the necessary friction on the roller. You may have to lubricate the V-notches also.

- Steam generators can be any enclosed container in which you can boil water. For a tea kettle, trim a one-hole stopper to fit the spout. Insert a short piece of metal or glass tubing, or even a ball point pen barrel into the stopper and attach a hose obtained from a home improvement store. For a 500 mL flask, insert glass tubing into a stopper and connect it to the hose.

2. If you took ΔL data with a micrometer, average the four micrometer readings in the margin of the Data section. Subtract the average from 2.00 mm in order to obtain ΔL. Record this value in Table 1. For a dial indicator, ΔL readings are provided directly, so this step is not necessary.

3. Determine the ΔT for each sample by subtracting T_1 from T_2 and enter the difference in the ΔT column of Table 1.

4. Compute the *experimental* coefficient of linear thermal expansion (α_e) for each metal, using Equation (3). Record the results in units of 10^{-6} $C^{\circ-1}$ in Table 1.

5. Compute the percent error between your experimental value and the accepted value of α for each metal and record these values in Table 1.

6. For the metal sample that was tested twice, compute the percent difference between the two experimental values of α.

metal _____

percent difference _____

Postlab Analysis

1. What key assumption, which forms the basis for the linear thermal expansion formula [Equation (3)], cannot be met with the types of apparatus used in this experiment? Explain your answer.

   The formula assumes that the entire length of the metal sample is being heated uniformly. In the experiment, the temperature declines from one end to the other as the steam flows through or around the sample.

2. What experimental procedure compensates for the concern noted in Question 1?

   The average temperature of the steam is determined, or the temperature is measured at the midpoint of the sample. It is assumed that the temperature decrease is uniform along the length of the tube or rod.

3. If you had measured the original length of the metal sample in inches and the apparatus indicated the change in length in inches, what would the unit for α be in this case? Explain your answer.

   The unit would still be 10^{-6} $C^{\circ-1}$ because the linear units cancel in the linear thermal expansion formula.

4. Which error in measurement will have a greater effect on the results of your calculations—a 1 mm error in measuring the original length or a 0.01 mm error in measuring the change in length? Prove your answer. Assume that $L_1 = 600.$ mm and $\Delta L = 0.60$ mm.

   Assuming a 600. mm sample, a 1 mm error in measurement is a 0.2% difference (1 mm ÷ 600. mm), which would produce an error of approximately 0.2% in α. However, assuming a change in length of 0.60 mm, a 0.01 mm error in measurement would produce a 2% error in ΔL (0.01 mm ÷ 0.60 mm) as well as α. Therefore, the effect of a 0.01 mm error in measuring the change in length is 10 times greater than the effect of a 1 mm error in measuring the original length.

5. Do you believe that you need an instrument more precise than a meter stick in order to measure the original length of the metal sample? Explain your answer.

No. The measurement of the length of the sample can be made to

0.1 mm precision with a meter stick. This precision will produce re-

sults that are well within the precision possible with the apparatus.

6. If you performed the test twice on the same sample, what does your percent difference between the two trials reveal? What does the average *percent error* reveal? Based on these values, discuss the precision and accuracy of the results you can expect to obtain from this experiment.

Student answers will vary. Percent difference between trials indicates

the precision of the experiment. High precision is revealed by low per-

cent difference, and low precision is revealed by high percent differ-

ence. Average percent error reveals the accuracy of the experiment. If

the percent error is high, students should conclude that the experi-

ment setup cannot produce accurate results.

7. __698.6 mm__ Engineers need to know how materials will change shape with temperature. Choose one of the samples that you used in this lab and assume that its length at room temperature is L_1. Using Equation (4) and the accepted value of α for the metal, predict the length of the sample if it were cooled to 0.0 °C.

The solution uses the typical data in Table 1. Actual answers will vary.

Given: $L_1 = 698.9$ mm; $T_1 = 26.1$ °C; $T_2 = 0.0$ °C; for copper,

$\alpha = 16.8 \times 10^{-6}$ C$^{°-1}$; $L_2 = ?$

Formula: $L_2 = L_1 + L_1 \alpha \Delta T$

Solution:

$L_2 = (698.9 \text{ mm}) + (698.9 \text{ mm})(16.8 \times 10^{-6} \text{ C}^{°-1})(0.0 \text{ °C} - 26.1 \text{ °C})$

$\doteq 698.6$ mm

Name _____

Date _____ Hour _____

PRELAB HOMEWORK

1. What factors determine how much a material will change size with temperature?

   The factors include the original length of the object, the change in temperature,

   and its coefficient of linear expansion, which is an inherent property of the material.

2. A bar of steel is heated 50 C°. How will the change in length of a 1 m bar compare to the change in length of a 10 m bar?

   The change in length of an object is proportional not only to the change in temper-

   ature but also to the original length, so the 10 m bar will expand 10 times as much

   as the 1 m bar.

3. Why is it possible in most school laboratory situations to substitute the initial length measured in the laboratory (L_1) for the reference length of an object measured at 25 °C (L_0) in the thermal expansion formula?

   Since the temperature of most school laboratories is usually within a few degrees

   of 25 °C, the difference between L_0 and L_1 is negligible.

4. Referring to Question 3, why do you *not* want to determine the reference length (L_0) of an object at 25 °C for use in the thermal expansion formula?

   You would have to change the object's temperature to 25 °C in order to measure its

   length, L_0. This procedure is impractical for school settings.

5. What is the symbol for the coefficient of linear thermal expansion, and what is the formula for calculating it?

   The symbol is α (Greek letter alpha). The formula is $\dfrac{\Delta L}{L_1 \Delta T}$. Accept $\alpha = \dfrac{\Delta L}{L_0 \Delta T}$ also.

6. What does the symbol $C^{\circ -1}$ mean?

   The symbol means "per Celsius degree."

7. Describe the general method used in this exercise for determining the coefficient of linear thermal expansion.

   A sample of metal in the form of a long rod or hollow tube is heated with steam.

   The sample's original length, its change in length, and its change in temperature

   are measured. The coefficient is then calculated using Equation (3).

8. __$16 \times 10^{-6}\ C^{\circ -1}$__ A tube of steel is measured and found to be 695.0 mm long. Room temperature is 24.5 °C. The tube is heated according to the instructions in this lab, and the change in length is noted to be 0.83 mm. The tube's temperature at its midpoint is 97.8 °C. Determine α for steel and report your answer in units of $10^{-6}\ C^{\circ -1}$.

   Given: $L_1 = 695.0$ mm; $T_1 = 24.5$ °C; $T_2 = 97.8$ °C; $\Delta L = 0.83$ mm; $\alpha = ?$

   Formula: $\alpha = \dfrac{\Delta L}{L_1 \Delta T}$

   Solution: $\alpha = \dfrac{0.83\ \cancel{mm}}{(695.0\ \cancel{mm})(97.8\ °C - 24.5\ °C)} = \dfrac{0.83}{50\,944\ C°} \doteq 16.3 \times 10^{-6}\ C^{\circ -1}$

   $\approx 16 \times 10^{-6}\ C^{\circ -1}$ (2 SDs allowed)

9. __697.0 mm__ If the tube in Question 8 could be heated to 200.0 °C, what would its new length be? Refer to Equation (4) in the Prelab Discussion.

Given: L_1 = 695.0 mm; T_1 = 24.5 °C; T_2 = 200.0 °C; α = 16 × 10^{-6} C$^{\circ -1}$; L_2 = ?

Formula: $L_2 = L_1 + L_1 \alpha \Delta T$

Solution: L_2 = (695.0 mm) + (695.0 mm)(16 × 10^{-6} C$^{\circ -1}$)(200.0 °C − 24.5 °C)

$\doteq$ 697.0 mm

Properly applying significant digit rules permits obtaining 4 SDs in the solution.

L_2 = (695.0 mm) + (695.0 mm)(16 × 10^{-6} C$^{\circ -1}$)(175.5 C$^\circ$)

= (695.0 mm) + (2.0 mm)

= 697.0 mm (4 SDs allowed)

Name _____

Date _____ Hour _____

SPECIFIC GRAVITY AND BUOYANCY

Purpose

This laboratory exercise will investigate phenomena associated with Archimedes' principle. The purpose is to

- determine the buoyant force exerted on an object supported by a fluid.
- determine the density of various objects and compare the experimental values to the accepted values.
- experimentally determine the specific gravity of several objects.
- compare the buoyant forces exerted by several different types of fluids on a given object.

Prelab Discussion

One key property of all fluids is the ability to exert a force that opposes the force of gravity on an object immersed in them. A **fluid** is any substance that has the ability to flow. Fluids include not only liquids and gases but also seemingly rigid materials such as rock and ice, which can flow very slowly under the influence of immense subterranean forces and gravity applied over long periods of time. You have experienced the fact that some objects float and others sink in water. From your textbook, you know that even an object that sinks in water weighs less in water than it does in air. This difference in weight is due to **Archimedes' principle,** which states that an object immersed in a fluid experiences an upward force exerted by the fluid that is equal to the weight of the fluid displaced by the object. This principle holds true for partially immersed objects that are floating as well as fully submerged objects. This upward force is called the **buoyant force.**

In an earlier chapter, you evaluated all of the forces acting on an object in order to determine if any change in motion might occur. For an object in a fluid, you can expect that if the weight of the object is greater than the buoyant force acting on it, it will sink. Similarly, if the buoyant force is greater than the weight of the object, the object will rise in the fluid until the fluid displaced by the object weighs no more than the object. What would happen if the fluid displaced by the fully immersed object had the same weight as the object? Consider the condition of a hot-air balloon or a submerged submarine. In both cases they neither rise nor sink as long as the buoyant force and their weight are exactly balanced.

There are many disciplines that use the concept of *buoyancy.* Shipbuilders, scuba divers, and hot-air balloonists are a few obvious examples. But architects, well drillers, geophysicists, and many other professionals must consider the effects of buoyancy. Builders of a dam or breakwater, for instance, must know if the rock to be used for the foundation will be dense enough to be stable when submerged. They need to know its **specific gravity (s.g.),** which is the ratio of the density of a substance (or object) to the density of water.

The density of an object (ρ) is determined by finding the ratio of its mass and volume. The mass of smaller objects may be measured directly with a lab balance. The volume of a *regular solid* can be determined mathematically. However, for irregular objects, such as a piece of rock, you must resort to the *water-displacement method* (see Lab 1-1) to find the volume of the object. If you know the mass and volume, you can calculate the density of the object. The s.g. is easily computed because the density of water is 1.00 g/cm^3, so the s.g. is numerically equal to the density of the object or substance.

Required Equipment

balance
beaker, 50 mL
graduated cylinder, 25 mL
liquid detergent
metric ruler
overflow can
specific gravity specimen set
string
water
wood block

Optional Materials

corn oil
corn syrup
denatured ethanol
glycerin or soap
isopropyl alcohol

Prelab Discussion

- Review the prerequisites for Lab 3-4 in the back of this manual.

- The concepts for this lab exercise are simple, but they may be applied across many fields of study, occupations, and recreational pursuits. Discuss various applications throughout the exercise.

- The term *buoyancy* may have a quantitative meaning when it is defined in a specific instance, but its more common meaning is qualitative. A more buoyant object floats higher in the water than a less buoyant one.

Equipment and Setup

- The recommended balance is a standard triple-beam balance mounted on a sturdy support stand or a rod inserted into the tabletop.

- If you are using a two-pan balance, you will need additional metric masses to balance the sample object.

- If you do not have a balance, you may use a spring scale to obtain the *weights* of the objects. The weights will have to be converted to masses in order to make the calculations in the Data tables. Note that spring scales do not usually have the 2-decimal-place precision of the mass balances.

- The recommended overflow can is easily constructed from common materials (see Home School Notes).

- The recommended metal samples are cylinders from a specific gravity kit. Any solid, nonporous object may be used for this exercise.

- Wood sample densities vary widely. You should carefully determine the density of each wood sample prior to lab time. You may then identify each sample with a letter and keep a table correlating density and sample letter.

- Wood or plastic objects that will not completely submerge should be spheres, cylinders, or rectangular solids so that their volumes can be easily calculated from their dimensions. Wood blocks sawn square or sections of wood dowels are ideal.

- The Optional Exercise is beneficial to illustrate the differences in buoyancy due to differing fluid densities. You may use glycerin, mineral oil, or even shampoo or motor oil in place of the suggested fluids. The densities listed in Table 2 are accurate. If you use fluids other than those in Table 2, you will have to

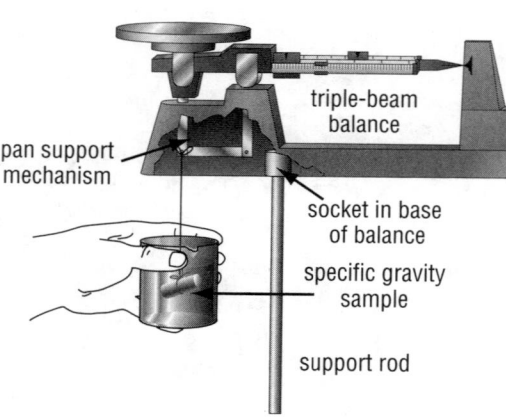

pan support mechanism

triple-beam balance

socket in base of balance

specific gravity sample

support rod

Figure 1

obtain their densities from the manufacturer, the MSDS file, or some other reference.

Procedure

- Point out to your students the locations where data is to be recorded during the lab.

- Refer to the Home School Notes for

Sometimes the s.g. must be determined for an object when its volume is either unimportant or impractical to determine. Specific gravity can also be measured indirectly by using water displacement. Note in the following specific gravity formula that the volumes of the object and the displaced water are the same, so they arithmetically cancel.

$$\text{s.g.} = \frac{\rho_{object}}{\rho_{water\ displaced}} = \frac{\frac{m_{object}}{V_{object}}}{\frac{m_{water\ displaced}}{V_{water\ displaced}}} = \frac{m_{object}}{m_{water\ displaced}} \qquad (1)$$

Specific gravity, therefore, is the ratio of the mass of the object and the mass of the displaced water. If you compute the corresponding weights of these two masses, you find that the s.g. of an object is also the ratio of its weight in air and the buoyant force when it is immersed in water (equal to the weight of the displaced water). Notice that s.g. is defined with reference to the density of *water;* therefore, you cannot find the s.g. by immersing the object in any other fluid.

In this exercise you will use the water-displacement method to determine s.g. by measuring the weight of several objects when they are in air and when they are immersed in water. The difference between these two measurements is the buoyant force exerted on each object. As you are aware, weight and mass are directly proportional. You will determine the objects' masses rather than their weights because balances are more precise than typical spring scales. You will also determine the volume and density of the objects and compare your results to the accepted values. Finally, you will determine the s.g. of each object from its density and compare the result to the value determined from the water-displacement method. As an optional exercise, you may evaluate the buoyant force exerted by different liquids on the same object and consider some consequences of these effects.

Procedure

Portions of this procedure assume that you are using a standard triple-beam balance (see Figure 1). If you are using a different instrument, your teacher will give you specific instructions to complete those steps.

1. Place the balance on top of the support rod by inserting the rod into the hole located in the underside of the balance base (see Figure 1).

2. Examine Figure 1. Note the vertical support mechanism for the balance pan, which can be seen underneath the left end of the balance base. Tie a 30 cm piece of string to the lower hinge pin of the pan support mechanism.

3. Immerse the string in a beaker of water until it is thoroughly soaked. Remove the beaker and determine the mass of the wet string. Record this value in the blank above Table 1.

4. Tie the string to the object to be measured. It should hang freely without touching anything. Use a slipknot to make untying easier. If you are using any material different from those listed in Table 1, write a description in the blank row in Table 1.

5. Determine the mass of the object and the string and record this value in Table 1.

6. Without removing the object from the balance and without touching the object in any way, completely immerse it (if possible) in the beaker of water (see Figure 1). Determine the mass of the object in the water and record this measurement in Table 1.

7. Repeat Steps 4–6 for each object. Note that one or more of the objects may float.

8. Remove the string from the balance pan support mechanism. Remove the balance from the support rod and place it on the tabletop. Verify that the balance is still zeroed.

9. Determine the mass of a *dry* graduated cylinder. Record this mass in the blank above Table 1.

10. Tie the string to one of the objects listed in Table 1.

11. Add one drop of the liquid detergent to the overflow can. Hold your finger over the spout and fill the can above the spout hole. (The detergent will reduce the surface tension of the water, permitting free flow of water out of the spout and thus a more accurate measurement of displaced water volume.)

12. Set the overflow can at the edge of a level table and place an empty beaker under the spout. Remove your finger and allow the water to flow out of the spout until it stops dripping.

13. After the dripping stops, remove the beaker and place the graduated cylinder under the spout. *Slowly* lower the object on the string into the overflow can, catching all of the water displaced by the object. *Do not touch the object in any way* and do not slosh the object around inside the overflow can—waves will cause more water to flow out than should be discharged (see Figure 2).

14. Read the volume of the displaced water and record in Table 1.

15. Determine the mass of the graduated cylinder and water. Record the combined mass in Table 1.

16. Repeat Steps 10–15 for the remaining objects listed in Table 1 and record the data for each object.

17. If any of your objects floated, calculate its volume geometrically and record this value in parentheses after the displaced water volume. Your teacher will provide geometrically regular objects for those that float.

Effect of Various Fluids on Buoyancy (Optional)

18. Assemble the balance and attach a string according to the instructions in Steps 1–4 above.

19. Write the names of the liquids to be tested in Table 2 and name the metal sample to be used in the blank above Table 2.

20. Your teacher will provide the densities of the liquids to be tested. Record the densities in Table 2. Record the mass in air for the metal specific gravity sample in the blank above Table 2.

21. Suspend the metal sample from the balance.

22. For the first liquid to be tested, add sufficient volume to the beaker to cover the sample. Submerge the sample in the liquid and determine the mass according to Step 6. Record the mass of the sample in liquid (after subtracting the mass of the wet string) in the corresponding row in Table 2.

23. Remove the sample from the liquid. If necessary, clean any remaining liquid adhering to it prior to testing another liquid.

24. Repeat Steps 4–6 for the remaining liquids. Record the masses of the sample in each liquid in Table 2.

25. When all data is collected, disassemble the balance apparatus and wash the metal sample in hot, soapy water in order to remove any residual liquid.

- alternative suggestions for supporting the balance.

- You may not want to account for the mass of the wet string when taking mass measurements, but doing so increases the accuracy of the measurements slightly.

Postlab Analysis

- This assignment includes several thought-provoking questions. Consider assigning the Optional Exercise questions even if you did not complete the Optional Exercise.

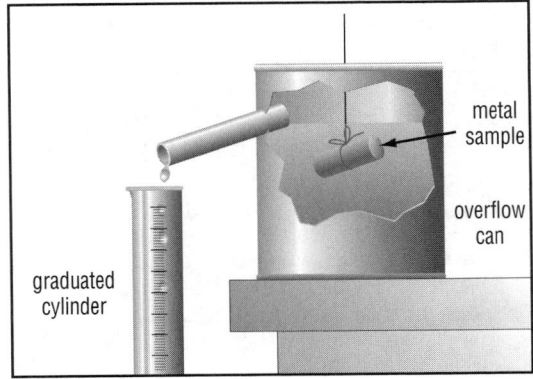

Figure 2

- (Question 2) Note that for large changes in depth (hundreds of meters), water does compress slightly, so its density gradually increases with depth due to pressure. However, nonrigid objects compress faster than the density of water increases due to hydrostatic pressure, so the buoyant force on a given object usually *decreases* with increasing depth because the displaced water volume is less.

- (Optional Exercise) Questions 13 and 14 refer to "trimming" a submarine. With the ship moving very slowly or stopped underwater, the crew pumps water into or out of the ship in order to make its weight exactly equal to its displacement and thus make it neutrally buoyant. They check the trim by noting if the ship tends to sink or rise by itself.

Home School Notes

- The balance can rest on a plank with a notch cut into one end so that

Data

Table 1
Mass and Volume Data

Mass of wet string ___0.50___ g   Mass of graduated cylinder ___48.30___ g

Object	Mass of Object and String	Mass in Air, m_a	Mass in Water, m_w	Displaced Water Volume, V_d	Mass of Cylinder and Water
Brass	55.07 g	54.57 g	48.20 g	6.4 mL	54.72 g
Aluminum	18.10 g	17.60 g	11.24 g	6.5 mL	54.79 g
Steel	50.40 g	49.90 g	43.51 g	5.9 mL	54.76 g
Copper	58.07 g	57.57 g	51.40 g	6.3 mL	54.80 g
Wood	5.36 g	4.86 g	0.00 g	4.0(6.72) mL	53.20 g
(Other)	g	g	g	mL	g

Actual data will vary. Data shown is typical.

the string can hang unobstructed under the balance base. The plank lies on or is clamped to the table with the balance extending over the edge sufficiently to provide the necessary clearance for the suspended objects.

- An overflow can may be constructed from any rigid can larger than 10 oz. (A 12 oz coffee can works well.) Obtain a short length of plastic tubing with an inner diameter of at least 3/8 in. from a home improvement store. Drill a hole in the can approximately one-quarter of its height down from the top—the hole's diameter should be slightly smaller than the tubing in order to provide a tight fit. Force the tubing into the hole so that about 1 cm extends into the can and cut the external tubing 5 to 10 cm from the can. Using caulk around the hole will prevent any leakage. Lower the outer end of the tubing so that water can easily flow from it.

- You may substitute nails, coins, springs or coils of wire, or rocks for the objects. At least one of them should be a pure element, such as copper, aluminum, or iron. In order to state an accepted value for the densities of the objects you use, you will have to determine the values yourself or obtain the information from an authoritative source.

Table 2 (Optional)
Data and Calculations

Sample ___copper___   Mass in air, m_a ___57.57___ g

Liquid	Density, ρ	Mass in Liquid, m_l	Mass Difference, Δm	Buoyant Force, F_b
Water	1.00 $\frac{g}{mL}$	51.40 g	6.17 g	0.0605 N
Corn Oil	0.918 $\frac{g}{mL}$	51.91 g	5.66 g	0.0555 N
Corn Syrup	1.38 $\frac{g}{mL}$	49.06 g	8.51 g	0.0835 N
Isopropyl Alcohol	0.785 $\frac{g}{mL}$	52.73 g	4.84 g	0.0475 N
Other	$\frac{g}{mL}$			

Sample type and data will vary. Data shown is typical.

Postlab Exercises

Table 3
Calculations

Object (Accepted Density)	Mass Difference, Δm		Displaced Water Mass, m_d		Mass Percent Difference	Exp. Density, ρ_e		Density Percent Error	Buoyant Force, F_b	Specific Gravity, s.g.
Brass ($8.47 \frac{g}{cm^3}$)	6.37	g	6.42	g	0.78 %	8.53	$\frac{g}{cm^3}$	0.71 %	0.063 N	8.50
Aluminum ($2.70 \frac{g}{cm^3}$)	6.36	g	6.49	g	2.02 %	2.71	$\frac{g}{cm^3}$	0.37 %	0.064 N	2.71
Steel ($7.86 \frac{g}{cm^3}$)	6.39	g	6.46	g	1.09 %	8.46	$\frac{g}{cm^3}$	7.63 %	0.063 N	7.72
Copper ($8.96 \frac{g}{cm^3}$)	6.17	g	6.50	g	5.21 %	9.14	$\frac{g}{cm^3}$	2.01 %	0.064 N	8.86
Wood ($0.75 \frac{g}{cm^3}$)*	4.86	g	4.90	g	0.82 %	0.72**	$\frac{g}{cm^3}$	−4.0 %	0.048 N	0.72**
Other ( )		g		g	%		$\frac{g}{cm^3}$	%	N	
Average					1.98 %			1.34 %		

Student answers will vary. Answers are calculated from typical data entered in Table 1.

*Accepted density for wood objects must be determined prior to the lab due to great variability.

**These results are calculated from the *total* volume of the wood object, obtained from its dimensions.

1. Determine the mass difference when the object is placed in water ($\Delta m = m_w - m_a$). Record the value in Table 3.

2. Determine the mass of the water displaced, m_d, by subtracting the mass of the graduated cylinder from the combined mass of the cylinder and the displaced water (from Table 1). Record the mass in Table 3 for each object.

3. According to Archimedes' principle, the weight "lost" by the object in the liquid should equal the weight of the liquid displaced. You can use the mass equivalent to this weight to simplify analyzing the data. Find the *percent difference* between the two masses from Steps 1 and 2 for each object and record the answer in Table 3.

$$\text{percent difference} = \frac{|\text{difference of the two values}|}{\text{average of the two values}} \times 100\%$$

4. Find the average mass percent difference and record it in Table 3.

5. Determine the experimental density ($\rho_e = m_a/V_d$) of each object from the data in Table 1. Recall that 1 mL = 1 cm³. Record the density (in g/cm³) in Table 3.

6. Find the *percent error* between your experimental density values and the accepted density values given in the Object column. Record your results.

$$\text{percent error} = \frac{(\text{experimental value} - \text{accepted value})}{\text{accepted value}} \times 100\%$$

7. Find the average density percent error and record the value in Table 3.

8. Determine the buoyant force (F_b) on each object in newtons. The buoyant force is the weight of fluid displaced, $F_b = m_d g$. Remember that mass must be stated in kilograms in order to determine the force in newtons. Record the value in Table 3.

9. Determine the s.g. of each object. Specific gravity is the ratio of the mass of the specimen and the mass of displaced water (m_a/m_d). For objects that floated, use the mass of the water equivalent to the calculated volume of the object. Record the value in Table 3.

Optional Exercise

10. For each liquid, subtract the mass in liquid from the mass in air to determine the mass difference (Δm) and record these values in Table 2.

11. Calculate the buoyant force equivalent to the mass difference, $F_b = (\Delta m)g$, for each liquid tested and record these values in Table 2.

Postlab Analysis

1. Assume that you place a beaker containing 50 mL of water on a balance and adjust the balance to zero. You then suspend an object on a string in the water so that it does not rest on the bottom of the beaker. Describe what will happen, if anything, and why.

   The beaker end of the balance will drop. The apparent increase in

   mass is produced by the buoyant force exerted on the object. The

   reaction to the buoyant force presses downward on the balance arm.

2. The buoyant force acting on a rock 1 m beneath the surface of a lake is 100 N upward. Discuss any changes in the buoyant force if the rock were moved to a depth of 10 m.

   The buoyant force on a rigid object is essentially insensitive to rela-

   tively small changes in depth, so the force will still be 100 N upward.

3. A branch breaks off a submerged tree stump 2 m below the surface of a lake. The branch has the same density as the water around it. Describe what will happen to the branch. (Will it rise or sink?)

   The log will neither sink nor rise because the buoyant force acting

   on it exactly balances its weight.

4. An empty *floating* ship that weighs 30 000 metric tons must displace at least _____30 000_____ tons of water.

5. If the ship in Question 4 has to carry cargo weighing 20 000 tons, what is the *minimum* weight of water displaced by the loaded ship?

   50 000 tons

6. If the mass of an object increases while its volume remains constant, what happens to its density?

   The density of the object increases.

7. If the weight of an object floating on the surface of the water increases while its volume remains the same, what happens to the *buoyant force* acting on the object?

   An increase of weight will result in forcing the object deeper into the

   water. The buoyant force will continue to increase with increasing

   water displacement until the object is totally submerged.

8. If the density of a submerged object increases while its volume remains the same, what happens to its s.g.?

   The object's density increases, so its s.g. increases.

Optional Exercise

9. State a generalization from your observations relating the density of a fluid to the buoyant force generated by that fluid on a given object.

   The denser the fluid, the greater the buoyant force exerted on an object immersed in it.

10. What will happen to a manned balloon as it suddenly moves into colder, denser air, assuming that the balloon remains at a constant volume and density?

    The balloon will tend to rise because the denser surrounding air generates greater buoyant force.

11. What will happen to the *volume* of the gas in the balloon in Question 10 as it cools to the surrounding air temperature (consider Charles's law).

    The volume will decrease proportionally with temperature.

12. What will happen to the balloon in Questions 10 and 11 *after* the gas starts to cool?

    The balloon will sink because buoyant force decreases as the volume of displaced air decreases.

13. A submerged submarine approaching an ice field in the Arctic Ocean is trimmed by the crew to be neutrally buoyant. The salinity of the water *under* the ice field usually declines because the fresh water melting from the ice floes dilutes the salt water. Decreased seawater salinity means decreased water density. As the submarine progresses under the ice field, what will happen to the submarine's depth without action by the crew?

    Initially the weight of the ship and the buoyant force of the seawater are equal. Under the ice, the submarine's depth will tend to increase (it will sink) because it is heavier than the weight of the displaced diluted seawater.

14. A submarine in the mid-Atlantic Ocean is trimmed to be neutrally buoyant at a depth of 50 m. It quickly changes depth to 150 m. The greater sea pressure at the new depth compresses the cylindrical steel hull slightly, reducing the volume of the ship. What happens to the submarine at the new depth without crew action?

    At 50 m, the buoyant force and the weight of the ship are the same.

    At 150 m, the submarine will tend to sink farther because it is not displacing as much water as it did at the shallower depth (less buoyant force), while the weight of the ship is unchanged.

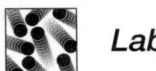

Laboratory Activity ━━━━━━━━━━━━━━━━━━━━━━━━━━ **3-4**

Name _____

Date _____ Hour _____

PRELAB HOMEWORK

1. State Archimedes' principle in your own words.

   Student answers should include the idea that an object immersed in a fluid experi-

   ences an upward force equal to the weight of the fluid displaced by the object.

2. Compare the weight of an object in air to its weight when fully submerged in water.

   The object's weight in water is less than its weight in air.

3. (True/False) A 1 kg object that is floating in water has a *net* force of 9.81 N acting on it. Explain your answer.

   Since the object is floating, the buoyant force exactly cancels the weight of the

   object. There is no net force acting on the object.

4. ___2.45 N___ A 250.0 cm³ block of steel has a mass of 2.00 kg before it is submerged in water. What will the magnitude of the buoyant force be when it is submerged? Express your answer in newtons to 3 SDs.

   Given: $V_{block} = V_{water\ displaced} = 250.0$ cm³; $\rho_{water} = 1.00$ g/cm³; $F_b = ?$

   Formulas: $m_d = V\rho$; $F_b = m_d g = V\rho g$

   Solution: The buoyant force is equal to the weight of the water displaced.

   $$F_b = \frac{250.0\ \cancel{cm^3}}{} \cdot \frac{1.00\ \cancel{g}}{\cancel{cm^3}} \cdot \frac{1\ kg}{1000\ \cancel{g}} \cdot \frac{9.81\ m}{s^2} \doteq 2.45\ N$$

5. ___8.00___ What is the s.g. of the steel block in Question 4?

   Given: $V = 250.0$ cm³; $m = 2.00$ kg; $\rho_{steel} = ?$; s.g.$_{steel} = ?$

   Formulas: $\rho = \dfrac{m}{V}$; s.g. $= \dfrac{\rho_{steel}}{\rho_{water}}$

   Solution: $\rho_{steel} = \dfrac{2.00\ \cancel{kg}}{250.0\ cm^3} \cdot \dfrac{1000\ g}{1\ \cancel{kg}} = 8.00\ \frac{g}{cm^3};$

   s.g. $= \dfrac{8.00\ \frac{\cancel{g}}{\cancel{cm^3}}}{1.00\ \frac{\cancel{g}}{\cancel{cm^3}}} = 8.00$

6. What is the simplified formula that can be used to determine s.g., using the water-displacement method?

   s.g. $= \dfrac{mass_{object}}{mass_{water\ displaced}} = \dfrac{m_a}{m_d}$

7. ___10.___ What is the s.g. of an object that has a mass of 60.0 g in air and displaces 6.0 g of water?

   Given: $m_a = 60.0$ g; $m_d = 6.0$ g; s.g. $= ?$

   Formula: s.g. $= \dfrac{m_a}{m_d}$

   Solution: s.g. $= \dfrac{60.0\ \cancel{g}}{6.0\ \cancel{g}} = 10.$

Laboratory Activity ━━━━━━━━━━━━━━━━━━ **3-5**

Name _____

Date _____ Hour _____

BOYLE'S LAW

Purpose

Understanding the behavior of gaseous matter in response to pressure changes is essential to many scientific and engineering endeavors. The purpose of this lab is to

- observe the change of gas volume in response to changes in pressure.
- calculate the ratio of volume to pressure in order to demonstrate Boyle's law.
- make comparisons of experimental values with theoretical calculations.
- graph volume-pressure relationships in two different ways.

Prelab Discussion

Unlike solids and liquids, gases do not have fixed volumes. They can expand indefinitely until they completely fill the container that they occupy or until they meet some other constraint. If a fixed quantity of gas is trapped in a container capable of changing shape, how does changing the pressure of the gas affect the volume of the gas? Is the change in volume predictable? In this experiment you will trap a quantity of gas in a syringe. The gas will be subjected to changes in pressure that will produce changes in the gas volume. By graphing V vs. P, you can discover what relationship exists.

Pressure is defined as force per unit area. Many different units exist for pressure, depending on the system of measurement (SI or British engineering), the scientific or engineering discipline involved, and occasionally, the type of instrument. A typical SI unit of pressure is N/m^2, also called the pascal (Pa), and the common British engineering pressure unit is $lb/in.^2$. The basic unit of atmospheric pressure to which all others are referenced is the atmosphere (atm); 1 atm is the average global pressure at sea level. This unit does not fit into any system of measurement, however, so we often use equivalents such as 101 325 Pa, 760 torr, 1013 mb, or 14.7 $lb/in.^2$. Appendix C contains a table of units equivalent to 1 atm. While there is no reason to memorize the table, it may be helpful to refer to it when working problems related to atmospheric pressure. It is important to remember that an object at the surface of the earth experiences 1 atm of pressure even if nothing else is exerting pressure on it. If additional pressure is applied to the object, that pressure must be added to atmospheric pressure.

In this experiment you will examine the effect on the internal volume of a sealed syringe as the force on the plunger is varied. This will be accomplished by placing masses on a platform attached to a syringe mounted vertically in a base. The syringe has 1 atm of pressure on (and within) it before any mass is added. You may assume that the atmospheric pressure is 1 atm, but if there is a barometer available, use the actual barometric pressure to obtain more accurate results.

In order to determine the pressure within the syringe, you must know the cross-sectional area of the syringe in square meters. This is calculated using the formula $A = \pi r^2$. The force acting perpendicular to the cross-sectional area determines the pressure within the syringe. If you place a 500. g mass on the platform of the syringe, you have added 4.91 N ($F_w = mg$) of force to the cross-sectional area of the syringe. However, the original pressure inside the syringe was approximately 101 000 Pa. In order to find the total pressure, you will need to determine the pressure from the additional mass in pascals, and add it to the original (atmospheric) pressure of the gas.

Prelab Discussion

- Review the prerequisites for Lab 3-5 in the back of this manual.

- This lab is intended to reinforce the gas law concepts students have learned in this course and possibly in previous chemistry courses.

- Two hidden objectives in this lab are to familiarize students with using alternative units for pressure and using scientific notation in calculations. Do not neglect the opportunity to review these topics.

- This lab provides the opportunity to compare predicted and experimental results for a process, using the same initial conditions. This is an important element of scientific methodology, and it should be discussed.

- If possible, review the Prelab Homework during the discussion introducing the lab. The determination of inverse pressure and the associated units of 10^{-4} kPa^{-1} may confuse some students. This unit was selected in order to provide inverse pressure numbers in the 50 to 100 range for ease of plotting on Graph 2. The unit itself is meaningless.

- Review the location of recorded data and the kind of calculations that will be required for each step in the Postlab Exercises.

Equipment and Setup

- The Boyle's law apparatus is a simple and inexpensive device obtainable from most science equipment suppliers. If you would rather build your own, see the Home School Notes.

- Prior to the lab, check each syringe to verify that the plunger moves freely and that it is not stuck at the bottom of the barrel. The plunger may be lubricated with a drop of silicone. Do not use a petroleum-based lubricant because this will deteriorate the plastic parts.

- Also check that the tip caps are in place. Push in each plunger firmly and check for leaks. Syringes that cannot hold air will not produce usable results.

- The lab requires at least three standard metric mass sets or the equivalent number of large masses. The quantity of mass that must be placed on each apparatus during the trials will probably require teams to wait until the necessary masses are available, and they will need to share their 1 kg and 500 g masses with other teams.

Procedure

- The procedure is easy to follow and should not present a problem. Collecting data usually requires less than 30 minutes.

- If the zero check in Step 9 reveals a leakage problem, you may attempt to fix it by lubricating the plunger, by pressing the tip cap back on tightly,

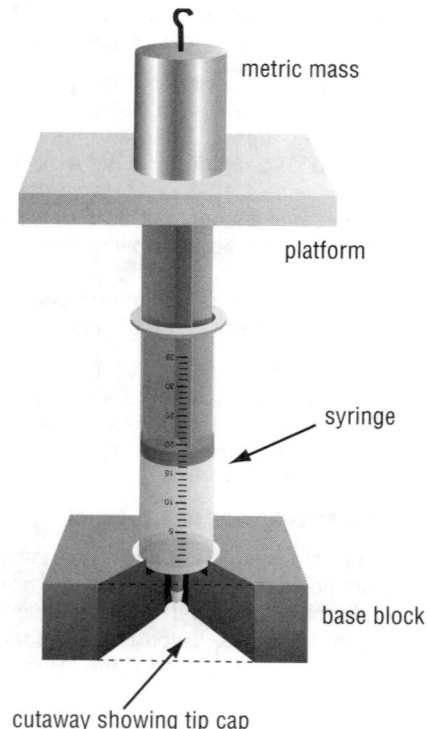

metric mass

platform

syringe

base block

cutaway showing tip cap

Figure 1

Boyle's law states that the volume of a dry gas varies inversely with the pressure if the temperature remains constant. The formula

$$V_1 P_1 = V_2 P_2 \qquad (1)$$

gives you the ability to calculate the expected change in volume if you change the pressure. In this lab you will change the pressure on a confined gas and measure the new volume. Then you will compare this volume with the volume predicted from Boyle's law.

One of the purposes of this lab is to demonstrate the inverse relationship between the pressure and volume of a sample of gas. This can best be done by plotting the two variable quantities V and P on a graph. Recall from your algebra courses that graphing a direct mathematical relationship ($y = kx$) will produce a straight line, but the graph of an inverse relationship ($xy = k$ or $y = k/x$) will produce a hyperbola.

Recall that in a direct variation (which has a linear graph that passes through the origin), the slope of the line is the positive constant k, and k can be calculated at any point (x, y) on the line, using the equation $k = y/x$. If the relationship of a gas's volume to its pressure were direct, then the ratio of any volume and its corresponding pressure (V/P) would be a constant, k, and the graph of V vs. P would be a straight line. However, if the relationship of volume and pressure is inverse (as Boyle's law predicts), then the *product* of volume and pressure is a constant ($VP = k$), and the volume of a gas can be predicted from the ratio of the constant and the corresponding pressure ($V = k/P$). If this inverse relationship is true, then a graph of volume and pressure will result in a hyperbola.

Due to the limited range of data you will obtain and the high probability of data scatter, it may be difficult to observe the hyperbolic curve of the graph of V vs. P, but if you rewrite the inverse volume-pressure formula as $V = k(1/P)$, the equation is now a function of $1/P$. In this form, the function appears to be a direct variation. If we graph V vs. $1/P$, a straight-line graph should result. This will be easy to evaluate, even with limited data. Therefore, you will produce two graphs from your experimental data, V vs. P and V vs. $1/P$. The graph that produces a straight line that passes through the origin reveals an inverse relationship between volume and pressure for a confined gas. (Recall that you graphed various representations of a variable in a similar way for Lab 2-6.)

Procedure

1. Remove the plunger from the syringe. Measure the inside diameter of the cylinder to the nearest 0.1 mm (0.01 cm). Record this value as the *diameter* in Table 1. Calculate the radius and record the value in centimeters as the *radius* in Table 1. Remember that the radius measurement determined this way cannot have greater precision than the diameter.

2. Record the initial (atmospheric) pressure in Table 1. Assume that the pressure is 101.3 kPa or use the actual barometric pressure. Use units of kilopascals in order to save space.

3. Remove the plastic cap from the tip of the syringe. Reinsert the plunger and set the inner edge of the plunger at the 30 cm³ mark. Replace the plastic cap. Assemble the apparatus as illustrated in Figure 1. Do not remove the cap again until the experiment is completed. If the cap comes off at any time during the remainder of the experiment, you will have to start over.

4. Gently pull up on the plunger slightly and release it. Repeat this two or three times. Note the position of the inner edge of the plunger against the scale printed on the cylinder.

5. Gently push down on the plunger and release it two or three times. Note the position of the plunger again.

6. Determine the position halfway between the readings noted in Steps 3 and 4. Record this volume as the *initial volume* (V_1) in Table 1. This step minimizes the effect of friction on the initial reading but will not be necessary when the masses are added to the platform.

7. Balance a 500 g mass on the platform. You may have to support the side of the mass in order to keep it from tipping, but do not hinder the motion of the plunger. Record the new volume and the mass that you added to the platform for Trial 1 in Table 2.

8. Continue as above for Trials 2 through 6. Use total masses in the following sequence:

Trial 2	1 kg
Trial 3	1.5 kg
Trial 4	2 kg
Trial 5	2.5 kg
Trial 6	3 kg

Record the syringe volume in Table 2 for each trial. Note that as the number of masses on the platform increases, the apparatus becomes unstable without support.

9. Remove all masses and place them in their storage containers. Without removing the syringe cap, perform Steps 3–5 again in order to verify the initial volume. If this volume varies from V_1 by more than a few cubic centimeters, you should ask for assistance from your teacher to determine the cause.

Data

Table 1
Initial Data

Syringe Diameter	2.30 cm	**Syringe Radius**	1.15 cm
Atmospheric Pressure, P_1	101.3 kPa	**Initial Volume, V_1**	30.0 cm^3

Actual data in Table 1 will vary. Values shown are typical.

Table 2
Boyle's Law Data

Trial	Total Mass, m		Experimental Volume, V_{2_e}	
1	0.500	kg	27.1	cm^3
2	1.000	kg	24.0	cm^3
3	1.500	kg	22.1	cm^3
4	2.000	kg	20.5	cm^3
5	2.500	kg	19.0	cm^3
6	3.000	kg	17.5	cm^3

Actual data in Table 2 will vary. Values shown are typical.

or by having the students use another syringe.

Postlab Exercises

- If you wish, you may have your students use a graphing calculator to perform a regression analysis of the data, including examining the residuals. See Appendix D.

- When calculating k from the Graph 2 plot, have students simplify the answer as much as possible, expressing their result in scientific notation and using the units cm^3·kPa.

Home School Notes

- The syringe may be obtained locally from a veterinary supply company. It should be a 50 cm^3 or larger syringe.

- The support is a piece of 2 × 4 wood with one side partially bored out to the diameter of the syringe and with a hole drilled through the center of the boring to receive the tip (see Figure 1).

- The platform is made from 1 in. lumber. Cut the syringe plunger thumb plate off so that the platform will be resting directly on the plunger itself. Bore a hole equal in diameter to the plunger stem halfway through the wood.

- A small-diameter protective cap for finishing wire-type closet shelving may be used as a tip cap.

- The metric masses may be replaced by a gallon milk jug containing the appropriate masses of water. Use a lab balance to determine the total mass of the container and water.

Postlab Exercises

1. Determine the cross-sectional area of the cylinder in square meters ($A = \pi r^2$). Convert the radius to meters before calculating the area. Record the value in the blank above Table 3.

2. Record the initial syringe volume from Table 1 in the blank above Table 3.

3. Determine the force exerted by the total mass ($F_w = mg$) for each trial and record the value in Table 3.

4. Determine the pressure exerted by the additional force ($P_{add} = F/A$). Record the value in kilopascals for each trial in Table 3.

5. Determine the total pressure within the syringe for each trial ($P_2 = P_1 + P_{add}$). Record the value in kilopascals for each trial in Table 3.

6. Calculate the inverse of total pressure and record the results in Table 3. Use units of 10^{-4} kPa^{-1}.

7. Calculate the *predicted* volume (V_{2p}) for each trial, using the formula $V_1 P_1 = V_2 P_2$, where V_1 is the initial syringe volume, P_1 is atmospheric pressure, and P_2 is the total pressure for each trial.

8. Transfer the experimental volume (V_{2e}) from each trial in Table 1 to Table 3.

9. Compare the predicted volume with the experimental volume and determine the percent difference for each trial and the average percent difference.

10. Plot V_{2e} vs. P_2 data on Graph 1 for each trial. Include the origin (0, 0) in your scale when labeling the axes. Draw a best-fit curve through the points on the graph.

11. Plot V_{2e} vs. $1/P_2$ data on Graph 2 for each trial. Include the origin in your scale when labeling the axes. Draw a best-fit curve through the points on the graph.

Table 3
Calculations
Initial volume, V_1 _____30.0_____ cm^3 Syringe area _____4.15×10^{-4}_____ m^2 Initial pressure, P_1 _____101.3_____ kPa

Trial	Added Force, F_w		Added Pressure, P_{add}		Total Pressure, P_2		Inverse Pressure, $1/P_2$ (10^{-4} kPa^{-1})	Predicted Volume, V_{2p}	Experimental Volume, V_{2e}		Percent Difference	
Initial	0.00	N	0.00	kPa	101.3	kPa	98.7	30.0 cm^3	30.0	cm^3		
1	4.91	N	11.8	kPa	113.1	kPa	88.4	26.9 cm^3	27.1	cm^3	0.741	%
2	9.81	N	23.6	kPa	124.9	kPa	80.1	24.3 cm^3	24.0	cm^3	1.24	%
3	14.72	N	35.5	kPa	136.8	kPa	73.1	22.2 cm^3	22.1	cm^3	0.451	%
4	19.62	N	47.3	kPa	148.6	kPa	67.3	20.5 cm^3	20.5	cm^3	0.00	%
5	24.53	N	59.1	kPa	160.4	kPa	62.3	18.9 cm^3	19.0	cm^3	0.528	%
6	29.43	N	70.9	kPa	172.2	kPa	58.1	17.6 cm^3	17.5	cm^3	0.570	%
Average											0.59	%

Actual data in Table 2 will vary. Data shown is typical.

Postlab Analysis

1. Does graphing V_2 vs. P_2 produce a straight line? Describe the graph.

   No. The graph is a small portion of a hyperbolic curve in the first

   quadrant of the Cartesian plane.

2. Does graphing V_2 vs. $1/P_2$ produce a straight line? Describe the graph.

   Yes, or nearly so. It should be a straight line that has a positive slope,

   and it should pass through the origin.

3. Based on the graphic results, how would you describe the relationship between the volume and pressure of a gas in an enclosed container?

   Plotting V vs. $1/P$ produced a straight-line graph, which indicates

   that volume is directly proportional to *inverse* pressure. Therefore,

   volume is inversely proportional to pressure.

4. _____Ans. vary._____ Determine the slope of the V vs. $1/P$ graph. Express your answer in $cm^3 \cdot kPa$.

   Answers will vary. Slope is determined by dividing the change in volume by the change in $1/P$. A typical value for k calculated from the data plotted on Graph 2 is $3.0 \times 10^3\, cm^3 \cdot kPa$.

5. The Prelab Discussion stated that the slope of the V vs. $1/P$ graph determined in Question 4 is the Boyle's law proportionality constant (k). Compare k with V_1P_1 and V_2P_2 for each trial and discuss any obvious pattern.

   Answers will vary. If the experiment was carefully conducted, stu-

   dents should note that the products of the associated volumes and

   pressures are equal or nearly so and that the products are close to

   the value they determined for the slope k.

6. What assumptions are necessary in order to apply Boyle's law to confined gases?

   It is assumed that the temperature and mass of the gas are

   constant.

7. What effect does increasing the *force* on the syringe plunger have on the *pressure* within the syringe?

   Increased force increases pressure.

8. What effect does increasing the external pressure imposed on a confined gas have on the volume inside a syringe?

   The volume of the gas decreases.

9. State three specific sources of potential experimental error in this exercise.

   Answers may include any three of the following: friction between the

   barrel and the plunger, gas leakage around the plunger, gas leakage

   by the tip cap, compression heating that was not accounted for, in-

   accurate volume calibrations on the syringe, or measurement errors.

Graph 1
Volume vs. Pressure

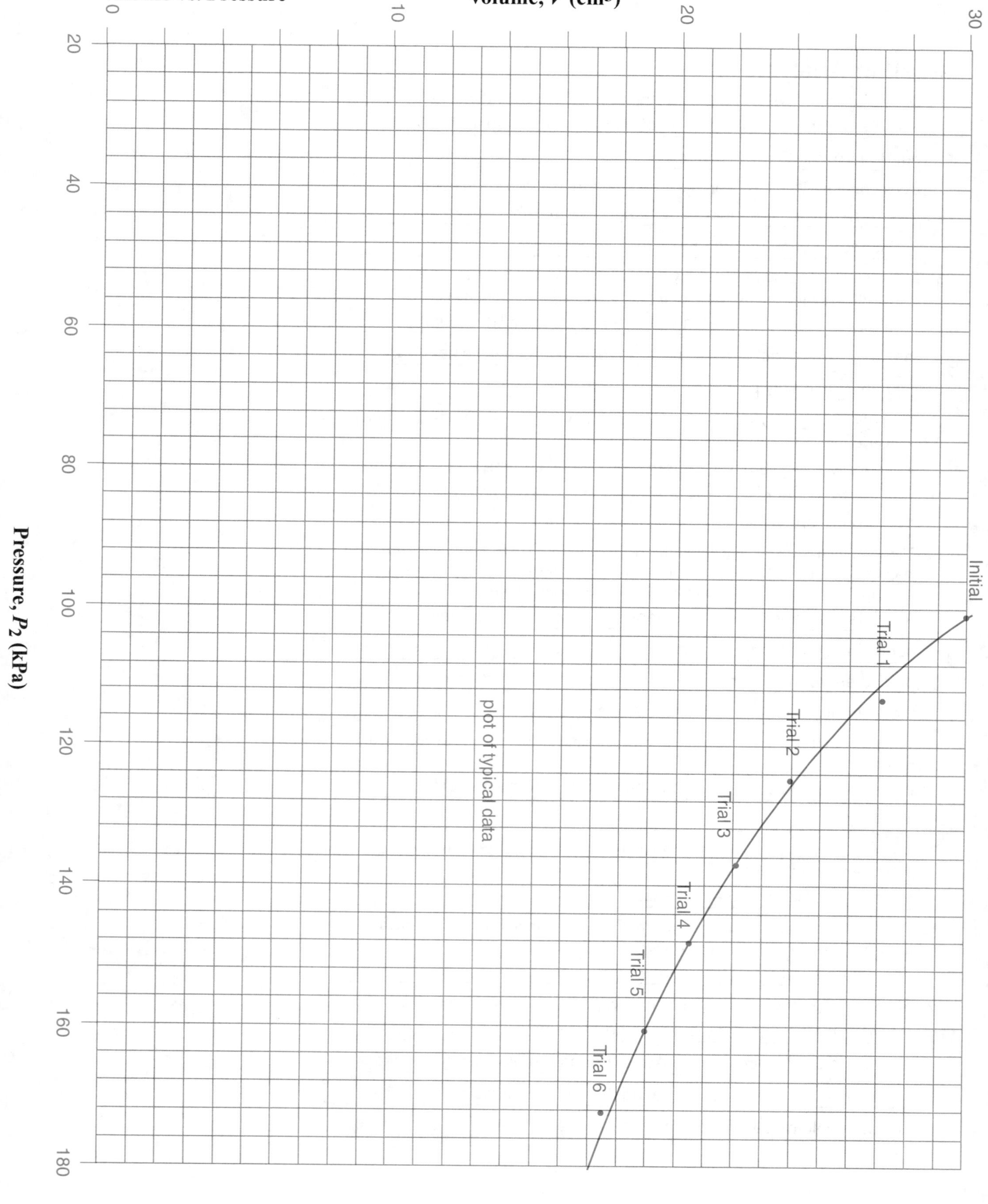
Volume, V (cm^3)
0
10
20
30
Pressure, P_2 (kPa)
20
40
60
80
100
120
140
160
180
Initial
Trial 1
Trial 2
Trial 3
Trial 4
Trial 5
Trial 6
plot of typical data

Graph 2
Volume vs. Inverse Pressure

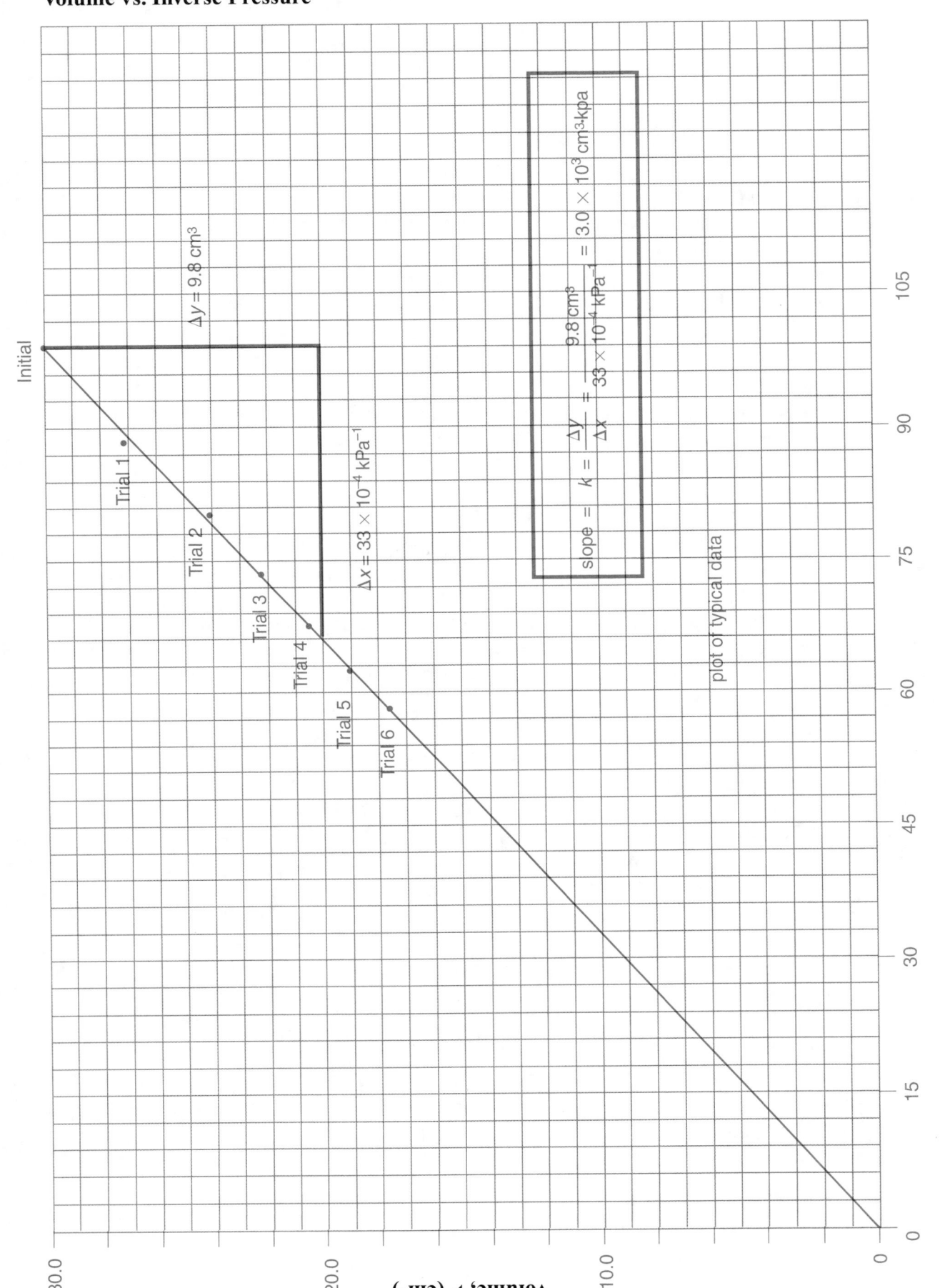

Volume, V (cm³)

Inverse Pressure, $1/P$ (10^{-4} kPa^{-1})

$\Delta y = 9.8$ cm³

$\Delta x = 33 \times 10^{-4}$ kPa^{-1}

Initial

Trial 1

Trial 2

Trial 3

Trial 4

Trial 5

Trial 6

slope $= k = \dfrac{\Delta y}{\Delta x} = \dfrac{9.8 \text{ cm}^3}{33 \times 10^{-4} \text{ kPa}^{-1}} = 3.0 \times 10^3$ cm³·kPa

plot of typical data

Name ————————————

Date ———————— Hour ———

PRELAB HOMEWORK

1. What is the general definition for pressure?

   Pressure is defined as the force applied per unit area.

2. Review the table of equivalent atmospheric pressures in Appendix C. Which pressure units listed are not based on metric force per area units ?

   Answers should include atm, lb/in.^{2}, mm Hg, in. Hg, and torr. All the others are

   based on either N/m^2 or dyn/cm^2.

3. From your knowledge of Boyle s law, state the conditions under which Boyle s law holds true.

   Boyle's law is true for a given mass of a dry ideal gas at constant temperature.

4. Write the formula that represents Boyle s law.

   $V_1P_1 = V_2P_2$

5. Write the formula for the cross-sectional area of a cylinder.

   $A = \pi r^2$

6. ———— 4.91 cm^2 ———— If the syringe in a Boyle s law apparatus has a diameter of 2.50 cm, what is its cross-sectional area?

   Given: $d = 2.50$ cm; $r = \dfrac{d}{2} = 1.25$ cm; $A = ?$

   Formula: $A = \pi r^2$

   Solution: $A = \pi(1.25 \text{ cm})^2 \doteq 4.91 \text{ cm}^2$

7. ———— 5.00×10^{-4} m^2 ———— Assuming that a syringe has a cross-sectional area of 5.00 cm^2, convert this area to m^2. Express your answer in scientific notation.

   $\dfrac{5.00 \text{ cm}^2}{} \left| \dfrac{1 \text{ m}^2}{10^4 \text{ cm}^2} \right. = 5.00 \times 10^{-4} \text{ m}^2$

8. ———— 4.91 N ———— Assume that you place a 500. g mass on the platform of a syringe with a cross-sectional area of 4.80×10^{-4} m^2. What is the additional *force* applied to the gas within the syringe?

   Given: $m = 500.$ g; $F_w = ?$

   Formula: $F_w = mg$

   Solution: $F_w = \dfrac{500. \text{ g}}{} \left| \dfrac{1 \text{ kg}}{1000 \text{ g}} \right| \dfrac{9.81 \text{ m}}{s^2} \doteq 4.91 \ \tfrac{\text{kg·m}}{s^2} = 4.91 \text{ N}$

9. ———— 1.02×10^4 N/m^2 ———— Calculate the additional pressure applied to the gas in the syringe in Question 8. Answer in newtons per square meter.

   Given: $F_w = 4.91$ N; $A = 4.80 \times 10^{-4}$ m^2; $P_{add} = ?$

   Formula: $P_{add} = \dfrac{F}{A}$

   Solution: $P_{add} = \dfrac{4.91 \text{ N}}{4.80 \times 10^{-4} \text{ m}^2} \doteq 1.02 \times 10^4 \ \tfrac{\text{N}}{\text{m}^2}$

10. ___1.115 × 10⁵ Pa___ Determine the total pressure on the gas in the syringe in
Question 8 with the 500. g mass placed on the platform. Assume normal atmospheric
pressure measured in pascals.

Given: P_{atm} (or P_1) = 101 325 Pa; P_{add} = 1.02 × 10⁴ Pa; P_{total} (or P_2) = ?
Formula: $P_2 = P_1 + P_{add}$
Solution: P_2 = 101 325 Pa + 10 200 Pa = 111 525 Pa ≈ 1.115 × 10⁵ Pa

11. ___32.0 cm³___ If the syringe under discussion originally had 35.2 cm³ of gas in
it, what do you predict the syringe volume to be *after* the 500. g mass was put in place?
Given: V_1 = 35.2 cm³; P_1 = 101 325 Pa; P_2 = 111 500 Pa; V_2 = ?
Formula: $V_1 P_1 = V_2 P_2$

Solution: $V_2 = V_1 \dfrac{P_1}{P_2} = (35.2 \text{ cm}^3)\left(\dfrac{101\ 325\ \cancel{Pa}}{111\ 500\ \cancel{Pa}}\right) \doteq 32.0 \text{ cm}^3$

12. ___89.7 × 10⁻⁴ kPa⁻¹___ Calculate the *inverse* of the total pressure in Question 10.
Express your answer with 3 SDs and a unit of 10^{-4} kPa⁻¹ (this is equivalent to $\frac{1}{10^7\ Pa}$).
Note that this unit does not *physically* mean anything, but converting your data to this unit
does provide useful values for plotting in the Postlab Exercises.

$$\frac{1}{P_2} = \frac{1}{1.115 \times 10^5 \text{ Pa}} = \frac{1}{111.5 \text{ kPa}} = \frac{1}{111.5} \text{ kPa}^{-1} \doteq 89.7 \times 10^{-4} \text{ kPa}^{-1}$$

━━━━━━━━━━━━━━━━━━━━━━━━ **3-5**

Name _____

Date _____ Hour _____

CHARLES'S LAW

Purpose

This laboratory exercise will investigate another significant property of gases. The purpose is to

- measure the change of gas volume in response to a change in temperature.
- calculate ratios of the temperature and volume of a gas in order to demonstrate Charles's law.
- compare observed experimental results with predicted theoretical values.
- gain experience graphing data and interpreting graphs.
- compare experimental and accepted values for absolute zero.

Prelab Discussion

Lab 3-5 demonstrated the interdependence of the volume and pressure of a confined gas (Boyle's law). If a confined gas is heated in a rigid container, gas pressure will increase (Gay-Lussac's law). However, if the container can expand as the gas is heated so that constant pressure is maintained, the volume of the gas will tend to expand. This phenomenon is known as Charles's law. Charles's law may be expressed by the formula

$$\frac{V_1}{T_1} = \frac{V_2}{T_2}, \tag{1}$$

where T is the kelvin temperature of the gas. Your textbook discusses the development of this formula, principally from Charles's work.

For this experiment you will be using the same syringe that you used for Lab 3-5 (but without the wood blocks). The syringe permits the gas confined within it to expand as it is heated and contract as it is cooled, while maintaining a nearly constant pressure. The plunger will tend to exert some friction on the barrel, which can be a source of error. As with the Boyle's law experiment, you will gently push and pull the plunger in order to eliminate most of the effects of friction.

In this lab you must change the temperature of the gas *inside* the syringe as well as measure the temperature *inside* the syringe. This must be done indirectly because of the limitations of the apparatus. If you adjust the temperature of the surroundings of the syringe, eventually the confined gas will arrive at the same temperature. If sufficient time is allowed for thermal equilibrium, measuring the temperature of the surroundings will also give you the temperature of the gas. Changes in volume are observed as the plunger position changes. Since controlling the surrounding air temperature for this lab is difficult and time consuming, you will use water baths at various temperatures to change the temperature of the confined gas. You must ensure during each trial that the enclosed gas volume of the syringe remains fully underwater at all times.

To provide four data points for comparison, you will measure temperature and volume by using baths of ice water, room-temperature water, hot tap water, and boiling water. The resulting volume-temperature ratios will be evaluated in order to validate Charles's law. You will also graph these data points as you reproduce Charles's experimental determination of absolute zero as discussed in your text. The extrapolation of temperature-volume data to minimum volume and absolute zero is not completely accurate because real gases do not behave exactly like ideal gases. With careful work, the results will still be within typical accuracies for other laboratory work you have done. You should find the comparison of your results with the accepted value of absolute zero interesting.

Required Equipment

beakers, 500 or 1000 mL, 2
beaker tongs
Boyle's law apparatus
hot mitts, 2
ice
lab thermometer
masking tape

Optional Equipment

Bunsen burner and lighter
support stand
wire gauze

Prelab Discussion

- Review the prerequisites for Lab 3-6 in the back of this manual. To successfully complete the Prelab Homework, your students need to review the discussions of heat engines, efficiency, and thermodynamic entropy in the textbook.

- This lab is a logical continuation of the investigation of the gas laws begun in Lab 3-5 (Boyle's Law). The instructions assume that Lab 3-5 has been completed and that the student is familiar with the apparatus.

- Review the algebraic steps required to solve for any of the variables in the Charles's law formula.

- As in Lab 3-5, experimental results will be compared with theoretical predictions. Emphasize that in science, real-world measurements rarely equal the values predicted by models, but scientists continue to try to improve the accuracy of the models.

Equipment and Setup

- Review the steps for preparing the syringes presented in the teacher's notes for Lab 3-5.

- The syringe and thermometer should be capable of sustaining immersion in boiling water.

- Be sure to have a sufficient supply of crushed ice or ice cubes on hand as well as hot and boiling water.

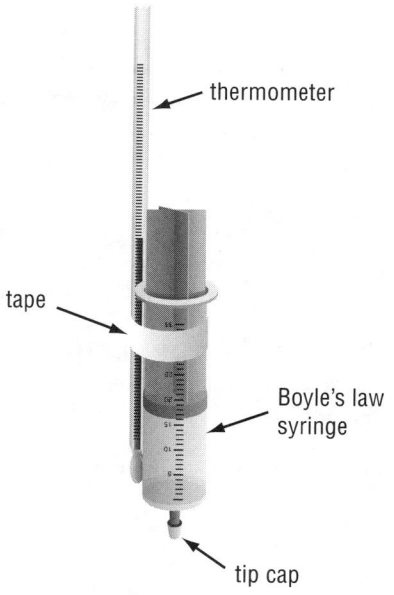

Figure 1

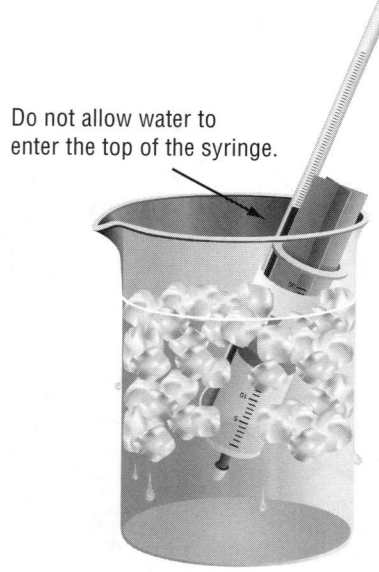

Do not allow water to enter the top of the syringe.

Figure 2

Procedure

- Allow students to practice the procedure for relieving the frictional forces on the plunger before they begin. The pulls and pushes should be gentle so that any resulting plunger movement is due more to the differences in air pressure than to manipulation.

- Do not allow any ice water to enter the barrel of the syringe stem. The

Procedure

1. Remove the plastic tip cap from the syringe. Set the syringe on 20 cm³ and replace the cap. Do not remove the cap again during any part of the experiment.

2. Tape the thermometer to the syringe. The bulb of the thermometer should be adjacent to the air space of the syringe (see Figure 1). Do not obstruct the volume scale graduations with the tape or thermometer.

3. Allow the syringe to sit in the air for a few minutes and do not touch the barrel near the air space.

4. Record the thermometer reading both in degrees Celsius (T_C) and kelvins (T_K) for Trial 1 in Table 1 ($T_K = T_C + 273.2$). Use the room temperature for T_1 when calculating the *predicted* volume.

5. Determine the volume of the syringe as you did in the Boyle's law experiment (Lab 3-5). Gently pull on the plunger and release it. Observe the volume reading. Push on the plunger and release it. Observe the volume reading again. Determine the volume halfway between these two points and record the value for Measured Volume in Table 1. This value is the initial volume, V_1, when calculating the *predicted* volume.

6. Fill a 1000 mL beaker or similar container (1 qt pan or jar) with enough ice water so that the syringe barrel can be submerged to the upper rim.

7. Place the apparatus into the ice water. **Note:** Do not allow water to enter the plunger end of the barrel (see Figure 2). Allow the temperature of the air in the syringe to reach equilibrium (3 to 5 minutes). Handle the apparatus only at the end of the plunger stem and keep the air space completely submerged at all times. Gently stirring the water will facilitate thermal equilibrium.

8. When you are confident that equilibrium has been reached, determine the volume, using the push-pull technique in Step 5. Keep the syringe submerged and avoid touching the barrel of the syringe near the air space. Record the temperature of the water and the volume of the syringe for Trial 2 in Table 1.

9. For Trial 3, empty the ice water and add hot tap water (~55 °C) to the beaker. Repeat Steps 7 and 8. Record the temperature and the volume for Trial 3 in Table 1.

10. For Trial 4, pour out the hot water and replace it with boiling water, if available. Immersing the syringe in boiling water over a heat source is best, but pouring boiling water into the beaker from a tea kettle will work. After several minutes, remove the syringe from the boiling water and *quickly* determine the volume, using the push-pull technique. **Caution:** The syringe will be hot; use hot mitts. (If this step can be completed with the syringe in the water, the data may be more accurate.) Record the temperature and the volume for Trial 4 in Table 1.

Data

Table 1
Charles's Law Data and Calculations

Trial	Celsius Temp., T_C	Kelvin Temp., T_K	Measured Volume, V_m	Predicted Volume, V_p	V_m and V_p Percent Difference
1	22.3 °C	295.5 K	20.3 cm³	20.3 cm³	0%
2	2.3 °C	275.5 K	19.2 cm³	18.9 cm³	1.57 %
3	50.0 °C	323.2 K	21.9 cm³	22.2 cm³	1.36 %
4	92.0 °C	365.2 K	24.9 cm³	25.1 cm³	0.80 %

Actual data in Table 1 will vary. Data shown is typical.

Postlab Exercises

1. Complete the calculations in Table 1.

2. Plot V_m vs. T_C for Trials 1, 2, 3, and 4 on Graph 1. On the graph, use a straightedge and draw a line of best fit through the data points. Extrapolate the line to the left until it crosses the *x*-axis.

Postlab Analysis

1. Describe the shape of the best-fit line that accounts for the data within the limits of this experiment.

   Answers will vary depending on the quality of data. The line should be

   a straight line.

2. Report the temperature at the point at which the extrapolation of the graph crosses the horizontal axis on your graph.

   Answers will vary. The plot of typical data was extrapolated to −289 °C.

   Consider valid graphs with an *x*-intercept falling within 15° of −273 °C

   to be excellent.

3. What is the accepted value for absolute zero in degrees Celsius to 5 SDs?

   The accepted value of absolute zero is −273.15 °C.

4. ___5.86%___ Report your percent error for determining absolute zero.

   $$\text{percent error} = \frac{[-289\ °C - (-273\ °C)]}{-273\ °C} \times 100\% = 5.86\%$$

   Answers will vary. The solution is based on typical data shown in the

   lab.

5. Did the percent differences between experimental and predicted values for Trials 2–4 indicate that there were significant errors (>5%) in the experimental data?

   Answers will vary. If only one data point is outside the 5% limit, the

   data is reasonable. If two or more are outside, then the data or the

   experimental setup may be suspect.

6. If there was excessive friction between the plunger and the barrel, how would that condition affect the data?

   The volume would expand less than predicted for the hotter tempera-

   tures and contract less than predicted for the colder temperatures.

   The data would produce a line with a smaller slope, and the extrapo-

   lation to zero volume would produce a lower (more negative) value for

   absolute zero.

negative pressure developed in the gas space may draw water into the syringe. This would result in water vapor pressure being added to the air pressure at the higher temperatures.

- Caution the students about the hot temperature of the syringe when it is removed from the boiling water. The volume check at that temperature must be made quickly, so handling the syringe with hot mitts is mandatory.

- The temperature-volume graph should fill the graph paper as much as possible. See the plot of typical data for guidance.

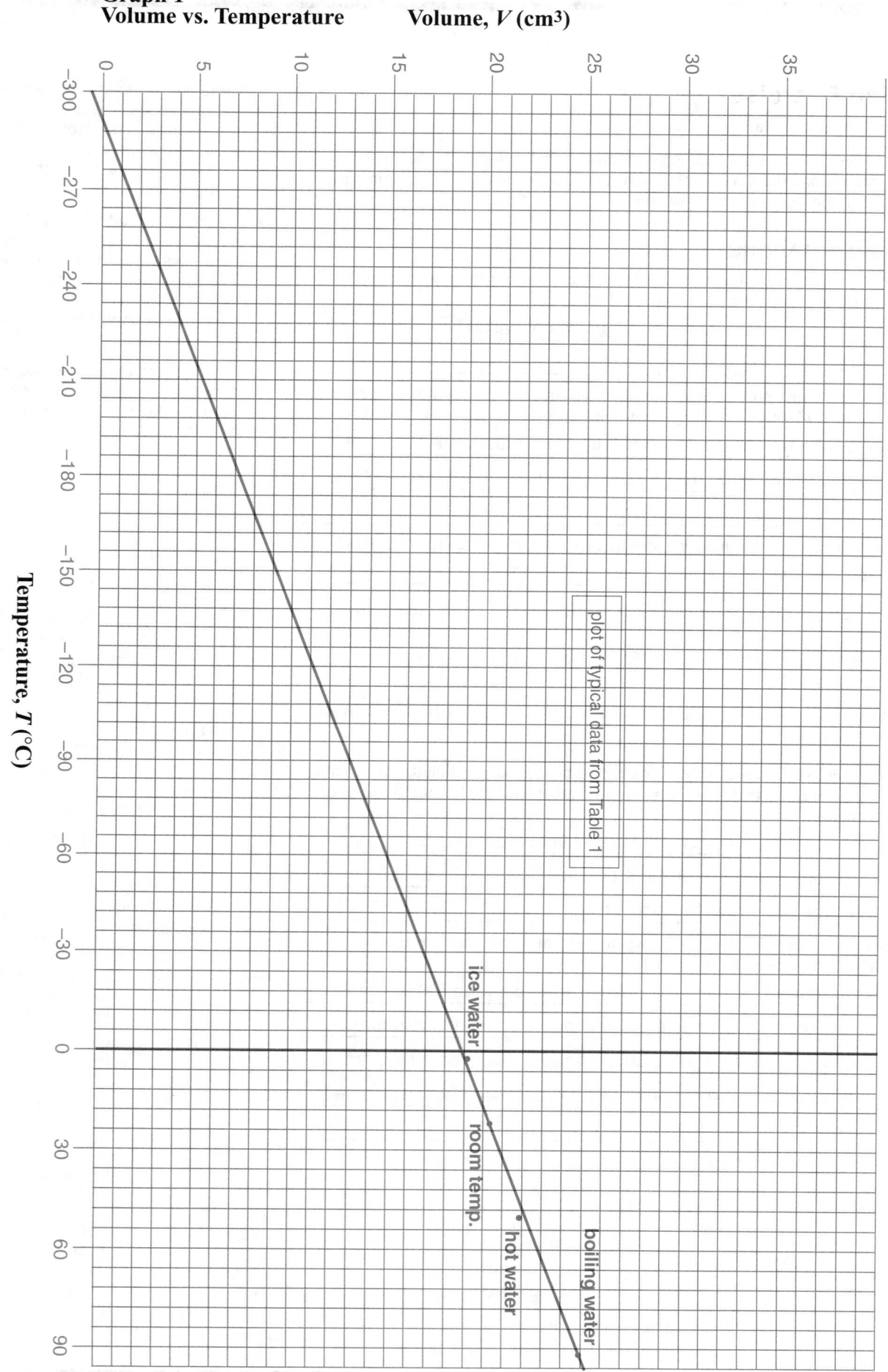

Graph 1
Volume vs. Temperature

Volume, V (cm³)

Temperature, T (°C)

plot of typical data from Table 1

ice water

room temp.

hot water

boiling water

Name _____

Date _____ Hour _____

PRELAB HOMEWORK

1. Write the general formula that summarizes Charles's law.

$$\frac{V_1}{T_1} = \frac{V_2}{T_2}$$

2. In this experiment, how do you determine the volume of the syringe at each temperature?

The volume is determined by reading the scale printed on the barrel of the syringe.

3. In this experiment, how is the air sealed inside the syringe heated to more than 95 °C?

The syringe is placed in a bath of boiling water.

4. ___27.2 cm³___ Suppose that at room temperature (25.0 °C), the volume of a syringe is 22.0 cm³. What would you predict the volume of the syringe to be at 95.0 °C?

Given: T_1 = 25.0 °C + 273.2 = 298.2 K; T_2 = 95.0 °C + 273.2 = 368.2 K;

V_1 = 22.0 cm³; V_2 = ?

Formula: $\dfrac{V_1}{T_1} = \dfrac{V_2}{T_2} \Rightarrow V_2 = V_1\left(\dfrac{T_2}{T_1}\right)$

Solution: $V_2 = (22.0\ \text{cm}^3)\left(\dfrac{368.2\ \cancel{K}}{298.2\ \cancel{K}}\right) \approx 27.2\ \text{cm}^3$ (3 SDs allowed)

Temperature increased; therefore, volume increased according to Charles's law.

5. ___20.2 cm³___ Suppose that the syringe at room temperature in Question 4 is placed into ice water (0.0 °C). What would you predict the volume to be at thermal equilibrium?

Given: T_1 = 298.2 K; T_2 = 0.0 °C + 273.2 = 273.2 K; V_1 = 22.0 cm³; V_2 = ?

Formula: $\dfrac{V_1}{T_1} = \dfrac{V_2}{T_2} \Rightarrow V_2 = V_1\left(\dfrac{T_2}{T_1}\right)$

Solution: $V_2 = (22.0\ \text{cm}^3)\left(\dfrac{273.2\ \cancel{K}}{298.2\ \cancel{K}}\right) \approx 20.2\ \text{cm}^3$ (3 SDs allowed)

Temperature decreased; therefore, volume decreased according to Charles's law.

6. At what Celsius temperature would you expect the confined volume in the syringe to be a minimum?

Charles's law states that the volume of a quantity of gas will be a minimum at approximately −273 °C.

7. Remember that a hypothesis is not simply a guess. It is a statement of what you would expect in light of the information that you have at your disposal. Based on the Prelab Discussion and your textbook, what effect would increasing the temperature have on the volume of gas inside the syringe? Explain your answer based on molecular kinetics.

You would expect the volume of the gas to increase. Since the air molecules gain kinetic energy when heated, they exert more force per collision, which produces a greater pressure. If the boundaries of the container are not rigid, the extra pressure will cause the boundaries to expand until the molecules are spread out enough to restore the original pressure at the higher temperature.

8. Review the discussion of the thermodynamics of heat engines and entropy in your textbook. Which of the laws of thermodynamics suggests that a real system cannot attain absolute zero?

   The third law suggests that absolute zero is not attainable by real systems.

9. If attaining absolute zero were possible, a heat engine could theoretically operate at 100% efficiency, which could make it a ____perpetual____ motion machine.

Name _____

Date _____ Hour ____

PERIOD OF A PENDULUM

Purpose

Understanding the factors that produce periodic motion is key to studying phenomena involving oscillations and waves. The purpose is to

- determine the period of a pendulum.
- determine what factors affect the period of a pendulum.
- calculate g by using a pendulum.

Prelab Discussion

Your textbook discusses the characteristics of **simple harmonic motion (SHM),** which is periodic motion that is caused by a **restoring force.** In the total absence of friction, the restoring force (F_r) is equal to the product of a constant (k) and the displacement of the vibrating object from an **equilibrium position.** An example of a real system that approximates ideal SHM is an oscillating mass attached to a spring. A pendulum is often considered another example of SHM, but it does not quite match the definition because the mass does not move in a straight line parallel with the restoring force and because the restoring force is not directly proportional to the displacement from the equilibrium position. However, if the amplitude is small, a pendulum provides a good approximation of SHM. The **period (T)** of a pendulum is the time required for it to complete one cycle. The formula for the period of a pendulum is

$$T = 2\pi\sqrt{\frac{l}{g}}, \qquad (1)$$

where l is the length of the pendulum arm. Note that this formula is similar to the formula for a spring, but l/g replaces the term m/k in the spring formula. Your text deals with the derivation of this relationship, and you should take time to review the process. Note that the location of the variables in the formula determines their relationship to the period. You should see that the *length* of the pendulum is in the numerator and under a square root sign. Thus, the period of a pendulum is proportional to the *square root* of its length. This means that if you make the length four times greater, the period will be two times greater than it was. A greater period means that the pendulum takes a longer time to make one cycle of its motion. In other words, the pendulum is swinging more slowly.

How would you expect the *mass* of the pendulum to affect its period? You might think that a heavier object would swing more slowly than a lighter object because it has more inertia. But remember that the downward force (mg) is greater for the heavier mass, so it might seem to others that the pendulum would swing more rapidly. Notice from the formula that, unlike the spring, a pendulum's motion is not affected by its mass. In this experiment you will verify this observation by examining the results when several different masses are used.

What would you expect regarding the *amplitude?* It would seem logical that lifting the pendulum higher would increase the potential energy and thus increase the speed with which it moves. However, lifting the mass higher increases the distance that the mass must travel. So even though the speed may increase, the distance through which the pendulum must travel also increases, and the total time required to complete one cycle does not substantially change. You will also test this statement for validity by examining the effects of several different amplitudes. Note, however, that as the amplitude of a pendulum increases, its motion conforms less and less to SHM. Using

Required Equipment

meter stick
metric mass set
stopwatch
string
support rod
support stand

Optional Equipment

metric measuring tape

Prelab Discussion

- Review the prerequisites for Lab 3-7 in the back of this manual. It is essential that students understand the derivation of the pendulum period formula from the SHM formula for springs before attempting this lab.

- Review the Prelab Homework yourself prior to assigning it in order to understand the emphasis needed to prepare students for the lab.

- Discuss the order in which the data is collected and point out the locations in Table 1 for recording data. Note that the data for Trial 3 for the

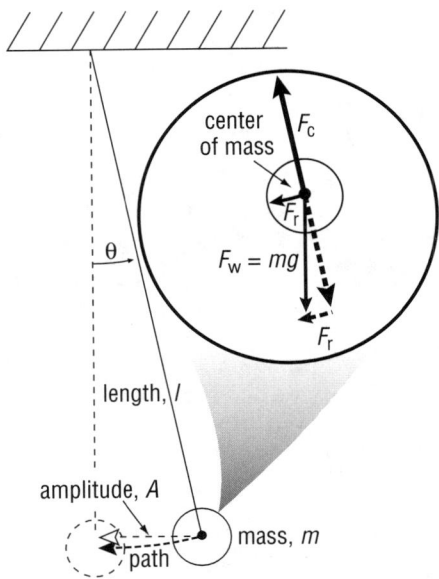

Figure 1

short pendulum and Trial 5 for the long pendulum are included in all three of the parameter groups for the respective pendulums.

Equipment and Setup

*   There are two setups for this lab, depending on a number of factors. If time or space is limited and you have the necessary support stands,

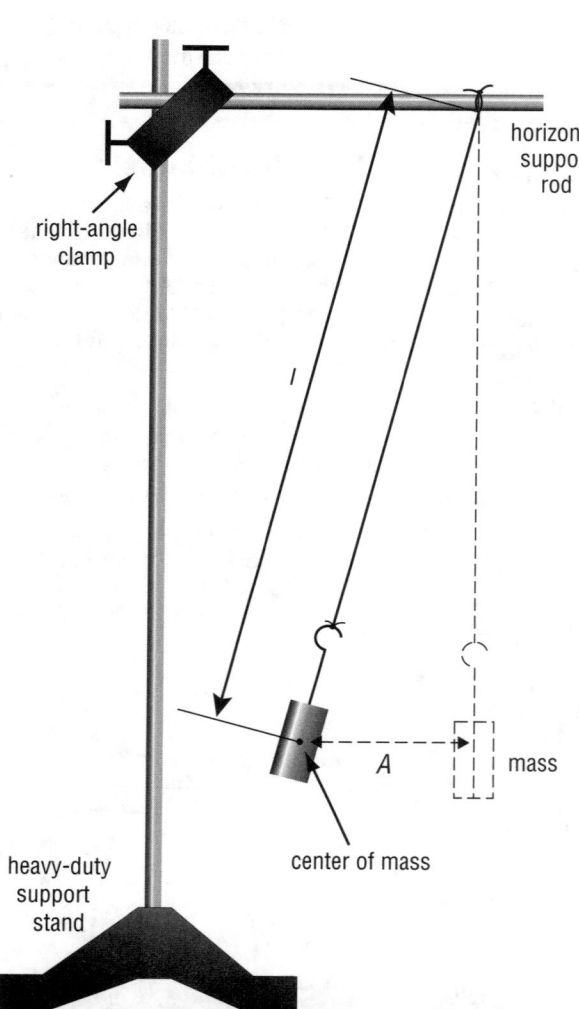

Figure 2

you can perform the lab as written for the short pendulum, which requires 10 data trials and can be performed on a tabletop. If you have more time and have the room or facilities to work with a longer pendulum, you should consider performing the lab as written for the long pendulum, which requires 16 data trials. The 1.6 m pendulum may be suspended from a C-clamp

Equation (1) assumes that the suspended object follows a horizontal, straight-line path to the rest position of the pendulum. The path followed is actually longer than the straight-line assumption because it is curved (see Figure 1). Also, as amplitude increases, the higher velocity of the center of mass produces a larger centripetal force component, which contributes significantly to the restoring force, causing it to vary in both magnitude and direction. The SHM formula for a pendulum is valid only for very small amplitudes. Included in this experiment is an investigation of how extreme amplitudes affect the pendulum period.

Procedure

Setup

1. Assemble the support stand, horizontal bar, and pendulum string according to Figure 2. Your setup may look quite different, depending on the apparatus provided by your teacher. Your teacher will give you specific instructions, if required.

2. Determine the mass of the first object to be suspended in the pendulum. The procedure assumes that you start with a 200 g mass. Measure the mass to 0.1 g, even if you are using a metric mass. Record this value in Table 1 as the mass for Trial 1.

Varying Length—Trials 1–3 (1–5)

Note: The numbers in the parentheses for each trial group represent the trial numbers for experiments using a long pendulum. Your teacher will tell you which set of trial numbers to use.

3. Assume that the support string has negligible mass. Estimate the location of the center of mass of the pendulum mass and mark this point on its exterior surface with a pencil or erasable marker. If you are not using standard metric masses, estimating the center of mass may be difficult. This difficulty may introduce an error when determining the pendulum arm length, *l*. Try to estimate the center of mass as accurately as possible.

    a. **Short Pendulum** Suspend the mass from the string in such a way that the length of the entire pendulum from the pendulum pivot point to the center of mass is 20.0 cm.

    b. **Long Pendulum** Suspend the mass from the string in such a way that the length of the entire pendulum from the pendulum pivot point to the center of mass is 10.0 cm.

4. When you are ready to begin collecting data, pull the mass to the side approximately 2 cm. Measure 2.0 cm horizontally from the equilibrium position to the *center* of the mass.

5. Start the stopwatch at the same instant that you release the mass. Allow the pendulum to swing freely while you determine the amount of time it takes to complete 10 cycles, *t*. A cycle is complete when the mass returns to the release position.

6. Record the time (*t*) in Table 1.

7. For the remaining trials in this section, keep the amplitude and the mass the same and double the length of the pendulum arm.

   a. **Short Pendulum** Use $l = 40.0$ cm for Trial 2 and $l = 80.0$ cm for Trial 3.

   b. **Long Pendulum** Use $l = 20.0$ cm for Trial 2, $l = 40.0$ cm for Trial 3, $l = 80.0$ cm for Trial 4, and $l = 160.0$ cm for Trial 5.

Varying Amplitude—Trials 4–8 (6–12)

8. Repeat the procedure as described above, keeping the pendulum length and the mass the same as the last trial of the previous section, but doubling amplitude for each trial.

   a. **Short Pendulum** Use $A = 4.0$ cm for Trial 4 and $A = 8.0$ cm for Trial 5.

   b. **Long Pendulum** Use $A = 4.0$ cm for Trial 6, $A = 8.0$ cm for Trial 7, $A = 16.0$ cm for Trial 8, and $A = 32.0$ cm for Trial 9.

9. For Trials 6–8 (10–12) you will evaluate larger amplitudes.

   Note that the starting position for the final trial in this section is with the pendulum horizontal (parallel to the floor). Ensure that the string is taut so that the mass swings smoothly when it is released.

   a. **Short Pendulum** If you completed Trial 5 with a pendulum length equal to 80.0 cm, then use $A = 20.$ cm for Trial 6, $A = 40.$ cm for Trial 7, and $A = 80.$ cm for Trial 8, measuring A perpendicularly to the pendulum equilibrium position.

   b. **Long Pendulum** If you completed Trial 9 with a pendulum length equal to 160.0 cm, then use $A = 64$ cm for Trial 10, $A = 128$ cm for Trial 11, and $A = 160.$ cm for Trial 12, measuring A perpendicularly to the pendulum equilibrium position.

Varying Mass—Trials 9–10 (13–16)

10. Repeat the trial procedure as described above, using the same length as the previous section and an **amplitude of 2 cm,** but doubling the mass for each trial. Attempt to hook the masses such that the length of the pendulum arm to the center of mass is the same for each trial. Readjust pendulum arm length if l changes from previous trials.

    a. **Short Pendulum** Use $m = 400$ g for Trial 9 and $m = 800$ g for Trial 10. (You may have to borrow masses from other teams in order to complete this step.)

    b. **Long Pendulum** Use $m = 400$ g for Trial 13, $m = 800$ g for Trial 14, $m = 1.6$ kg for Trial 15, and $m = 3.2$ kg for Trial 16. (You may have to borrow masses from other teams in order to complete this step.)

Summary

Short Pendulum When you are finished, you will have three trials in which the length is the variable (1, 2, 3), six trials in which the amplitude is the variable (3–8), and three trials in which the mass is the variable (3, 9, and 10).

Long Pendulum When you are finished, you will have five trials in which the length is the variable (1–5), eight trials in which the amplitude is the variable (5–12), and five trials in which the mass is the variable (5, and 13–16).

attached to a door frame or tied to the framework of a suspended ceiling. The greater number of trials permits better data analysis in the Postlab Exercises.

- The recommended stand for the short pendulum lab is a heavy-duty lab support stand or a rod inserted into the lab table with a horizontal rod clamped to it. Two standard ring stands with a crossbar will serve. Whatever arrangement is used, it must be rigid so that the swing of the pendulum does not cause the support to wobble.

- It is recommended that you use single masses whenever possible. When multiple masses must be connected together for a particular trial, hook them into a common loop at the end of the string rather than hooking the masses in a chain. Hooking multiple masses together complicates the determination of the length of the pendulum arm, which must be measured to the estimated center of mass.

- The recommended hooked metric masses are ideal because the mass is a simple geometric shape, making it easier to determine the location of the center of mass.

- Use very lightweight, flexible thread for the string, but be sure it is strong enough to support the necessary weight.

- For the short pendulum, the loss of energy due to friction at the attachment point of the pendulum arm and the support can be essentially eliminated by replacing the loop and knot in the string as follows. Use a drill or a set punch to create a shallow indentation on the top of the horizontal support rod. File the end of a heavy-duty paper clip wire to a point, and bend it so that when the pointed end is positioned in the indentation in the support rod, the rest of the wire will wrap around the rod without touching it. Tie the string to the paper clip below the rod. As the pendulum swings, the arm pivots on the point of the paper clip, which is essentially frictionless.

Procedure

- After studying the procedure, you and your students may find it more

Data

Table 1
Pendulum Data and Calculations

Trial	Amplitude, A		Mass, m		Pendulum Arm Length, l		Time (10 cycles), t		Period, T		Experimental g		g Percent Error	
1	2.0	cm	0.2000	kg	0.100	m	6.4	s	0.64	s	9.6	$\frac{m}{s^2}$	−2.14	%
2	2.0	cm	0.2000	kg	0.200	m	9.0	s	0.90	s	9.7	$\frac{m}{s^2}$	−1.12	%
3	2.0	cm	0.2000	kg	0.400	m	12.7	s	1.27	s	9.79	$\frac{m}{s^2}$	−0.204	%
4	2.0	cm	0.2000	kg	0.800	m	17.8	s	1.78	s	9.97	$\frac{m}{s^2}$	1.63	%
5	2.0	cm	0.2000	kg	1.600	m	25.2	s	2.52	s	9.95	$\frac{m}{s^2}$	1.43	%
6	4.0	cm	0.2000	kg	1.600	m	25.5	s	2.55	s	9.71	$\frac{m}{s^2}$	−1.02	%
7	8.0	cm	0.2000	kg	1.600	m	25.6	s	2.56	s	9.64	$\frac{m}{s^2}$	−1.73	%
8	16.0	cm	0.2000	kg	1.600	m	25.4	s	2.54	s	9.79	$\frac{m}{s^2}$	−0.204	%
9	32.0	cm	0.2000	kg	1.600	m	25.5	s	2.55	s	9.71	$\frac{m}{s^2}$	−1.02	%
10	64	cm	0.2000	kg	1.600	m	25.4	s	2.54	s	*	$\frac{m}{s^2}$	*	%
11	128	cm	0.2000	kg	1.600	m	26.8	s	2.68	s	*	$\frac{m}{s^2}$	*	%
12	160.	cm	0.2000	kg	1.600	m	30.0	s	3.00	s	*	$\frac{m}{s^2}$	*	%
13	2.0	cm	0.4000	kg	1.600	m	25.3	s	2.53	s	9.87	$\frac{m}{s^2}$	0.612	%
14	2.0	cm	0.8000	kg	1.600	m	25.2	s	2.52	s	9.95	$\frac{m}{s^2}$	1.43	%
15	2.0	cm	1.6000	kg	1.600	m	25.3	s	2.53	s	9.87	$\frac{m}{s^2}$	0.612	%
16	2.0	cm	3.2000	kg	1.600	m	25.4	s	2.54	s	9.79	$\frac{m}{s^2}$	−0.204	%
Average											9.80	$\frac{m}{s^2}$	−0.148	%

Data in Table 1 is typical for the long pendulum procedure. Actual student data will vary.

*These calculations are omitted for large amplitude trials.

efficient to write in the values for length, amplitude, and mass appropriate for the pendulum to be used in Table 1 and then perform the trials, using Table 1 as a guide.

- It is very important that students carefully determine the length of the pendulum arm to the *center of mass* of the arm. For metric masses, that point will be approximately the center of the mass itself. It can be measured on the mass

Postlab Exercises

1. Compute the period ($T = t/10$) for each of the trials from the data in Table 1.

2. For each trial, with exception of the extreme amplitude trials, compute your experimental value for g from the formula you derived in Prelab Homework Question 3 and enter the results in Table 1. Determine the average experimental value of g.

3. For each trial, compute the percent error between your experimental value of g and the accepted value of 9.81 m/s². Average the percent errors, observing the signs of the values.

4. Refer to the Summary section of the Procedure for specific trials. Plot the data from the variable length trials in Graph 1, the data from the variable amplitude trials in Graph 2, and the data from the variable mass trials in Graph 3. The independent variable for each graph will be the pendulum parameter of interest, and the dependent variable will be the period from Table 1. Sketch a best-fit curve through the data points in each graph.

Postlab Analysis

1. Examine your data and Graph 1. Does increasing the length of the pendulum have a significant effect on the period if mass and amplitude remain constant? If so, what is the ratio of the periods of the longer pendulums to the periods of the shorter, and are these ratios predicted by the period formula?

   Answers will vary, but a *yes* response is expected. If the pendulum
   arm is doubled, the period should approximately equal the shorter
   pendulum's period multiplied by $\sqrt{2}$, or 1.41.

2. Examine your data and Graph 2. Do *small* changes in the amplitude of the pendulum have a significant effect on the period if mass and length remain constant? If so, what seems to be the effect as amplitude is increased? If any effect is noted, is it predicted by the period formula? (Ignore the large amplitude portions of the data and graph when answering this question.)

   Answers will vary, but a *no* response is expected. Students may note
   a slight increase in period with increasing amplitude. The period
   formula does not predict any effect on the period with changes in
   amplitude.

3. Examine your data and Graph 3. Does increasing the mass have a significant effect on the period if the length and amplitude remain constant? If so, what seems to be the effect as mass increases? If any effect is noted, is it predicted by the period formula?

   Answers will vary, but a *no* response is expected. The formula does
   not predict any effect on the period with a change in mass.

4. What kind of function is the formula for the restoring force in SHM ($F_r = kx$)?

   The formula represents a linear function (or a direct variation).

5. Write a formula relating the restoring force to the angle of the pendulum from the vertical position. Assume that the amplitude of the pendulum is small so that F_r is essentially horizontal.

   The restoring force varies as a function of the sine of the angle of
   the pendulum to the vertical. $F_r = mg \sin \theta$

6. For small amplitudes of motion (small pendulum angles), can you correctly assume that the restoring force is directly proportional to displacement? Explain your answer from a trigonometric perspective.

   Yes, you can correctly assume this because a function involving the
   sine of an angle is essentially linear at small angles.

7. How does the distance that the center of mass of a pendulum actually travels compare to the amplitude of the pendulum?

   The path that the center of mass travels is slightly longer than the
   amplitude.

cylinder with a ruler. A more precise method involves tying a string around the middle of the mass cylinder and determining the balance point. Mark the position with a pencil.

- Amplitude is measured perpendicularly (horizontally) from the hanging position of the pendulum to the center of mass. For the large pendulum, making this determination may be difficult. If the pendulum is suspended near a desk or wall, a reference line can be marked or supported on the vertical surface for determining amplitude.

- Large Amplitude Precautions

   1. For the short pendulum, the string will have to be attached directly to the support before performing these trials. The paper clip pivot described above will not work under the conditions of these trials.

   2. Ensure that the string is taut before releasing the mass.

   3. It is not recommended that large masses be used for the large amplitude trials because of the significant centripetal forces generated during the oscillations.

Postlab Exercises and Analysis

- Have the students complete the calculations and graph the data outside of class. The homework is designed to require some thoughtful answers based on the students' observations.

- For Graph 1, the curve should be based on a square-root function (half of a parabola lying on its side), opening to the right. See the graphs of typical data provided.

- If students have an advanced graphing calculator, such as the TI-83 Plus, they can perform regression analysis, using various functions to evaluate the data points for period vs. length and determine whether the square-root function is the best fit. See Appendix D.

Home School Notes

- In place of the standard metric masses, you can use a can supported by a string that is looped through two holes punched in the rim. Fill the can with varying amounts of water or sand in order to obtain the masses required. The mass of the can must be included in the mass of the pendulum. The shape and mass of the can must be taken into account when determining the location of the center of mass.

8. For small amplitudes, would you expect the period of a real pendulum to be longer or shorter than the theoretical pendulum experiencing SHM? Consider your answers to Questions 4–7 in your explanation.

   The real pendulum should have a slightly longer period than the theoretical pendulum because it follows a slightly longer path. The force varies at essentially the same rate, based on its displacement from the equilibrium position.

9. Would you expect the value of g determined by a real pendulum to be greater than or less than the accepted value of g (review the answer to Question 3 in the Prelab Homework)?

   Since the actual period of a pendulum is slightly greater than the theoretical period, the experimentally determined g will be less than the accepted value.

10. How does your conclusion in Question 9 compare to your observations for swings with larger amplitudes? Calculate the value of g, based on the periods of the trials with large amplitudes from the data in Table 1 to support your answer.

    Answers will vary. At relatively small amplitudes, the students probably obtained values for g that were very slightly lower than the accepted value. However, at very large amplitudes, the periods increase significantly and the calculated value of g becomes increasingly smaller than the accepted value.

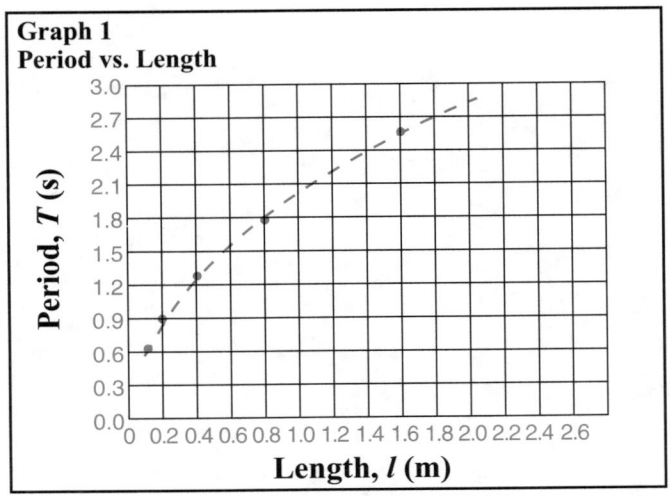

Graph 1
Period vs. Length

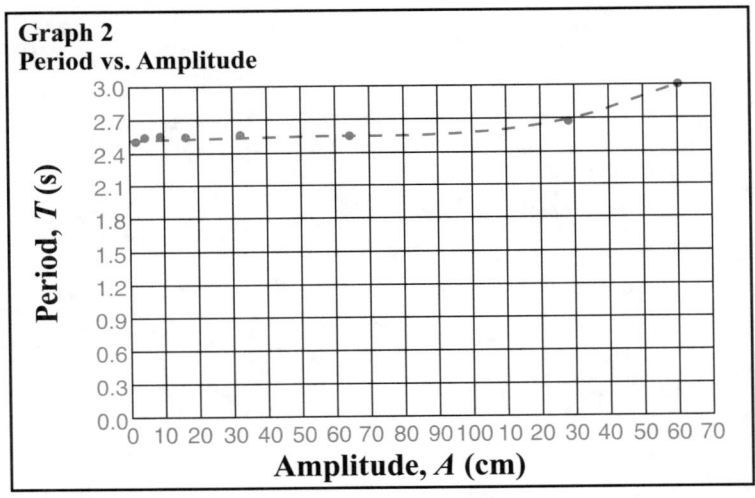

Graph 2
Period vs. Amplitude

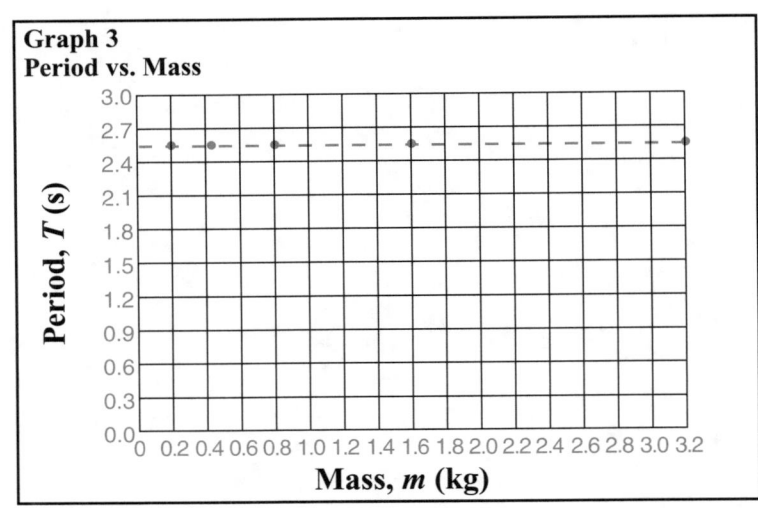

Graph 3
Period vs. Mass

Name _____

Date _____ Hour _____

PRELAB HOMEWORK

1. What is the difference between simple harmonic motion and the motion of a pendulum?

   Simple harmonic motion involves the periodic movement of an object in line with a restoring force that tends to return it to an equilibrium position. A pendulum's center of mass takes a longer path to the equilibrium position than it would for true SHM, and the restoring force varies in both magnitude and direction as a function of displacement.

2. Write the formula for the period of a pendulum.

   $$T = 2\pi \sqrt{\frac{l}{g}}$$

3. From Equation (1), derive the formula for determining the acceleration due to gravity, g.

   $$g = \frac{4\pi^2 l}{T^2}$$

4. __0.667 s/cycle__ If a pendulum swings back and forth 15 times in 10.0 s, calculate its period.

   Given: $t = 10.0$ s; $n = 15$ cycles; $T = ?$

   Formula: $T = \dfrac{t}{n}$

   Solution: $T = \dfrac{10.0 \text{ s}}{15 \text{ cycles}} \approx 0.667 \frac{\text{s}}{\text{cycle}}$ (3 SDs allowed)

5. Why is measuring the duration of a number of swings a better way to determine the period of a pendulum than measuring a single cycle?

   Obtaining the time for one swing averaged over many cycles will produce a value much closer to the actual period than attempting to measure a single cycle because any measurement errors will be reduced by the averaging process.

6. __9.87 m/s²__ If a pendulum swings with a period of 1.00 s and has a length of 0.250 m, calculate the acceleration due to gravity.

   Given: $T = 1.00$ s; $l = 0.250$ m; $g = ?$

   Formula: $g = \dfrac{4\pi^2 l}{T^2}$

   Solution: $g = \dfrac{4\pi^2 (0.250 \text{ m})}{(1.00 \text{ s})^2} \doteq 9.87 \frac{\text{m}}{\text{s}^2}$

7. __+0.408%__ Assume that the experimental value determined for g was 9.85 m/s². Determine the *percent error* compared to the accepted value for g.

   $$\text{percent error} = \frac{(9.85 \frac{\text{m}}{\text{s}^2} - 9.81 \frac{\text{m}}{\text{s}^2})}{9.81 \frac{\text{m}}{\text{s}^2}} \times 100\% \doteq +0.408\%$$

8. During an experimental trial, if you increase the mass of the pendulum by hooking an additional mass to the bottom of the original one, what happens to the pendulum length, l? Explain your answer.

   If the mass is added to the bottom of the existing mass, then the estimated center of mass will be farther from the pivot point of the pendulum, so the length of the pendulum arm (l) will be longer.

9. If the length of a given pendulum is doubled, what would you expect to happen to the *period?*

   The period of a pendulum is proportional to the square root of the length of the

   pendulum, so the period would increase (by a factor of $\sqrt{2}$, or approximately 1.41).

10. If the mass of a given pendulum increases while the amplitude and the length remain the same, what happens to the *frequency* of the swings?

    The frequency is the reciprocal of the period. The period of a pendulum does not

    depend on its mass, so no effect would be observed in the frequency of the

    pendulum.

11. If the small amplitude of a given pendulum is increased *slightly* while the mass and the length remain the same, what happens to the period?

    As long as the amplitude of a pendulum is small, the period does not depend on

    the amplitude according to Equation (1), so no effect would be seen.

12. How would the *period* of a pendulum on Mercury compare to the period of the same pendulum on Earth? (Mercury's acceleration due to gravity is 38% of Earth's.)

    According to the period formula, T is inversely proportional to the square root of

    the gravitational acceleration. Since $g_{Mercury} \ll g_{Earth}$, the period will be much

    longer on Mercury for a given pendulum.

13. How would the *frequency* of a pendulum on Mercury compare to the frequency of the same pendulum on Earth?

    The applicable formula is $f = \dfrac{1}{T}$.

    Therefore, if $T_{Mercury} > T_{Earth}$ (from Question 12), then $f_{Mercury} < f_{Earth}$.

Name _____

Date _____ Hour _____

SPEED OF SOUND IN AIR

Purpose

Many natural and man-made phenomena involve the transmission of energy in waves. Sound is one form of wave-transmitted energy. The purpose of this lab is to

- demonstrate the existence and predictability of standing waves in a resonating column.
- measure the wavelength of sound in a resonating column.
- determine the speed of sound in air.
- compare your experimentally determined speed of sound with the accepted value.

Prelab Discussion

Sound is a longitudinal mechanical wave consisting of **rarefactions** and **compressions** in a medium. One compression and rarefaction constitute a **wave cycle.** The distance between points of maximum compression (or any other corresponding points) of two consecutive wave cycles is called the **wavelength,** symbolized by λ (Greek letter lambda). The maximum extent of the compression or rarefaction of the medium is called the **amplitude.** This is analogous to the height of a water wave. The displacement of a wave per unit time in the direction of propagation is called the wave **speed,** or speed of sound, represented by v, and the number of waves passing a point in space per unit time is called the **frequency,** f.

Multiple waves passing through the same point in the medium can **interfere** *constructively,* so that the wave amplitudes add together, or *destructively,* so that the amplitudes subtract from each other. When a wave reflects off a boundary in the medium, the reflected wave can interfere with the original wave in the same way that waves having separate sources do. The interference pattern produced by a wave and its reflection is called a **standing wave.** A standing wave consists of **nodes,** points at which complete destructive interference occurs and the medium is essentially motionless, and **antinodes,** points at which the medium experiences maximum oscillations. Figure 1 is a diagram of a standing wave pattern.

If you forcefully blow across the mouth of a soft drink bottle just right, you can produce a fairly loud, low-frequency sound. If you rub a damp fingertip around the rim of a good-quality crystal glass, you can produce a clear, medium-frequency tone. Both of these cases illustrate the phenomenon of **acoustic resonance.** Objects that are rigid or substances within cavities (enclosed spaces) can be caused to vibrate at a particular frequency known as their **natural frequency.** Vibrating objects or cavities are called **oscillators.** If energy is added to the object at the same frequency as its natural frequency, it will vibrate with increasingly larger amplitudes in a standing wave pattern. When the vibrations occur within the frequency range of human hearing, you hear resonant tones such as those mentioned above. Note that resonance does not have to be audible in order for it to occur. The famous destruction of the Tacoma Narrows Bridge in 1940 and the earthquake in Gujarat, India, in 2001 provide dramatic examples that resonance can occur at subaudible frequencies with devastating results.

Resonance depends on several factors, the most significant being the dimensions of the vibrating object (the oscillator) and the speed of sound within the oscillator. The material properties of the oscillator also determine resonant frequency, but these factors can be ignored in this exercise. You know from the

Prelab Discussion

- Review the prerequisites for Lab 3-8 in the back of this manual.

- The first paragraphs are included only as a brief overview of sound wave theory and terminology. Ensure that this material is thoroughly discussed prior to performing this lab.

- The end correction is often left out of basic labs of this type. However, the end correction is needed because not all of the vibrational motion and transfer of energy between the air molecules at the open end of the tube is parallel to the axis of the

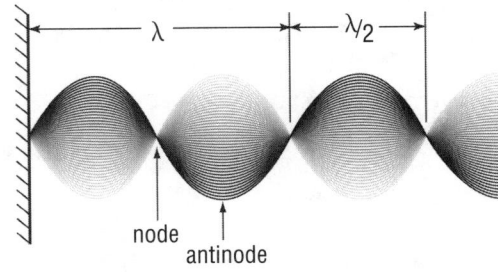

node
antinode

Figure 1

tube. Neither does it take place only within the length of the air column, but extends beyond the end of the tube.

- You may want to discuss the resonance of an open tube. Antinodes are present at both ends, so all possible fourths of a wavelength (both even and odd) can be present. This is the reason that an open-tube instrument like a trumpet has more overtones (harmonics) than an instrument closed at one end like a flute.

• The analysis of Equation (4) includes the definition of the ΔT term. Some references include only the term T, which is room temperature. This works arithmetically, but the units are wrong for the sound speed temperature correction factor in the formula. By convention in this manual, ΔT is expressed in C°, which indicates an increment of temperature change (equivalent to 1 K), while °C is the unit of a specific point on the temperature scale.

Equipment and Setup

• The recommended equipment consists of a tall graduated cylinder (at least 500 mL, but 1000 mL is better), a glass or plastic resonance tube at least 30 cm long, and two tuning forks with frequencies greater than 500 Hz. The rubber mallet is a convenience to avoid potential damage to the forks.

• If a support stand with a sufficiently long rod is available, the resonance tube may be clamped in position, making the measurement of the air column length much easier.

• Science suppliers provide a classic apparatus that will permit obtaining multiple resonance points for frequencies above 500 Hz as well as for some frequencies below. It costs about twice as much as a 1000 mL graduated cylinder.

• See the Home School Notes for alternative materials.

Procedure

• Tuning forks do not need to be struck hard in order to provide the required sound. DO NOT strike the forks with or against a hard object. If a rubber mallet is not available, students may strike the fork on a knee or an elbow without damage.

• It is unlikely that students will obtain more than one resonance point when using the recommended equipment and a fork with a frequency less than or equal to 512 Hz. The sound wavelength is too long. Use forks with frequencies between 800 and 1000 Hz in order to obtain multiple resonance points.

study of wave characteristics that the speed of a wave (v) is determined by the kind of medium through which it passes and that its frequency (f) is determined by the frequency of the source that generated it. The wavelength (λ) is directly proportional to the speed of the wave and inversely proportional to its frequency. You can express this relationship in the equation

$$\lambda = \frac{v}{f}. \tag{1}$$

Sound enters an oscillator with a large variety of frequencies. Resonance occurs when those waves that are multiples of the oscillator's natural frequency produce standing waves within the oscillator. Usually, the oscillator's physical characteristics are fixed. However, if an oscillator's dimensions can be adjusted and if a sound source producing a single frequency of sound is used, you can vary the size of the oscillator until resonance occurs and then determine the wavelength of the sound produced. If you know the frequency of the sound source and the wavelength of the sound, then you can determine the speed of sound in the oscillator by solving Equation (1) for v:

$$v = \lambda f. \tag{2}$$

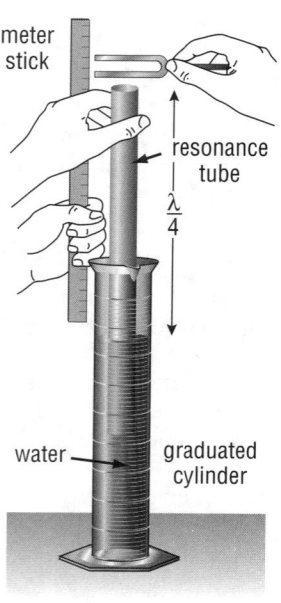

meter stick

resonance tube

$\frac{\lambda}{4}$

water | graduated cylinder

Figure 2

In this lab you will use the air column within a cylindrical tube as the oscillating medium. The air column will be closed at one end by placing the end of the tube in water. The source of sound will be a tuning fork with a *known frequency*, which produces a nearly pure tone with few harmonics (see Figure 2). When a standing wave is produced in a closed tube, a node exists at the closed end, where no displacement of air molecules occurs, and an antinode exists at the open end, where maximum displacement occurs. In any standing wave, the distance between a node and an adjacent antinode is 1/4 of a wavelength, or $\lambda/4$. Therefore, the minimum possible air column length that can produce resonance will be approximately $\lambda/4$. The length is *approximate* because the antinode is actually slightly beyond the end of the cylinder due to the friction of the sound wave interacting with the air outside the cylinder. This distance, called the **end correction,** is a function of the diameter of the cylinder. The resonating length, L, can be more accurately estimated by the formula

$$L = l + 0.4d, \tag{3}$$

where l is the length of the air column in the tube and d is the diameter of the tube. The wavelength of the sound producing the standing wave in a $\lambda/4$ air column is therefore $4L$.

If you raise the tube farther out of the water to lengthen the air column, the standing wave will disappear because the antinode will no longer be located at the open end of the tube. You will note a distinct decrease in resonant sound volume. If you continue to raise the tube, eventually another antinode will coincide with the open end. This will be accompanied by a distinct increase in resonant sound. Antinodes are $\lambda/2$ apart, so the length of this air column will be $3\lambda/4$ long ($\lambda/4 + 2\lambda/4 = 3\lambda/4$). If you could continue to increase the length of the air column, you would note resonant points at lengths equal to $5\lambda/4$, $7\lambda/4, \ldots, n\lambda/4$, where n is an *odd* integer. Note that these lengths represent *odd fourths* of the fundamental wavelength, which is characteristic of an air column oscillating in a tube with a closed end. When determining the wave length of the standing wave, you can eliminate the uncertainty of the end correction by finding the difference between any two adjacent resonant lengths to yield the value $\lambda/2$. The wavelength of the sound produced by the tuning fork is twice this length.

As a check on your work, you can compare the experimentally determined value of the speed of sound with the accepted value of the speed of sound in air. The speed of sound in air at 0 °C (v_0) is 331.5 m/s. As temperature rises, the speed increases at 0.60 (m/s)/C°. The speed of sound at a Celsius temperature T, v_T, can be calculated according to the formula $v_T = v_0 + 0.60\Delta T$ m/s, or

$$v_T = (331.5 + 0.60\Delta T) \text{ m/s}, \qquad (4)$$

where $\Delta T = T - 0.0$ °C (in Celsius degrees). Note that the *change* in the speed of sound between any two typical environmental temperatures may be calculated by the term $0.60\Delta T$.

Procedure

1. Measure the room temperature and record it in the blank above Table 1.

2. Measure the inner diameter of the resonance tube (in meters) and record the value in the blank above Table 1.

3. Add water to the graduated cylinder until it is at least three-fourths full.

4. Note the frequency stamped on the first tuning fork to be used and record this value in hertz in Table 1 for each trial in which it is used.

5. Hold the resonance tube vertically in the graduated cylinder so that the water seals the bottom of the tube. The length of the air column is the distance from the surface of the water to the upper lip of the resonance tube.

6. Strike the tuning fork with a rubber mallet. Hold the vibrating tuning fork so that it is horizontal and as close as possible to the mouth of the tube.

   Caution: Do not let the tuning fork touch a glass resonance tube—it could shatter the glass.

   Move the fork and tube up and down as a unit in order to vary the air column length. You will note one or more positions at which the sound is re-inforced and therefore resonates noticeably louder.

7. Lower the tube in order to find the shortest length that produces a resonant sound. Raise and lower the tube and fork slightly to verify the point of best resonance and have a partner measure the air column length. Record this measurement (l) in meters in Table 1.

8. If you are using a graduated cylinder that is tall enough, you may be able to raise the tube and vibrating tuning fork to the next point at which a resonant reinforcement occurs and record l for this position. Record the frequency of the fork and the air column length as Trial 2 in Table 1.

9. Repeat Step 8 for longer resonance lengths until you are unable to find another resonance point without lifting the resonance tube out of the water.

10. If you have a second tuning fork with a different frequency, repeat Steps 6–9 and record the data in Table 1 for as many resonance points as you can.

- Students should practice determining the resonance points. Students with acute hearing should be able to locate the point within half a centimeter.

Home School Notes

- A person handy with basic shop tools can construct a very service-able resonance tube apparatus from basic materials.

  1. Materials
     1 in. ID PVC pipe, 1 m
     1/4 in. ID plastic hose, 1 m
     1/4 in. self-threading hose nipples, 2
     rigid clear plastic cup 16 oz or larger
     small scrap of Plexiglas
     two-part epoxy sealer

  2. Instructions

     a. Finish one end of the pipe flat, perpendicular to its length, and smooth.

     b. Drill a hole for a hose nipple about 1 in. from the finished end. Make sure that it is the right size to accept the self-tapping thread of the nipple.

     c. Coat the threads of a nipple with a small amount of the epoxy sealer and thread it into the drilled hole. Do not plug the channel of the nipple with epoxy!

     d. Glue the finished end of the pipe to the scrap of Plexiglas with the epoxy sealer and set it aside to cure.

     e. Drill a hole in the bottom of the cup to accept the other nipple. Coat the threads of the nipple with epoxy and thread the nipple into the cup.

     f. When all epoxy joints have cured, work the ends of the hose onto the nipples. Fill the apparatus with water and check for leaks.

  3. Use

     a. To fill the apparatus, hold the cup so that its bottom is about 10 cm below the top of the pipe. Add water until the water level visible in the hose is at the bottom of the cup.

Data

Table 1
Speed of Sound Data and Calculations

Room temperature ____23.5____ °C   Tube diameter ____0.025____ m

Trial	Tuning Fork Frequency, f		Air Column Length, l		Corrected Air Column Length, L		Wavelength, λ		Experimental Speed of Sound, v_e		Accepted Speed of Sound, v_T		v_e and v_T Percent Error	
1	512	Hz	0.156	m	0.166	m	0.664	m	340.	m/s	346	m/s	−1.75	%
2	512	Hz	0.496	m	0.506	m	0.675	m	346	m/s	346	m/s	0.0	%
3		Hz		m		m		m		m/s		m/s		%
4		Hz		m		m		m		m/s		m/s		%
5		Hz		m		m		m		m/s		m/s		%
6		Hz		m		m		m		m/s		m/s		%
7		Hz		m		m		m		m/s		m/s		%
8		Hz		m		m		m		m/s		m/s		%
Average									343	m/s	346	m/s	−0.871	%

Data and calculations in Table 1 are typical. Actual data and results will vary.

b. One or more heavy rubber bands can secure the cup to the tube, leaving your hands free for the experiment.

c. The water level in the pipe coincides with the water's surface in the cup. You can adjust the water level in the pipe by lowering or raising the cup as necessary. Measure the distance between the water's surface in the cup and the top of the pipe in order to determine the air column height.

d. One advantage to this apparatus is that the resonance tube and tuning fork can be held stationary and the water level can be varied as described above.

Postlab Exercises

1. For each value of l, make the end correction, using Equation (3), and enter these values for L in Table 1.

2. Calculate the wavelength of the sound wave by multiplying L by the appropriate factor depending on the resonance length. For the shortest length ($\lambda/4$), multiply by 4. For the next position ($3\lambda/4$), multiply by 4/3, and so on to obtain λ. Record these wavelengths in Table 1.

3. Compute the experimental speed of sound (v_e) for each trial, using Equation (2), and record the values in Table 1.

4. Determine the temperature-corrected accepted value for the speed of sound (v_T) based on the temperature measurement made at the beginning of the lab, using Equation (4). Record these values in Table 1 for each trial.

5. Compute the percent error between the experimental and accepted values for the speed of sound in air at room temperature and record these results in Table 1.

6. Determine the average of your experimental speeds of sound. Determine the average percent error from this result. Record your values in Table 1.

Postlab Analysis

1. If you were not aware of end correction and just assumed that the air column length of the resonance tube was $\lambda/4$, which frequency range would produce a greater error in determining wavelength—higher frequency (shorter resonance length) or lower frequency (longer resonance length), assuming that you use the same tube?

   End correction is dependent on the diameter of the tube, so it is the

   same for both frequency ranges. The error of ignoring end correction

   would be proportionately less for the lower frequency range.

2. Once you have determined the speed of sound for your lab conditions, explain how you could find the frequency of a tuning fork that does not have a frequency stamped on it.

   Perform the experiment again in order to obtain the wavelength of the

   standing wave with the unmarked fork. Calculate the frequency from

   the formula $f = v/\lambda$, using the speed of sound previously determined.

3. ___329 m/s___ Calculate the speed of sound at 0.0 °C (v_0), using Equation (4) and the average of *your experimentally determined speeds of sound* at room temperature.

   Student answers will vary. The solution uses the typical values in Table 1.

   Given: $v_T = \dfrac{(340\ \frac{m}{s} + 346\ \frac{m}{s})}{2} = 343\ \frac{m}{s};$

   $\Delta T = T_{room} - 0.0\ °C = 23.5\ C°;\ v_0 = ?$

   Formula: $v_T = v_0 + 0.60\Delta T\frac{m}{s} \Rightarrow v_0 = v_T - 0.60\Delta T\frac{m}{s}$

   Solution: $v_0 = 343\ \frac{m}{s} - (0.60\ \frac{m}{s\cdot C°})(23.5\ C°) = 328.9\ \frac{m}{s} \approx 329\ \frac{m}{s}$

   (3 SDs allowed)

4. ___348 m/s___ The Prelab Discussion noted that the wavelength of the standing wave in a tube could be determined without considering the end correction. Using the difference of two adjacent resonant lengths (l) from your data for a given tuning fork, calculate the speed of sound. (Omit this question if you could obtain only a single resonant length for a given tuning fork.)

   Student answers will vary. The solution uses the typical values in Table 1.

   Given: $\dfrac{\lambda}{4} = 0.156\ m;\ \dfrac{3\lambda}{4} = 0.496\ m;\ f = 512\ Hz = 512\ s^{-1};\ v_e = ?$

   Formula: $v = \lambda f$

   Solution: First, find the difference of the two adjacent resonant lengths.

   $\dfrac{3\lambda}{4} - \dfrac{\lambda}{4} = \dfrac{2\lambda}{4} = \dfrac{\lambda}{2} \Rightarrow \dfrac{\lambda}{2} = 0.496\ m - 0.156\ m = 0.340\ m;$

   $\lambda = 2(0.340\ m) = 0.680\ m$

   $v_e = (512\ s^{-1})(0.680\ m) = 348.16\ \frac{m}{s} \approx 348\ \frac{m}{s}$ (3 SDs allowed)

5. Considering the experimental apparatus, what two factors probably contributed the *most* to errors in the results?

   Students should recognize that the subjective nature of aurally deter-

   mining the resonance point and the awkward arrangement for mea-

   suring the air column length will contribute the most to errors in the

   final results.

Name _____

Date _____ Hour ____

PRELAB HOMEWORK

1. A sound wave differs from a water wave in that the particles in a sound wave move longitudinally, forming _____rarefactions_____ and _____compressions_____ in the medium.

2. The distance between two corresponding points on adjacent waves is called the _____wavelength_____.

3. In a wave, the maximum change in the medium from the neutral position or condition is called the _____amplitude_____.

4. When more than one wave system is present in a medium at the same time, _____interference_____ occurs between the systems of waves.

5. When a reflected wave passes back through the incident (original) wave, a pattern called a _____standing wave_____ is formed.

6. A point in a standing wave at which maximum oscillation in the medium takes place is called a(n) _____antinode_____.

7. The frequency at which an object can be made to audibly vibrate most easily is called its _____natural or resonant_____ frequency.

8. When the object in Question 7 is vibrating at that particular frequency, it is experiencing acoustic _____resonance_____.

9. In the wavelength formula, Equation (1), indicate which variables are independent and which are dependent. Explain.
   Frequency and speed are the independent variables in the relation because frequency is determined by the source of the wave and the speed is determined by the medium. Wavelength is dependent on the other two.

10. Why is the standing sound wave that is formed in a tube that is closed at one end not an *exact* multiple of one-fourth of a wavelength?
    The wave interacts with the air at the open end so that the antinode is a short distance beyond the end of the tube.

11. How is the end correction calculated in this experiment?
    The end correction is calculated by adding $0.4d$ to the length of the air column, where d is the diameter of the tube.

12. What precaution must you take with glass resonance tubes when adjusting the height of the air column while using a vibrating tuning fork?
    The vibrating tuning fork must not touch the glass because it might shatter the tube.

13. _____0.176 m_____ If a 4.0 cm diameter tube resonates with an air column of 16.0 cm, what is the *corrected* resonant length of the air column in meters?
    Given: d = 4.0 cm = 0.040 m; l = 16.0 cm = 0.160 m; L = ?
    Formula: $L = l + 0.4d$
    Solution: $L = 0.160$ m $+ 0.4(0.040$ m$) = 0.176$ m

14. ___0.680 m___ If the *shortest* corrected resonant length L is 0.170 m in this experiment, what is the wavelength of the sound wave?

The shortest resonant length in this experiment is $\lambda/4$ long.

$\lambda = 4L = 4(0.170 \text{ m}) = 0.680 \text{ m}$

15. ___343 m/s___ The wavelength of the sound wave produced by a 512 Hz tuning fork was experimentally determined to be 0.670 m. Calculate the speed of sound.

Given: $f = 512$ Hz; $\lambda = 0.670$ m; $v_e = ?$

Formula: $v_e = \lambda f$

Solution: $v_e = (0.670 \text{ m})(512 \text{ Hz}) \doteq 343 \frac{\text{m}}{\text{s}}$

16. ___346 m/s___ The accepted speed of sound varies with temperature and is determined by Equation (4). If the room temperature is 24.0 °C, what is the accepted speed of sound, v_T?

Given: $T = 24.0$ °C; $v_T = ?$

Formula: $v_T = (331.5 + 0.60\Delta T)\ \frac{\text{m}}{\text{s}}$

Solution: $v_T = 331.5\ \frac{\text{m}}{\text{s}} + (0.60\ \frac{\text{m}}{\text{s}\cdot\text{C}^\circ})(24.0 \text{ °C} - 0.0 \text{ °C}) =$

$331.5\ \frac{\text{m}}{\text{s}} + (0.60\ \frac{\text{m}}{\text{s}\cdot\cancel{\text{C}^\circ}})(24.0\ \cancel{\text{C}^\circ}) \approx 346\ \frac{\text{m}}{\text{s}}$ (3 SDs allowed)

17. ___−1.16%___ Assume that the accepted speed of sound for the existing lab conditions is 344 m/s. Compute the percent error between an experimental value of 340. m/s and the accepted value.

$$\text{percent error} = \frac{340.\ \frac{\text{m}}{\text{s}} - 344\ \frac{\text{m}}{\text{s}}}{344\ \frac{\text{m}}{\text{s}}} \times 100\% \doteq -1.16\%$$

Name _____

Date _____ Hour _____

ELECTROSTATIC CHARGES

Purpose

The study of electrostatic charges is the foundation for more advanced studies in electricity, magnetism, and even light. The purpose of this lab is to

- demonstrate how different materials gain and hold electrostatic charges.
- observe the effects of charged objects on one another.
- demonstrate the transfer of static charges by induction and contact.

Prelab Discussion

All matter is composed of particles some of which bear an electrical charge. Electrons are one of these charged particles, and protons are the other. Removing or adding electrons usually produces a net charge on objects because some electrons are easily removed from the surface of an object by **friction.** Protons are fixed in the nuclei of atoms and are not easily displaced.

Early scientists experimented with the effects of friction on amber and glass. By convention, objects that behaved like amber were called *resinous,* and objects that behaved like glass were called *vitreous.* Ben Franklin gave the term *positive* to vitreous substances and *negative* to resinous substances because he considered the flow of charge to be the flow of an electrical fluid. He reasoned that vitreous substances had an excess of the fluid and that resinous substances were deficient in the fluid—thus the "flow" from positive to negative. While Franklin's concept is inconsistent with modern electron theory, much of the terminology remains. Glass or Lucite rubbed with a silk cloth will develop a positive charge, while a rubber rod rubbed with fur will produce a negative charge. Rather than having an excess or deficiency of "electric fluid," the real cause of charge is associated with the presence of electrons. Electrons may be easily removed from some substances by simple friction.

When two different materials are rubbed together, friction causes some of the electrons to be transferred from the surface of one of the materials onto the surface of the other material. As a result, both materials become temporarily charged. The material that gains the negatively charged particles acquires a negative charge, while the material that loses the negatively charged particles acquires a positive charge. *Note that a positive charge is the result of the removal of electrons, not the addition of positive charges.* Electrically neutral atoms have an equal number of electrons and protons.

Objects that are electrically charged will attract or be attracted by other objects that are overall electrically neutral and by objects that have an opposite electrical charge. Two objects with the same charge will repel. The **law of charges** summarizes these two principles. In order to prove that an object is electrically charged, it must repel another charged object. Attraction is *not* an acceptable test for identifying the kind of electrical charge because a neutral object will also attract a charged object by a process called *induction.* In order to determine the kind of charge for an object, it must repel a second object with a known charge.

While friction is the most common method for experimentally charging objects, it is by no means the only method. Objects can also be charged by **contact** with a charged object. For example, electrons will flow from a negatively charged object touching a neutral object until the surface charges on both objects are equal (equilibrium is established). At this point, both objects have a negative charge, and the two objects will repel each other. Electrons can also flow from a neutral object in contact with a positively charged object until equilibrium is established. Then both objects have a positive charge, and the two objects repel each other.

Prelab Discussion

- Review the prerequisites for Lab 4-1 in the back of this manual.

- This lab is very elementary in content and presentation. You may want to consider assigning the exercise for homework or presenting it as a class demonstration.

- The concept of induction is often misunderstood. Use this lab to demonstrate how induction occurs for both negatively charged and positively charged objects.

Equipment and Setup

- The necessary electrostatic rods and pads are sold as a kit by most science equipment suppliers. However, all of the items may be substituted with common household items. See the Home School Notes.

- The wire support for the pith ball can be forced into a cork stopper sized to fit a flask. The flask then acts as a support base.

- The electroscope portion can be completed using foil-leaf electroscopes if they are available.

Procedure

- This lab is designed to give students the opportunity to experiment with the electrostatic properties of different materials.

- As an optional activity, ask students to evaluate the effectiveness of different combinations of rods and friction pads. Some combinations will produce a greater charge than others.

- For the sake of accuracy, ensure that students acknowledge that when two objects attract, the unknown charge cannot be determined without additional testing.

Home School Notes

- Equipment substitutions are simple.

  1. Glass rods may be replaced with glass tubing melted closed at one end.

  2. A comb can replace the rubber rod.

  3. Pith balls can be obtained from trees locally if you know where to look, or you may use un-coated cereal pieces made from pithy grains such as puffed wheat or oats. Trim the pieces so that they are spherical. Use the lightest weight string available to suspend them.

  4. The two hangers can be made from wire clothes hangers and bent into shape as in Figures 1 and 2.

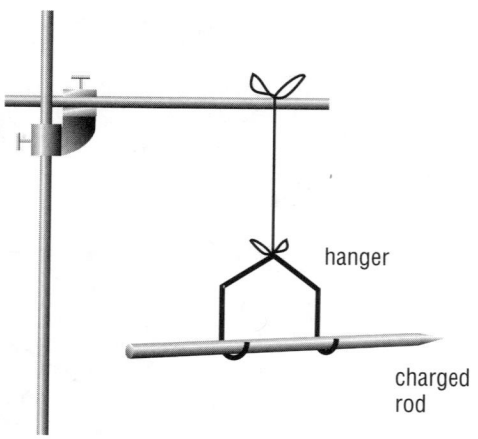

hanger

charged rod

Figure 1

It is also possible to charge an object by **induction.** The following example may help you understand induction. In dealing with persons, *induce* means to persuade or convince by influence. You might think of the term *influence* when thinking about induction. There is no contact between the objects, but one object influences the other object. When a negatively charged object comes close to a large nonconducting surface, the electrons in the negatively charged object will repel the electrons on the surface, and those electrons will move as far from the influence of the charged object as possible. Therefore, the charged object and the large surface in the vicinity of the object will have opposite charges and will attract each other much more strongly than if induction did not occur. At contact, an exchange of electrons may also take place. If the electrons move to the large surface, the object will then be positively charged, and the large surface will receive a negative charge so that they "stick" together. Perhaps you have charged a balloon by rubbing it on your hair and then "stuck" it to the ceiling. The balloon will cling to the ceiling until it collects sufficient electrons from colliding air molecules to reduce its positive charge relative to the ceiling.

An **electroscope** is a device that shows the influence of charged objects. There are many different kinds of electroscopes. Some common high-school laboratory versions include a simple suspended rod, suspended pith balls, and metal-foil electroscopes. There are more sophisticated forms that can provide quantitative indications of charge, but all serve the same purpose.

Procedure

Detecting Charges

1. Suspend the coat hanger "stirrup" support for the rod by means of a string from a support stand or another convenient location (see Figure 1).

2. Prepare a rod with a known charge.

   a. Wrap a piece of masking tape around one end of the rubber rod.

   b. Hold the taped end of the rod and charge it, using fur or wool.

   c. Place the charged rod into the stirrup. The end that you held in your hand is likely to be neutral because electrons can easily flow onto your hand from the rod or vice versa. Nonmetals are poor conductors, so the charge from the rubbed end will not quickly move to the end that you were holding. Use only the charged end of the rod (the one without the tape) for testing purposes.

   d. Record the type of rod you are using and the charge on that rod in the blanks above Table 1. This is your known rod. The other items to be tested will be called test objects.

3. Charge a second rubber rod with fur or wool. (You may need to borrow a second rod from another group. Otherwise, use a rubber comb or experiment with different materials until you find a material that will repel the suspended rod.)

4. Bring the test rod near the known rod, but do not allow them to touch. If the rods do touch, you will need to recharge the known rod. In Table 1, notice that the data cell under the rubber rod rubbed with fur has the word *repel* and a negative sign under the charge. If the rubber rod does not repel the known rod, recharge the known rod before proceeding. These two rods must repel each other before you can be assured of the charge on the known rod.

5. Charge each of the three objects with silk and fur as indicated in Table 1. If the object repels, write a "−" under Charge. If it attracts, write a "+" *and* the letter "N" under Charge. (You are indicating that the object may be oppositely charged or neutral.) Remember that if the rods touch, you will need to recharge the known rod before proceeding.

6. Remove the rubber rod from the stirrup. Touch the stirrup in order to neutralize any charge that may have built up.

7. Now charge the Lucite rod with silk. Suspend the Lucite rod in the stirrup. To determine the charge on the Lucite rod, rub another Lucite rod with silk and notice whether it is attracted or repelled. (You may need to borrow a Lucite rod from another group, or you may use a strip of transparent tape—a 30 cm piece folded back sticky side to sticky side works well.) You should be able to determine the charge by using the observations in Table 1 and your current observations.

8. Test the objects listed in Table 2 and record your observations as you did for Table 1.

Data for Detecting Charges

Table 1
Negative Charge Test Data

Suspended rod is ____rubber____. Charge is assumed to be ____negative____.

Test Object	Silk		Fur	
	Attract or Repel?	**Charge**	**Attract or Repel?**	**Charge**
Rubber Rod	repel	–	repel	–
Lucite Rod	attract	+, N	attract	+, N
Glass Rod*	attract	+, N	attract	+, N

*If the humidity is high, you may have difficulty getting the glass rod to show the same characteristics as the Lucite rod. If this occurs, don't worry. Record the results as you observe them. Don't alter the results to conform to what you think they should be.

Table 2
Negative Charge Test Data

Suspended rod is ____Lucite____. Charge is assumed to be ____positive____.

Test Object	Silk		Fur	
	Attract or Repel?	**Charge**	**Attract or Repel?**	**Charge**
Lucite Rod	repel	+	repel	+
Rubber Rod	attract	–, N	attract	–, N
Glass Rod*	repel	+	repel	+

Observations in Tables 1 and 2 are typical. Actual answers may vary.

Electroscopes, Induction, and Contact

9. Use string to suspend a ball of pith wood from a support. The pith must not touch the support (see Figure 2).

10. Rub the rubber rod with fur. Bring the rod *near* the pith (without touching it).

    Is the pith attracted or repelled by the rod? ____attracted____

11. Now *touch* the rod to the pith and remove it (if the pith does not spring away from the rod). Bring the rod near the pith again. Is the pith attracted

    or repelled by the rod? ____repelled____

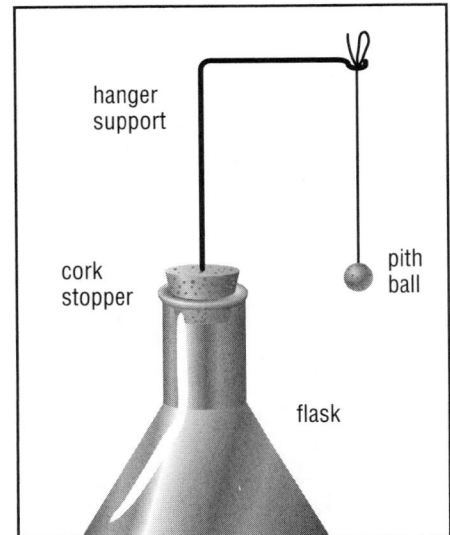

Figure 2

12. Rub the Lucite rod with silk. Bring the rod *near* the pith. Is the pith attracted or repelled by the rod? _____attracted_____

13. Now *touch* the rod to the pith and remove it. Bring the rod near the pith again. Is the pith attracted or repelled by the rod? _____repelled_____

14. Bring the charged Lucite rod *near* the pith. (If the rod does not repel the pith, recharge the pith by touching it with the charged rod. Repeat until the rod repels the pith.) While the rod is near the pith and repelling it, reach out and touch the pith with your finger. Remove your finger from the pith. Is the pith attracted or repelled by the rod? _____attracted_____

15. Bring a charged rubber rod *near* the pith. Is the pith attracted or repelled by the rod? _____repelled_____

16. Repeat Step 14 with the rubber rod. Is the pith attracted or repelled by the rod? _____attracted_____

17. Bring the charged Lucite rod near the pith. Is the pith attracted or repelled by the rod? _____repelled_____

18. Explain in your own words how induction is demonstrated in Steps 10–17. Answers should conform to the description of induction in the Prelab Discussion. For Steps 14–17, students should state that touching the ball with the hand provides an avenue of escape for electrons when the rubber rod is near. (The electrons are repelled from the pith onto the hand.) When the Lucite rod is used, the electrons flow onto the pith from the hand. This method of charging is called induction.

Name _____

Date _____ Hour _____

PRELAB HOMEWORK

1. State the law of charges in your own words.

   Answers will vary but should essentially state that like charges repel and unlike

   charges attract.

2. What happens to materials that lose electrons when they are rubbed?

   The materials become positively charged.

3. What must be true if two electrostatically charged objects repel each other?

   The two objects have the same charges.

4. What *can* be true if two objects attract each other electrostatically?

   The objects may be oppositely charged; or one may be neutral, and the other may

   be either positively or negatively charged.

5. What device detects and indicates the presence of electrostatic charges?

   electroscope

6. By what three methods can an electrostatic charge be produced on an object?

   A charge can be produced by rubbing, by coming in contact with another charged

   object, or by induction.

True or False. If the statement is true, write *True* in the shorter blank. If the statement is false, write *False* in the shorter blank and use the longer blank to explain why the statement is incorrect.

7. _____True_____ A Lucite rod that has been rubbed with a silk cloth will gain a positive charge.

   _____

   _____

8. _____False_____ A rubber rod that has been rubbed with fur will gain a positive charge.

   Rubber will normally acquire electrons when rubbed by another material.

   _____

9. _____False_____ When a charged rubber rod and a charged Lucite rod come near each other, they will repel.

   Charged rubber and Lucite rods have opposite charges, so they will attract.

   _____

10. _____False_____ If a negatively charged rod attracts another rod, then the second rod must be positively charged.

    Two objects can attract each other if they are oppositely charged or through the

    process of induction if one is neutral.

Laboratory Activity ━━━━━━━━━━━━━━━━━━━━━━━━

Name _____

Date _____ Hour _____

RESISTANCE

Purpose

This lab is an introduction to basic electricity principles and components. The purpose is to

- provide practice connecting electrical components in an electrical circuit.
- observe the effects of a short circuit and the action of an electrical fuse.
- determine the resistance of a resistor from color coding.
- provide practice using an ohmmeter.
- read and sketch electrical schematic diagrams.

<table>
<tr><td>Required Equipment
Elenco Learning Center kit
Elenco M-1000B multimeter</td></tr>
</table>

Prelab Discussion

Read pages 6–11 of the Elenco Learning Center manual. Be sure that you understand the material covered on those pages as well as the material discussed in this Prelab Discussion before proceeding with the lab.

Batteries

An electrical circuit is a path for an electrical current to follow. For current to flow, there must first be a source of electrons. The Learning Center circuit board uses a 9 V battery to provide current to the circuit. Two or more connected **voltaic cells** are called a battery. Your 9 V battery is actually six 1.5 V dry cells connected in series. Your teacher will demonstrate what happens when batteries are connected in series and in parallel. Later you may wish to duplicate the demonstration if you have extra batteries in your classroom. You will be able to measure the voltage of these connections after you learn the proper use of an electrical test meter.

Figure 1 shows the connections for a pair of batteries in a series (one path). Figure 2 shows the same electrical connections drawn as an **electrical schematic diagram.** A schematic diagram is a simplified diagram that substitutes symbols for more complex drawings. Each symbol represents a specific electrical component. Straight lines that connect components indicate **wires** or other conductors. Dots at which component symbols and wires are joined represent **junctions** or **terminals.** You may refer to Appendix F for a list of some common electronic component symbols. The symbol for a dry cell is simply a long line next to a short line. You can think of the short line in the symbol as a negative sign to help you locate the negative end of the battery. For your purpose, a long and short line symbol represents a 1.5 V battery. Batteries with larger voltages are symbolized by more pairs of lines. The output voltage of batteries connected in series is the sum of the individual battery voltages. Series connections produce higher voltages than a single battery can attain.

Prelab Discussion

- Review the prerequisites for Lab 4-2 in the back of this manual. Refer to Appendices F and G for additional information on electrical component symbols and resistor color codes.

- The Elenco Electronic Playground and Learning Center will be called the Learning Center in this manual for brevity's sake.

- You should spend some time in a regular class period introducing the multimeter and the Learning Center. Discuss the precautions described in this lab and in the multimeter manual.

- The term *test lead* is probably unfamiliar to your students but is in common use in technical occupations. In this context, *lead* is pronounced "leed," not "led."

- Show the students how batteries (or other components) can be connected in series and in parallel.

- When sketching circuit schematics, be sure to include junction dots, which act as nodes and delimit electrical components from one another.

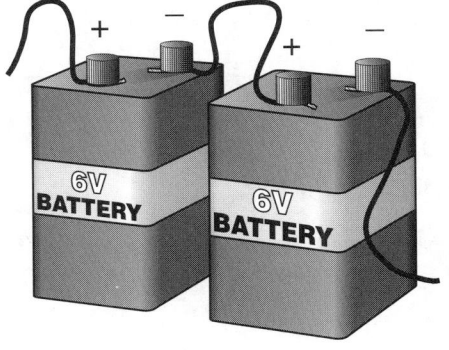

Figure 1

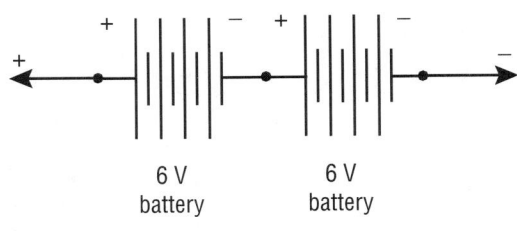

6 V battery   6 V battery

Figure 2

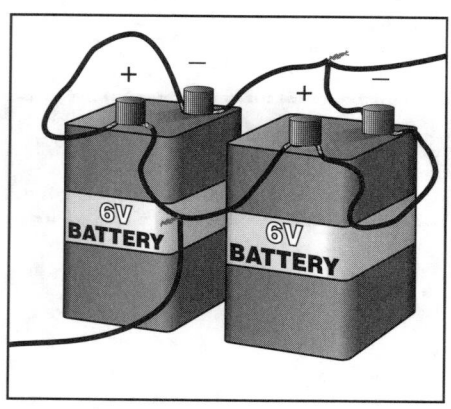

Figure 3

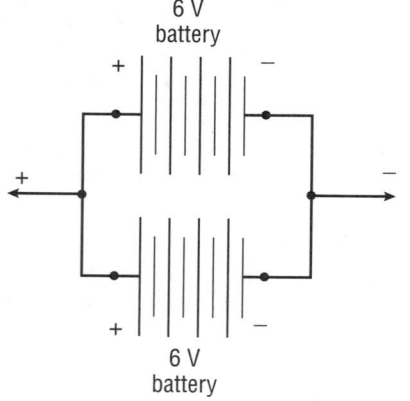

Figure 4

- There are several good electronic circuit emulation computer programs on the market. You will find that demonstrating the attributes of a complex circuit (component voltage, current, inductance, etc.) is very easy with such software.

Equipment and Setup

- The recommended equipment is readily available through BJUP from a longtime supplier of instructional aids. The multimeter is not a toy but a fully functional multimeter.

- Install fresh batteries in your Learning Centers prior to the first use for the school year. Check the function of all multimeters prior to class. In particular, check the current scales by using a medium-sized resistor in series with the battery, because the meter's protective fuse is easily blown.

- In the event that the specified equipment is not available, any multimeter

Figure 3 is a diagram of the connection for two batteries in parallel (multiple paths). Figure 4 is the parallel battery connection drawn as a schematic diagram. When batteries are connected in parallel, the output voltage is the same as a single battery, but electrical capacity is increased. Prolonged battery life is the advantage of a parallel connection.

Open, Closed, and Short Circuits

Simple circuits may be classified as either closed or open. In a **closed circuit,** the electrical current can flow throughout the circuit. An **open circuit** has an intentionally or unintentionally broken path, preventing the flow of current.

A **switch** is a device that is placed in a circuit for the purpose of intentionally opening the circuit in order to control an electrical device. Most power distribution circuits also have an automatic means of opening the circuit to prevent hazardous conditions from developing. A **short circuit** is an unintentional second path for electrical current to follow. The path has low resistance and can produce high temperatures from the resulting large currents. Fires often result from short circuits. Devices that provide protection in the event of a short circuit or an overload are called **fuses** or **circuit breakers.** A fuse is a one-time-use device that simply places a conductor with a low melting point into the circuit. If the circuit is overloaded due to a short circuit or if too many electrical loads are operating, the high current will cause the fuse to overheat and melt, opening the circuit. A circuit breaker works similarly, except that the high temperature causes a switch to open. The circuit breaker can be shut (reset) and used again when the overload condition is corrected.

The Learning Center uses an LED as both a load and an indicator that there is a closed circuit. An LED is a **light-emitting diode.** You will learn more about the operation of the LED in a later lab. Note that an LED is easily damaged if too much current passes through it.

Procedure

Note: The numbers in the text refer to the terminal numbers on the Elenco Learning Center. If you are using an electronics kit from another supplier, your teacher will provide the equivalent terminal numbers for your kit so that you can write them in the blanks following the numbers.

Open, Closed, and Short Circuits

1. Install a 9 V battery in the Learning Center by attaching the battery connector and then inserting the battery into the battery holder.

2. Connect the spring connecting posts, also called terminals, with wires provided in the Learning Center as follows:

   27 (____) to 56 (____)

   55 (____) to 41 (____)

   40 (____) to 3 (____)

   4 (____) to 26 (____)

   > Note: Never connect the LED without a resistor in the circuit.

3. Press down on the switch. Record your observations.

   The LED glows brightly as soon as the switch is pressed.

4. Describe what happens when you release the switch.

   The LED extinguishes instantly.

5. You have constructed a *circuit.* It is *open* when the switch is released, and it is *closed* when the switch is pressed.

6. Connect another wire from the 1 kΩ resistor (41 ___) to the negative terminal of the battery (26 ___).

7. Briefly press the switch. Does the LED illuminate?

no

It should *not* illuminate because you have created a short circuit. Do not press the switch for very long at a time. Short circuits put an excessive drain on the battery and quickly deplete it.

8. Remove the wire that connects the battery (27 ___) to the switch (56 ___). Replace it with a fine strand of steel wool. Press the switch again and hold it for a few seconds. Record your observations.

The LED glows briefly, the strip of steel wool glows and then burns

up, and the LED goes out.

The steel wool should melt and open the circuit.

9. Remove the remnants of the steel wool, and reconnect the wire between the battery and the switch (27 ___ to 56 ___). Remove the shorting wire (41 ___ to 26 ___). Test the circuit and make sure that the LED glows again.

Look at the schematic diagram for the circuit that you have connected (see Figure 5). You should become familiar with the symbol for each component that is connected. Notice that in Figure 5, the schematic uses a symbol showing only two dry cells (two pairs of lines normally means 3 V) instead of six (9 V). This convention provides a simple means of representing *any* battery. The actual battery voltage will be written next to the symbol.

Notice also that the "arrow" in the LED symbol points in the direction of **conventional current flow.** *Conventional current flow occurs from positive to negative, which is the opposite of electron flow.* The LED must be connected so that the flow of conventional current is in the direction of the arrow.

10. Reverse the wires connected to terminals 26 (___) and 27 (___). Press the switch and record your observations.

The LED no longer glows when the switch is pressed.

Resistors

You can determine the value of a resistor by examining the color code printed on it. Refer to the keys given on page 10 of the Learning Center manual and in Appendix G of this manual. The first two bands represent the significant digits of the resistance. The third band represents the power of 10 by which the significant digits are multiplied (the "multiplier"). The last band represents the **tolerance,** or the permissible variation of the actual resistance compared to its color code value, expressed as a percentage. For example, the 1 MΩ resistor has brown, black, green, and gold bands. The first two bands indicate that the significant figures are 1 and 0. The third shows that the significant figures should be multiplied by 10^5, and the last indicates a tolerance of ±5%. The color code resistance is 10×10^5 Ω, or 1 000 000 Ω (1 MΩ). Record this value in Table 1 under 1 MΩ. The tolerance is ±50 000 Ω (1 000 000 Ω × 0.05), so the **range** of the resistor is between 1 050 000 Ω and 950 000 Ω [(1 000 000 Ω + 50 000 Ω) to (1 000 000 Ω − 50 000 Ω)]. Record these values also; then read the other resistor color codes and record the resistance, tolerance, and range of each resistor in Table 1. You will complete the meter reading and the other tolerance and range readings later in this lab. In the first

can be substituted, and most science equipment suppliers sell equivalent electronic learning kits.

- If you are using a different electronics kit, make a conversion chart for the corresponding terminal numbers in the Learning Center and your electronics lab. Provide students with the substitute terminal list so that they can fill in the blanks in the procedure.

Procedure

- For maximum effectiveness, students should follow the procedure in the order in which it is written.

- Check the calculation of meter tolerance in Table 1 during the lab. The recommended multimeter has two resistance scale tolerances, so verify that the students are using the correct value.

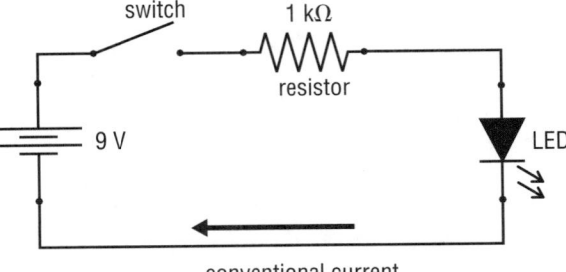

Figure 5

Home School Notes

- While it is possible to construct a suitable homemade electronics breadboard, the cost and time consumed doing so may be prohibitive.

- You will need the following components to duplicate the features of the Elenco Learning Center:

LEDs, red (includes two 100 Ω protective resistors)	2
speaker, small	1
diode	1
transistors, NPN	3
transformer, 3-tap, small	1
battery holder, 9 V	1
capacitor, tuning	1
capacitors (0.0047 µF, 0.047 µF, 10 µF, 100 µF)	1 ea.
resistors (470 Ω, 1 kΩ, 3.3 kΩ, 10 kΩ, 33 kΩ, 100 kΩ, 1 MΩ)	1 ea.
resistor, variable, 0 Ω to 50 kΩ	1

switch, push-button   1
antenna, air core wire wound 1

- Attach the components on a sufficiently large Masonite Peg-Board, using small bolts and nuts. The electrical connections should be soldered.

- Obtain a spool of 18- to 24-gauge insulated wire, cut it into various lengths in sufficient numbers to complete the labs. Strip approximately 1 cm of insulation from each end. "Tin" twisted wire ends by melting solder into the strands of wire to make them more resistant to damage from use.

- Any true multimeter will suffice. The Elenco multimeter is very economical.

circuit, you connected a resistor in series with the LED in order to reduce the current just enough to protect the LED.

11. Remove the wires from the 1 kΩ resistor (40 ____ and 41 ____) and move them to the 100 kΩ resistor (51 ____ and 52 ____).

12. Press the switch and notice the difference in the brightness of the LED. Record your observation.

    The LED is noticeably dimmer.

    You may need to cup your hand over the LED to see that it is lighted because the 100 kΩ resistor reduces the flow of electrons so much that the LED emits very little light.

13. Try each of the resistors on your board to see how the brightness of the LED varies with each. **Caution:** Do not press the switch for very long at a time when testing the lower-value resistors. Otherwise, you could burn out the LED. When you are finished, reconnect the 1 kΩ resistor (40 ____ and 41 ____).

14. Remove the wire from terminal 40 (____). Press the switch. Reconnect the wire and then remove the wire from terminal 41 (____). Press the switch. Reconnect the wire and then remove the wire from terminal 3 (____). Press the switch. Reconnect the wire and then remove the wire from terminal 4 (____). Press the switch. Reconnect the wire and then remove the wire from terminal 26 (____). Press the switch. Summarize your observations.

    Disconnecting any part of the circuit prevents the LED from lighting.

15. After you finish, remove all wires from the Learning Center.

Table 1
Resistance Data

Resistance	470 Ω	1 kΩ	3.3 kΩ	10 kΩ	33 kΩ	100 kΩ	1 MΩ
Color Code	470 Ω	1×10^3 Ω	33×10^2 Ω	1×10^4 Ω	33×10^3 Ω	1×10^5 Ω	1×10^6 Ω
Tolerance ±	24 Ω	50 Ω	170 Ω	500 Ω	1700 Ω	5000 Ω	50 000 Ω
Range	446 Ω to 494 Ω	950 Ω to 1050 Ω	3130 Ω to 3470 Ω	9500 Ω to 10 500 Ω	31 300 Ω to 34 700 Ω	95 000 Ω to 105 000 Ω	950 000 Ω to 1 050 000 Ω
Meter Reading	459 Ω	986 Ω	3.24 kΩ	9.82 kΩ	32.3 kΩ	98.1 kΩ	1012 kΩ
Tolerance ±	4 Ω	8 Ω	0.03 kΩ	0.08 kΩ	0.3 kΩ	0.8 kΩ	10 kΩ
Range	455 Ω to 463 Ω	978 Ω to 994 Ω	3.21 kΩ to 3.27 kΩ	9.74 kΩ to 9.90 kΩ	32.0 kΩ to 32.6 kΩ	97.3 kΩ to 98.9 kΩ	1002 kΩ to 1022 kΩ

Color code values are obtained from Learning Center resistors. Meter values are typical.

Using an Ohmmeter

An ohmmeter is a device used to experimentally determine the resistance of a circuit component or of several components connected together. To determine the resistance, the electrical element must be disconnected from the circuit because the ohmmeter has its own power supply.

Note: If you are using a meter other than the Elenco M-1000B, you will need to adjust the directions to comply with the meter that you are using. Follow the instructions that come with your particular meter.

The recommended instrument you will use is called a **multimeter.** This electrical test instrument can function as several instruments in one. Plug in the cables, or **test leads,** of the meter. The *red* test lead should be plugged into the connector marked VΩmA. The *black* test lead should be plugged into the connector marked COM, which stands for *common.* Always plug the test leads into these connectors when using the multimeter as an ohmmeter. The center dial selector switch of your meter should also be placed in the ohmmeter mode.

16. Turn it to the left past the scale labeled DCV to the scale labeled Ω. Stop at the 2000K position. The number indicates the *maximum* resistance value that can be read at this particular scale setting.

17. Touch one of the test probes to terminal 53 (＿＿＿) of the 1 MΩ resistor and the other test probe to terminal 54 (＿＿＿). Record the meter reading in Table 1.

Observe that moving the selector switch to the 200K position while testing the 1 MΩ resistor causes the meter to display a 1 in the window. This indicates that the meter scale setting is less than the resistance being measured. Selecting 20K, 2000, or 200 does not alter the reading but simply moves the decimal point placement in the display. As long as the 1 remains in the display, the meter's resistance scale setting is less than the value for the resistor.

The display reading on the meter will have the same metric unit prefix as the prefix indicated on the scale. A K indicates readings that are measured in thousands of ohms, or kΩ. If there is no prefix, the units will be Ω. A reading of "998" in the display when the selector switch is pointing to the 2000K setting would be recorded as 998 kΩ. A reading of "000" in the 200K setting would indicate that the resistor has a value less than 1000 Ω (1 kΩ) and that you need to switch to a smaller scale in order to obtain a reading. The 2000 setting has no prefix, so a reading of "998" in this position would be recorded as 998 Ω. Notice that the meter display with the 200 scale is precise to tenths of an ohm.

When testing a resistor, always set the meter at the highest scale position; then sequentially switch through the lower scales until the window displays an out-of-range reading (1). Switch back to the next higher scale and use the display value and the metric prefix from that position.

All meters have an **instrument tolerance** that indicates the maximum expected variation of the display from the actual value being measured. It is usually found in the instruction manual. If you are using the Elenco M-1000B meter, the tolerance is ±1% for the 2000K scale and ±0.8% for all other resistance scales. Notice that these tolerances are smaller than the manufacturer's tolerance indicated by the resistor color code (5%). Consequently, you can determine a resistor's actual value more accurately. Multiply the meter resistance reading by the meter tolerance; then calculate the possible resistance range by adding the calculated tolerance to the meter reading for the higher limit and subtracting it from the meter reading for the lower limit.

18. Determine the resistance of each of the resistors in the Learning Center, using the ohmmeter. Record the values in Table 1 in the Meter Reading row. Include a "k" if the display value requires it.

19. Calculate the meter tolerance of the measured resistance for each of the resistors in the Learning Center. Round the tolerance to the decimal place of the least significant digit of the meter reading. Record the tolerance values in Table 1.

20. Calculate the lower and upper resistance limits based on meter tolerance for each resistor and record the ranges in Table 1.

Variable Resistors

It is often desirable to use a variable resistor to adjust a circuit. Circuits with variable resistor elements help control volume in your radio and TV and function as light dimmers. As the name implies, the resistance can be adjusted from a maximum value to a minimum value.

21. Using a no. 2 or softer pencil, fill in the box below. Press fairly hard and make the area as dark as possible.

```
┌────────────────────────────────────────┐
│                                        │
└────────────────────────────────────────┘
```

22. Select 2000K on the Ω scale of the multimeter. Place the black test probe of your meter at one end of the shaded area and the red probe at the other end. Notice the reading. Slowly move the red probe toward the black probe, keeping it within the shaded area at all times. Pressing the *side* of the metal probe against the graphite will improve electrical contact. Record your observations.

    The display resistance readings decrease as the probes get closer

    together.

23. The variable resistor on the Learning Center works in a similar manner. Pages 10–11 of the Learning Center manual discuss the variable resistor. Learn the schematic symbol for a variable resistor.

24. Insert the red test probe into terminal 48 (____) on the Learning Center and the black test probe into 49 (____).

25. The variable resistor is labeled 50KΩ, so set the selector switch of your meter to the appropriate position to read that value. Rotate the resistor knob clockwise and then counterclockwise. Record your observations.

    (Answers may vary.) The meter display changes from approximately

    50 kΩ to 0 Ω and back to approximately 50 kΩ as the resistor knob

    is turned.

26. Move the red test lead to terminal 50 (____) and turn the resistor knob clockwise, then counterclockwise. Record your observations.

    (Answers may vary.) The meter changes from 0 Ω to approximately

    50 kΩ when the resistor knob is turned. The variation is the opposite

    of what is recorded in Step 25.

Notice that the numbers on the resistor scale do not indicate ohms but rather a percent of the total 50 kΩ resistance. Some resistors may be installed backward compared to the scale on the Learning Center. Inform your teacher so that the scale can be corrected.

27. Insert the black test probe into terminal 50 (____) and the red probe into 48 (____). Turn the resistor knob clockwise and then counterclockwise. Record your observations.

    The meter reads approximately 50 kΩ and does not change as the

    resistor knob is turned.

From the diagram on page 11 in the Learning Center manual, you should be able to explain why there is no change in the reading when the dial is moved.

28. Connect the circuit shown in Figure 6. Follow the schematic carefully.

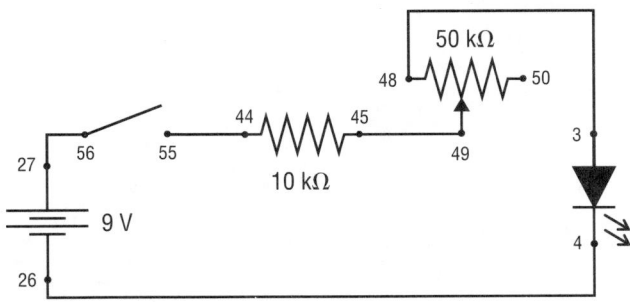

Figure 6

29. Press the switch and rotate the knob on the variable resistor. Observe and record what happens to the brightness of the LED.

    The LED gets brighter as the resistor is turned to minimum resis-

    tance and dimmer as it is turned the other way.

30. Move the wire from 49 (____) to 50 (____). Repeat Step 29 and describe what happens when the knob is rotated.

    The LED does not respond when the dial is rotated; it remains the

    same brightness. Terminals 48 and 50 are not connected to the vari-

    able part of the resistor. It works like any other resistor.

Some variable resistors are designed in such a way that three terminals can be used to increase the current in one branch and to decrease the current in another branch at the same time. These resistors are often called **potentiometers,** or "pots" for short.

31. Move the wire from terminal 50 (____) back to 49 (____) as in Figure 6. Connect a wire from terminal 50 (____) to LED 1 terminal 1 (____). Then connect another wire from terminal 2 (____) to the negative terminal of the battery (26 ____).

32. Press the switch and turn the knob on the variable resistor. Describe your observations.

    One bulb gets brighter as the dial is turned from maximum to mini-

    mum resistance while the other bulb gets dimmer. When the dial is

    turned the other way, the opposite occurs.

33. Remove all of the wires from the Learning Center and turn off the multimeter.

Name _____

Date _____ Hour _____

PRELAB HOMEWORK

1. What does the schematic in Figure 7 represent? Include in your answer any values that you can determine.

   The schematic represents two 9 V batteries in series.
   _____

2. Name two kinds of devices that protect a circuit from an overload condition.

   The two protective devices are fuses and circuit breakers.
   _____

3. What is a schematic diagram?

   A schematic diagram is a simplified representation of a complex system,

   using symbols to represent components of the system.

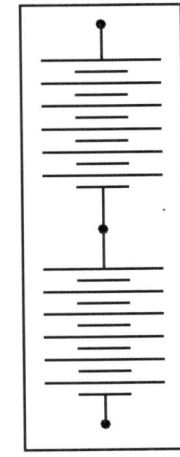

Figure 7

4. Name the following electrical components.

   a.  resistor

   d. terminal (junction)

   b. light-emitting diode

   e. switch

   c. 1.5 V cell

   f. variable resistor

   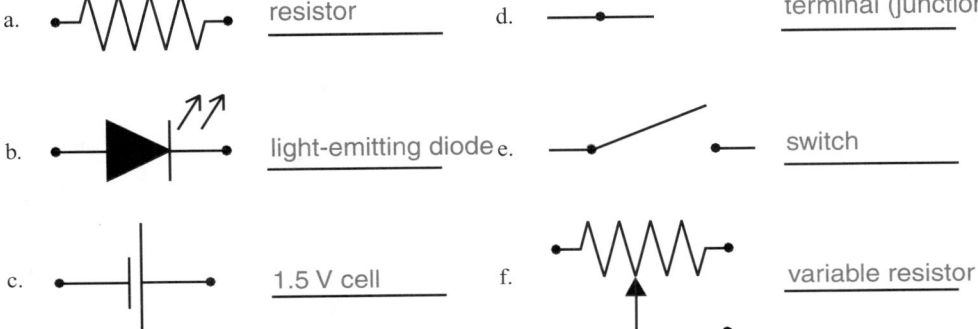

5. What preventive measure is necessary when connecting an LED in a circuit? Why?

   An LED must always be connected in series with a resistor to protect it from

   excessive current (to avoid burning it out).

6. Describe conventional current flow.

   Conventional current flow occurs in the opposite direction from electron flow in a

   circuit.

7. What is the value of a resistor having the following color bands?

   a. red, yellow, orange, gold ___24 kΩ___   c. blue, violet, gold, gold ___6.7 Ω___

   b. brown, green, violet, gold ___150 MΩ___   d. orange, white, yellow, gold ___390 kΩ___

8. What does tolerance mean in reference to the color code value of a resistor? What is the tolerance of the Elenco Learning Center resistors?

   Resistor tolerance is the variation allowed for the actual resistance value from the

   color code value, expressed as a percentage of the color code value. The toler-

   ance of the Learning Center resistors is ±5%.

9. What does tolerance mean when referring to a test meter's displayed reading? What is the tolerance of the meter for resistance readings?

Meter tolerance is the maximum expected variation of the displayed value from the value actually being measured; it is expressed as a percentage of the displayed value. The tolerance is ±1% for the 2000K scale and ±0.8% for all other scales.

10. What must you do to an electrical component before you can measure its resistance?

The component must be disconnected from the circuit before measuring its resistance.

Name _____

Date _____ Hour _____

SERIES CIRCUITS

Purpose

This lab continues familiarization with basic DC circuits. The purpose is to

- provide practice connecting series circuits.
- become familiar with the function and use of voltmeters, ohmmeters, and ammeters.
- practice reading and sketching schematic diagrams.

Prelab Discussion

Simple circuits may be classified as **series** or **parallel.** Series circuits are circuits in which current has only one path to follow. Interrupting a series circuit anywhere in the circuit stops the flow of current in the entire circuit. Parallel circuits allow current to branch so that there is more than one path for it to follow. Most circuits are combinations of both series and parallel circuits; these combinations are often referred to as **series-parallel** circuits.

It would be awkward if all of the lights in your house went out every time a light bulb burned out. It would also be difficult to control a reading light if the light got dimmer every time someone turned on another light in the house. For this reason, lights in your home are connected in parallel rather than in series. Switches, on the other hand, are designed to turn off one or more lights, so switches are always connected in series with the light(s).

In Lab 4-2, you used the multimeter as an ohmmeter. Your multimeter can also be used as a **voltmeter.** Review the theory and usage of voltmeters in Appendix E of this manual. **Voltage** can be considered "electrical pressure." It follows the water analogy discussed in the Learning Center manual even though the concept is not entirely accurate. Recognize that the water analogy simply helps you understand some of the electrical terminology; it is not meant to be a literal description of how electricity works. You would do better to think of voltage as a *drop in electrical potential* as the current flows through a circuit. If voltage is 9 V at the positive terminal of a battery connected to a circuit, you would expect current to flow down the "voltage hill" to zero potential (0 V) at the negative terminal of the battery. Recall that conventional current flows from positive to negative.

The electrical potential change across a resistance in a circuit is often referred to as **voltage drop.** The voltage drop is the same across all components in the parallel-connected portion of a circuit. *The total voltage drop in a series-connected circuit, however, is the sum of the voltage drops across each resistance.* The analogy of the potential energy of a river illustrates the principle well. The river has great potential energy high in the mountains. The potential decreases as the river flows downhill until the potential becomes zero at sea level. Think of each resistor as a large waterfall. The potential energy is greater at the top and lower at the bottom. There may be many waterfalls in a river on its trip from the mountain heights to sea level. The river may even have many tributaries (similar to parallel circuits). The potential is related to the distance above sea level, so at any particular height, the potential energy is always the same in each tributary.

Current is the rate of flow of charge through an electrical path. In a series circuit there is only one path for current, so the current is the same in all components of a series-connected circuit. You will verify this statement in this exercise. Current is measured with a device called an **ammeter.** A multimeter can function as an ammeter as well as an ohmmeter and voltmeter. Review the theory and use of ammeters in Appendix E. To prepare the Elenco multimeter as an ammeter, plug the black test lead into the COM connection and the red lead into the 10ADC (10 amps DC) connection. Set the selector switch to the 10A position (see Figure 1). Notice that the

Required Equipment

Elenco Learning Center kit
Elenco M-1000B multimeter

Prelab Discussion

- Review the prerequisites for Lab 4-3 in the back of this manual.

- Have students read page 13 in the Learning Center manual with emphasis on the water flow analogy.

- Review the operation of the Elenco M-1000B multimeter, referring to Appendix E in the back of this manual. If you are using a different meter or several meters, be sure to explain the differences in operation.

Equipment and Setup

- The equipment used in this lab is the same as the equipment used in Lab 4-2.

- If you must use an electronics lab kit different from the Elenco Learning Center, see the note regarding terminal numbers in Lab 4-2.

- If you use a different kit, the resistor values will likely be different from

© Elenco Electronics Inc. Used by permission.

Figure 1

those specified in this lab. Revise the procedure and verify that the lab works prior to performing it in class.

• It is recommended that spare fuses for the multimeters be available in the event that a meter is connected across a battery. Fuse specifications are given in the manual for the meter.

Procedure

• Monitor the use of the multimeters during the lab to ensure that the proper readings are being obtained and that the meters are not being damaged.

• When measuring current, it is best to push the tip of the test probe through the side of the spring terminals between the coils to ensure good electrical contact. Just inserting the probe into the top of the terminal will probably produce unstable readings.

• Some multimeters that normally select an appropriate scale automatically (autorange) can be manually set to read a particular scale. The meter's instruction manual will describe how to inactivate the autoranging feature.

• The values of current and voltage drop given in the Teacher's Edition will vary with battery voltage; they are provided primarily to show the expected arrangement of displayed digits.

• In the last circuit connected in the procedure, current is measured before and after the components. Help your students streamline these measurements even more than indicated in Step 49 as follows. Note that the "after" battery reading is also the "before" reading for the 1 kΩ resistor and that the "after" reading for the 33 kΩ resistor is the "before" reading for the battery. The "before" and "after" readings for the battery are also the combined current readings for the three resistors as well as for the circuit.

Home School Notes

• Refer to the Lab 4-2 Home School Notes for information about constructing an electrical breadboard similar to the Elenco Learning Center kit.

VΩmA connection on the multimeter that you used for measuring resistance includes milliamps (mA). The VΩmA connection is used for measuring very small currents. If you are not sure of the magnitude of the current to be measured, always use the 10ADC connection first. Then if the current is too small to register on the display when the meter is set to 10ADC, unplug the red test lead, insert it into the VΩmA connection, and turn the selector switch to a DCA scale setting.

Resistance in a series circuit branch is the sum of the resistances in each of the individual resistors. In the next lab you will learn how to determine the total resistance for parallel-connected resistors. You are already aware that resistance is measured with an ohmmeter and that an element should be disconnected from the circuit when measuring resistance.

Procedure

Resistors in Series

1. Insert the test leads of your multimeter for use as an ohmmeter. Review Appendix E for the proper use of ohmmeters.

2. Measure the resistances of the 470 Ω and 1 kΩ resistors, using the methods learned in Lab 4-2. Adjust the meter selector to display the maximum number of significant digits possible for each resistance. Record the measured resistance values.

470 Ω __470 Ω (±24 Ω)__

1 kΩ __1000 Ω (±50 Ω)__ (Both readings use the 2000 scale.)

3. Connect a wire from terminal 39 (___) to 41 (___). Insert the red test probe into 38 (___) and the black test probe into 40 (___). The resistors and ohmmeter form a series circuit in which the ohmmeter supplies the voltage that produces current in the circuit. Record the resistance displayed by the meter.

__1470 Ω (±74 Ω)__ (2000 scale)

You should find the display to be close to the sum of the two readings that you recorded in Step 2. The water diagram on page 13 in the Learning Center manual will help you understand why this is so.

4. Draw a circuit diagram for the connection in Step 3. Recall that the symbol for an ohmmeter is a circle with the letter O in its center.

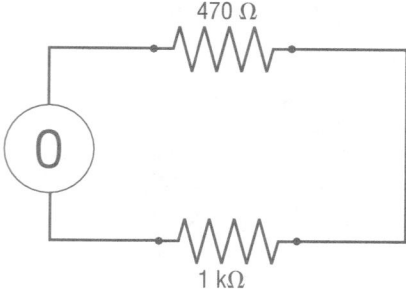

5. Remove the black test lead from terminal 40 (___). Connect a wire from 40 (___) to 42 (___). The wire from 39 (___) to 41 (___) will remain connected. Now insert the black test probe into 43 (___) and the red probe into 38 (___). Adjust the scale selector as required and record the meter reading.

__4.77 kΩ (±0.24 kΩ)__ (20K scale)

Notice the circuit path: from the meter through the 3.3 kΩ resistor, through the 1 kΩ resistor, through the 470 Ω resistor, and then back to the meter. The current must flow through each resistor in order to return to the meter. This is also a series circuit. You should note that the total resistance is the sum of the three resistors.

6. Draw a circuit diagram for the connection in Step 5.

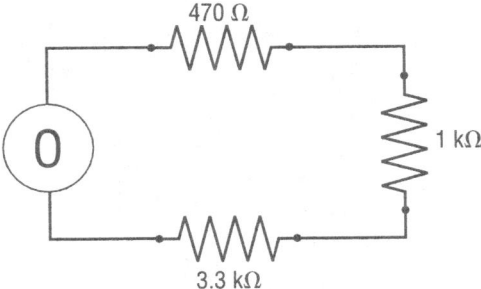

7. Disconnect all of the wires from your circuit board and connect the circuit shown in Figure 2.

8. Press the switch and record your observations.

   The LED lights up, but it is very dim.

9. Switch the wires so that the components follow the sequence 3.3 kΩ resistor-100 kΩ resistor-LED.

10. Press the switch and record your observations.

    There is no visible difference in the brightness of the LED.

11. Switch the wires so that the order of components is 3.3 kΩ resistor-LED-100 kΩ resistor.

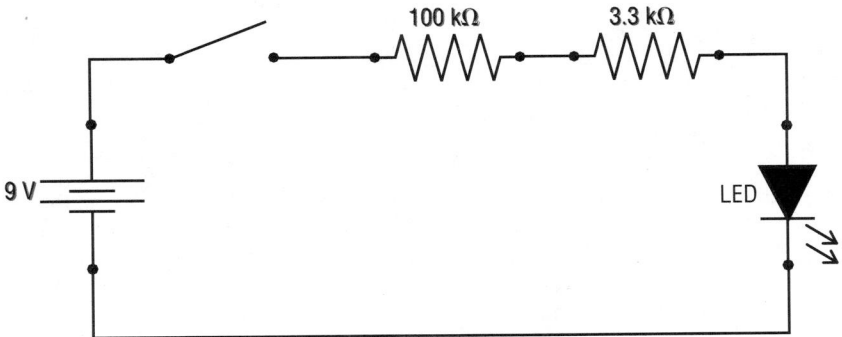

Figure 2

12. Press the switch and record your observations.

    There is no visible difference in the brightness of the LED.

13. Switch the wires so that the order of components is LED-3.3 kΩ resistor-100 kΩ resistor.

14. Press the switch and record your observations.

    There is no visible difference in the brightness of the LED.

Notice that in the series circuit, it makes no difference where the resistors are located because the current is the same throughout a series circuit.

Current Measurement in Series Circuits

Before proceeding, review the precautions for connecting ammeters in Appendix E.

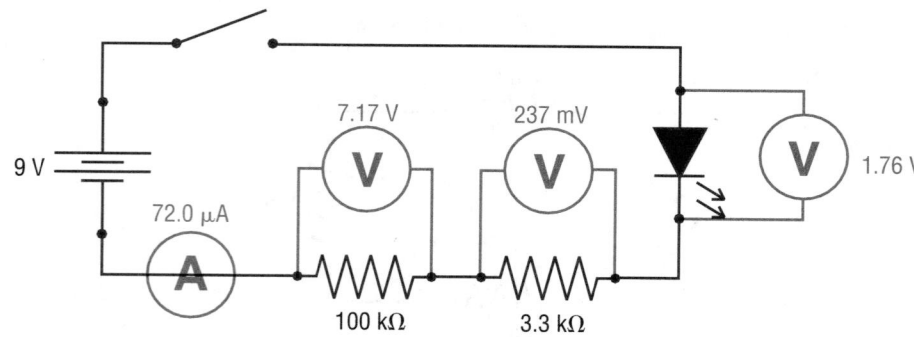

Measured values are typical. Actual values will vary.

Figure 3

15. The Learning Center should still be connected as in Figure 3. To use your multimeter as an ammeter, plug the black test lead into the COM connection and the red lead into the 10ADC connection. Set the selector switch to the 10A position.

16. Disconnect the wire from the battery (27 ____) to the switch (56 ____). Insert the red probe of the ammeter into the battery terminal (27 ____). Insert the black probe into the switch terminal (56 ____). The red lead is always connected to the positive end of an electrical circuit.

    Note: If your multimeter is an "autoranging" instrument that automatically selects the most useful scale, skip Steps 17–22. If you are not sure, ask your teacher.

17. Press the switch. Observe the LED as well as the meter. Record your observations and the reading on the ammeter.

    The LED illuminates. The meter display is 0.00 (A).

    The meter reads zero because the current is too small to register on the 10A scale setting. The LED should illuminate because the current is still able to pass through the meter. You will not have to use the 10A position in the remaining experiments with the Learning Center because all of the currents will be very small.

18. Unplug the red test lead and plug it into the VΩmA connection. Move the meter selector switch to the 200m position.

19. Press the switch. Observe the LED as well as the meter. Record your observations and the reading on the ammeter.

    The LED illuminates. The meter displays 00.0 (mA).

    A reading was not obtained at this position because the current is less than 0.1 mA. Observe the tenths decimal place in the meter window.

20. Move the meter selector switch to the next lower position (20m). Press the switch and observe the LED as well as the meter. Record your observations.

    The LED illuminates. The meter displays ~0.07 (mA).

    A reading is obtained on the 20m scale, but not the 3 SDs that should be visible.

21. Move the meter selector switch to the next lower setting (2000μ). Press the switch and observe the LED as well as the meter. Record your observations.

    The LED illuminates. The meter displays ~072 (μA).

    Again, a reading is obtained, but still not the 3 SDs that should be visible.

22. Move the meter selector switch to the next lower position (200μ). Press the switch and observe the LED as well as the meter. Record your observations.

    The LED illuminates. The meter displays ~72.0 (μA).

    Now there should be a 3 SD reading. The display should be approximately 75 μA. Notice that the symbol following the numerical selector switch setting is used as a prefix with the symbol for the ampere.

23. Disconnect the ammeter and reconnect the wire to terminals 27 (____) and 56 (____).

24. Remove the wire between the *negative* terminal of the battery (26 ____) and the 100 kΩ resistor. Insert the red test probe of the ammeter into the resistor terminal (on the positive side of the circuit) and the black probe into the negative battery terminal.

25. Press the switch and record your observations.

    The LED illuminates. The meter displays ~72.0 (μA).

    This reading should be the same as the previous reading because the current throughout a series circuit is the same.

26. Disconnect the meter and reconnect the wire removed in Step 24.

27. Remove the wire between the two resistors and connect the ammeter to those terminals, observing the proper polarity (black to the negative terminal and red to the positive terminal).

28. How does the current compare to that measured in Steps 22 and 25?

    The current should be the same.

29. Reconnect the wire between the two resistors.

30. The schematic symbol for an ammeter is a circle with the letter A inside it. In Figure 3, add the ammeter connected to the circuit in Step 24. Write the value that you observed on the ammeter above or below the symbol.

Voltage Measurement in Series Circuits

In this part you will measure the voltage drops across the components in a circuit.

31. Your circuit should be connected like the schematic in Figure 3. Press the switch to verify that the LED illuminates.

32. Set your multimeter to read voltage by turning the selector switch to the 20 position on the DCV scale.

33. Insert the red test probe into the terminal of the 3.3 kΩ resistor that is nearest the positive end of the circuit. Insert the black probe into the other terminal of the 3.3 kΩ resistor.

34. Press the switch. Notice that you must keep the wires connected and that the circuit must be energized when checking voltage drop. Record the meter display.

    The reading should be ~0.23 (V).

    If there is a negative sign visible in the display, the connections are reversed. Swap the test lead connections and check the voltage again. At this setting, only 2 SDs are displayed.

If there is a negative sign visible in the display, the connections are reversed. Swap the test lead connections and check the voltage again. At this setting, only 2 SDs are displayed.

35. Move the selector switch to the next lower position (2000m). Press the switch and record the meter display.

The reading should be ~237 (mV).

36. To check the voltage drop across the 100 kΩ resistor, set the meter selector switch back to 20 (DCV), and insert the red test probe into the terminal nearest the positive battery terminal (via the circuit) and the black probe into the other terminal.

37. Press the switch and record the reading.

The reading should be ~7.17 (V).

Notice that the larger resistor has a larger voltage drop than the smaller resistor. Next, the total voltage drop across both resistors will be determined.

38. Insert the black test probe into the terminal on the 100 kΩ resistor nearest the battery and the red probe into the terminal on the 3.3 kΩ resistor nearest to the LED.

39. Press the switch and record the displayed reading.

The reading should be ~7.41 (V).

You should observe that this is the sum of the voltage drops across each individual resistor.

40. Determine the voltage drop across the LED by inserting the red probe into the terminal closest to the positive terminal of the battery and the black probe into the other terminal.

41. Press the switch and record the displayed reading.

The reading should be ~1.76 (V).

42. Measure the voltage drop across the battery (red probe inserted into the positive terminal). Record the meter display.

The reading should be ~9.17 (V).

43. Are the voltage drops the same across all components of a series circuit?

no

44. Add together the voltage drops across the 3.3 kΩ resistor, the 100 kΩ resistor, and the LED. Record the sum.

The reading should be ~9.17 (V).

45. How does this value compare to the terminal voltage?

It should be the same.

Note that the sum of the voltages across each component in the series circuit is the same as the total voltage supplied to the entire circuit. The water analogy will help you remember that the current is the same in all parts of a series circuit and that the total voltage drop is the sum of the voltage drops across each resistance.

46. The schematic symbol for a voltmeter is a circle with the letter V inside the circle. In Figure 3, sketch three voltmeters connected to measure the voltage drops across the two resistors and the LED. Remember that the symbols for the voltmeters should indicate that they are connected in parallel.

From Theory to Practice with Series Circuits

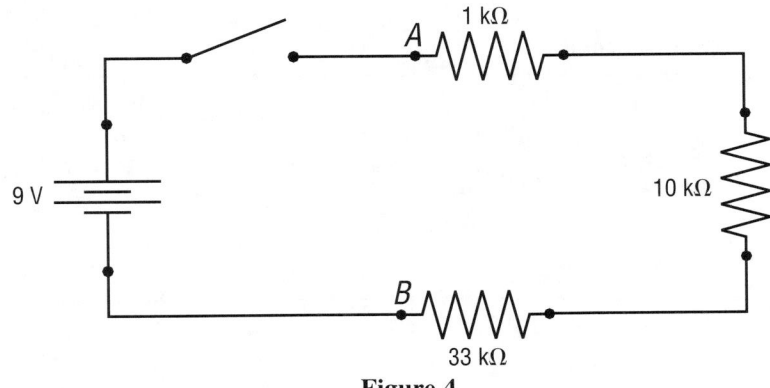

Figure 4

47. Connect the Learning Center as shown in Figure 4. Note that there is not an LED in the circuit.

48. Measure the resistance of each resistor in the circuit. Use the procedures you have learned in order to select the correct resistance scale. Remember that each resistor must be disconnected from the circuit in turn and that the circuit switch is not pressed for this check.

    a. Record the values of the resistors in Table 1.

    b. To test the resistance across all three of the resistors together, leave the wires connected between them (but disconnect the end resistors from the circuit) and touch the ohmmeter probes to the terminals at points A and B in Figure 4. Record this value as the measured resistance for the three combined resistors in Table 1.

    c. The total circuit resistance in Table 1 is the sum of the three individual resistances recorded in Step 48a.

49. Reconnect the resistors (see Figure 4) and measure the current passing through each resistor. Press the switch for each check.

    Caution: Connecting the ammeter across the terminals of the battery places it in parallel with the rest of the circuit. Since the circuit has more resistance than the meter, a large current will pass through the meter, and its protective fuse will blow.

    a. Two measurements will be made by connecting the meter "before" the component (on the positive side) and "after" the component (on the negative side). Note that the "after" measurements for the first and second resistors are the "before" measurements for second and third resistors, respectively.

    b. Remember that the ammeter must be connected in series with the resistor.

    c. Start with a higher scale setting on the DCA scale; then lower the setting until the meter displays 3 SDs.

    d. Measure the total circuit current in Table 1 on both sides of the battery.

    e. Record the "before" and "after" readings in Table 1 for each resistor.

50. Measure the individual voltage drops across the three resistors and their combined voltage drop. Press the switch for each check.

    a. Determine the combined voltage drop by touching the same two terminals that you used for checking combined resistance.

    b. Measure the total circuit voltage drop in Table 1 at the battery terminals.

    c. Record the respective readings in Table 1.

51. When you have finished taking measurements, disconnect all wires from the Learning Center and switch the multimeter off.

Data

Table 1
Series Circuit Resistance, Current, and Voltage Data and Calculations

Circuit Component	Measured Resistance, R_m	Measured Current, I_m Before	Measured Current, I_m After	Measured Voltage Drop, V_m	Calculated Current, $I_c = V_m/R_m$	Calculated Voltage Drop, $V_c = I_{m\,av}R_m$
1 kΩ	988 (Ω)	223 (μA)	223 (μA)	219 (mV)	222 μA	220 mV
10 kΩ	9.80 (kΩ)	223 (μA)	223 (μA)	2.16 (V)	220 μA	2.19 V
33 kΩ	32.1 (kΩ)	223 (μA)	222 (μA)	7.09 (V)	221 μA	7.16 V
3 Combined Resistors	42.9 (kΩ)	223 (μA)	222 (μA)	9.54 (V)	222 μA	9.57 V
Total Circuit	42.9 (kΩ)	223 (μA)	222 (μA)	9.55 (V)	223 μA	9.57 V

Data in Table 1 is typical. Actual data and calculations will vary.

Postlab Exercises

1. Calculate the current flowing through each part of the circuit listed in Table 1. Use the measured values for resistance and voltage drop in your calculations. Record the calculated currents in Table 1.

2. Calculate the voltage drop across each part of the circuit listed in Table 1. Use the measured values of resistance and the *average* of the "before" and "after" measured currents for each. Record the calculated voltage drops in Table 1.

Postlab Analysis

1. Within experimental accuracy, how did the total resistance in the circuit connected according to Figure 4 relate to the individual component resistances?

   The total resistance was equal to the sum of the individual resistances.

2. Within experimental accuracy, how did the current measured in the series circuit vary from component to component?

   The current was the same throughout the circuit.

3. Within experimental accuracy, how did the total voltage drop across the series circuit relate to the individual voltage drops of the circuit components?

   The total voltage drop across the circuit was equal to the sum of the individual voltage drops across the components.

4. Assume that you are required to measure the current through a resistor in an important circuit. You can see the resistor on the circuit board, and you can make any necessary measurements at its terminals, but you cannot disconnect the resistor or turn the circuit off. Describe how you could make the determination under these circumstances, using only a multimeter.

   The voltage drop across the resistor could be measured with the multimeter. The resistor value could be determined from the color code on the resistor. The current could then be calculated from $I = V/R$.

Name _____

Date _____ Hour _____

PRELAB HOMEWORK

1. Compare a series-connected circuit to a parallel-connected circuit.

   A series-connected circuit consists of a single path for current to pass through the
   components. A parallel-connected circuit has two or more paths for current to
   pass from one point to another in the circuit.

2. Describe the only case in which the voltage drops across each of the individual components in a series circuit would be equal.

   The voltage drop would be equal only if the resistances of all of the components
   were equal.

3. A voltage drop is more correctly referred to as a decrease in __electrical potential__.

4. Potential difference across a resistor is measured with a(n) __voltmeter__.

5. Describe how a voltmeter is connected to a component, the connection of the component, and the condition of the circuit (energized or de-energized) to measure the voltage drop across the component.

   A voltmeter is connected in parallel with the component. The component is
   connected to the circuit, and the circuit is energized.

6. What does the expression "the highest scale setting" refer to on a voltmeter or ammeter? What are some potential problems encountered when trying to measure a quantity greater than the scale setting selected?

   The highest scale setting is the maximum value (e.g., voltage) that can be measured and displayed by the meter. If the quantity is larger than the scale selected,
   the meter display will not show a meaningful value. If voltage or current is *much*
   larger than the scale selected, the meter could be damaged.

7. The rate of flow for charges through a circuit component is measured by a(n)
   __ammeter__.

8. Describe how an ohmmeter is connected to a component, the connection of the component, and the condition of the circuit (energized or de-energized) to measure the resistance of the component.

   An ohmmeter is connected in parallel with the component. The component should
   be disconnected from the circuit, and the circuit is de-energized.

9. Describe how an ammeter is connected to a component, the connection of the component, and the condition of the circuit (energized or de-energized) to measure the current through a circuit component.

   An ammeter is connected in series with the component. The component is connected to the circuit, and the circuit is energized.

10. Describe how the total resistance of the components in a series circuit is determined.

    Total resistance in a series circuit is determined by adding all of the individual
    resistances together or by measuring the combined resistances as a unit.

11. Describe how the total current in a series circuit is determined by direct measurement.
    <u>The current may be measured at any point in the circuit. It will be the same</u>
    <u>throughout the circuit.</u>

12. Describe how the total voltage drop in a series circuit is determined.
    <u>Total voltage drop in a series circuit is determined by adding all of the individual</u>
    <u>voltage drops together or by measuring the combined voltage drop of the compo-</u>
    <u>nents as a unit.</u>

13. Explain why you would *not* want to touch both terminals of the battery with the test leads of an ammeter.
    <u>Ammeters have very low resistances, so a very high current would result, blowing</u>
    <u>the protective fuse and possibly damaging the meter.</u>

Name _____

Date _____ Hour _____

PARALLEL CIRCUITS

Purpose

This lab investigates parallel DC circuits. The purpose is to

- demonstrate the connection of parallel circuits.
- provide additional practice using ohmmeters, ammeters, and voltmeters.
- demonstrate the properties of parallel circuits.
- practice reading and sketching electrical schematics.

Required Equipment
Elenco Learning Center kit
Elenco M-1000B multimeter

Prelab Discussion

Review pages 14–15 in your Learning Center manual. Be sure that you understand the material covered on those pages as well as the material presented in the Prelab Discussion of Lab 4-3 before proceeding with this lab.

In Lab 4-3, you demonstrated that the current flowing in a circuit, the battery voltage applied to the circuit, and the total resistance in the circuit are related by Ohm's law ($V = IR$). You also learned that the total resistance in a series circuit is the sum of the individual resistances of the series components. Some of these principles can be applied to parallel circuits, but there are some significant differences.

Prelab Discussion

- Review the prerequisites for Lab 4-4 in the back of this manual.

- Review the teacher's notes for Lab 4-3. The theoretical basis for this lab is essentially the same as the previous lab, and the instructions and precautions are appropriate for both.

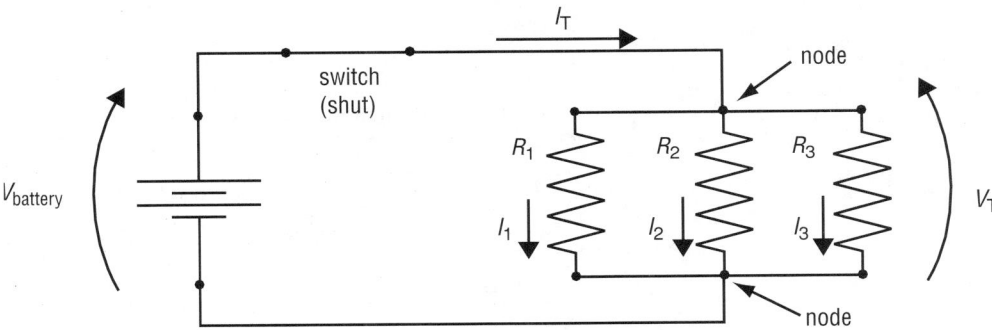

Figure 1

Refer to Figure 1 for the following discussion. The three resistors R_1, R_2, and R_3 are connected in parallel. You will assume that the wires connecting the components and the switch have no resistance. You can see that the voltage drop across each resistor is equal in magnitude to the battery voltage. Therefore,

$$V_T = V_1 = V_2 = V_3 = V_{battery}. \tag{1}$$

The current flowing out of the battery must split up when it comes to the point where the parallel resistances are connected (a **node**). After passing through the resistors, the current recombines at another node and returns to the battery. The principle stating that the sum of the currents entering a node must equal the sum of the currents leaving the node is called **Kirchoff's law.** The total current in the circuit, I_T, is equal to the sum of the individual currents flowing through the resistors. Since the resistance and the voltage drop for each resistor are known, the resistor currents can be determined by Ohm's law. Mathematically,

$$I_T = I_1 + I_2 + I_3 = \frac{V_1}{R_1} + \frac{V_2}{R_2} + \frac{V_3}{R_3}. \tag{2}$$

The total current in the circuit can also be calculated from Ohm's law, using the total voltage drop and the total resistance in the circuit. Equating this relationship with Equation (2) gives

$$I_T = \frac{V_T}{R_T} = \frac{V_1}{R_1} + \frac{V_2}{R_2} + \frac{V_3}{R_3}. \tag{3}$$

Equipment and Setup

- See Lab 4-3.

Procedure

- Measuring current through components in the Elenco kit can be tricky. If the ammeter display continuously changes and does not settle down to a constant value, then there is a loose connection somewhere.

- In Step 3, the 5% tolerance allows only 2 SDs. See Appendix A.

- In Step 23d, the wiring must be changed so that only the current flowing through the 10 kΩ resistor is measured. It cannot be measured otherwise. The wiring should be returned to the original plan in Figure 3 after the 10 kΩ resistor current has been measured.

Postlab Analysis

- Question 4 may give students difficulty. The plan of attack is unusual in that the unknown to be identified is not part of the calculation. The scenario is realistic.

- In Question 4, you know that the failed resistor is open rather than shorted because a voltage drop exists across the resistors. If the bad resistor were shorted, there would be no voltage drop at all and a very high current flowing through the resistors.

- Ask students why Equation (6) can be used instead of Equation (5) to solve Question 4.

Home School Notes

- Refer to the Lab 4-2 Home School Notes for information about constructing an electrical breadboard similar to the Elenco Learning Center kit.

Recall that all of the voltage drops are equal in a parallel circuit, so Equation (3) can be rewritten

$$\frac{V_T}{R_T} = \frac{V_T}{R_1} + \frac{V_T}{R_2} + \frac{V_T}{R_3}. \tag{4}$$

Dividing all terms by V_T yields the **parallel-resistance formula**

$$\frac{1}{R_T} = \frac{1}{R_1} + \frac{1}{R_2} + \frac{1}{R_3}. \tag{5}$$

This formula holds true for any number of resistances in parallel. For simple circuits consisting of only two parallel resistors, Equation (5) is often rewritten

$$R_T = \frac{R_1 R_2}{R_1 + R_2}. \tag{6}$$

In summary, the total current in a parallel circuit is the sum of the currents in the parallel branches; the voltage drop across each component in a parallel circuit is the same as the total voltage drop across the parallel portion of the circuit; and the reciprocal of the total resistance in a parallel circuit is equal to the sum of the reciprocals of the individual resistances.

Procedure

Parallel Circuits

1. Connect a wire from the 470 Ω resistor (38 ___) to the 1 kΩ resistor (40 ___). Connect another wire from the other end of the 470 Ω resistor (39 ___) to the end of the 1 kΩ resistor (41 ___).

2. Set the multimeter to the 2000 position on the Ω scale. Insert one test probe into terminal 38 (___) and the other test probe into 41 (___). Read and record the ohmmeter display.

   The ohmmeter should display ~315 (Ω).

3. Using Equation (5) or (6), calculate the theoretical total resistance of the two parallel resistors.

   $$R_T = \frac{R_1 R_2}{R_1 + R_2} = \frac{(470\ \Omega)(1000\ \Omega)}{470\ \Omega + 1000\ \Omega} \doteq 320\ \Omega$$

   Notice that the total resistance is less than the individual resistance of either of the resistors because the current has two paths to take. The idea is somewhat like having two doors in your classroom, one narrow and one wide. The time that it would take to evacuate 100 students through either of the doors would be greater than the time required if both doors are used. Likewise, the total resistance to the flow of electrons is less if two resistors are used than if only one is used—as long as they are connected in parallel. The water analogy shown on page 14 of your Learning Center manual provides another way of visualizing the effect of combining resistors in parallel.

4. Connect a third resistor with the first two by connecting a wire from the 1 kΩ resistor (41 ___) to the 3.3 kΩ resistor (43 ___) and another wire from 40 (___) to 42 (___).

5. Insert the test leads into terminals 40 (___) and 41 (___). The electrons from the meter's battery can flow through any one of the three resistors. The total resistance of the three resistors should be even less than when only two resistors were connected in parallel. Read and record the ohmmeter display.

   The ohmmeter should display ~288 (Ω).

6. Using Equation (5), calculate the total resistance of the three resistors in parallel.

$$\frac{1}{R_T} = \frac{1}{R_1} + \frac{1}{R_2} + \frac{1}{R_3} \Rightarrow \frac{1}{R_T} = \frac{1}{470\ \Omega} + \frac{1}{1000\ \Omega} + \frac{1}{3300\ \Omega}$$

$$\frac{1}{R_T} = \frac{(1000\ \Omega)(3300\ \Omega) + (470\ \Omega)(3300\ \Omega) + (470\ \Omega)(1000\ \Omega)}{(470\ \Omega)(1000\ \Omega)(3300\ \Omega)}$$

$$R_T = \frac{(470\ \Omega)(1000\ \Omega)(3300\ \Omega)}{(1000\ \Omega)(3300\ \Omega) + (470\ \Omega)(3300\ \Omega) + (470\ \Omega)(1000\ \Omega)} \approx 290\ \Omega$$

(2 SDs allowed)

7. Draw the circuit. Include the three resistors and the ohmmeter.

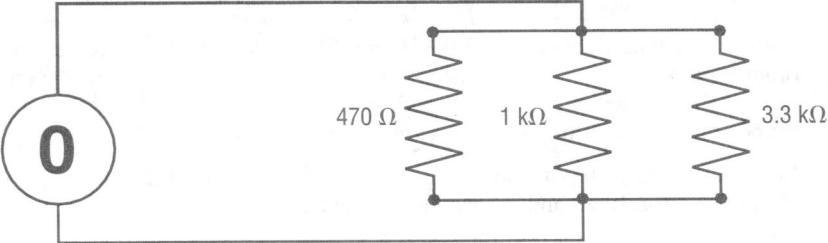

8. Remove all of the wires from the Learning Center.

9. Connect the circuit shown in Figure 2.

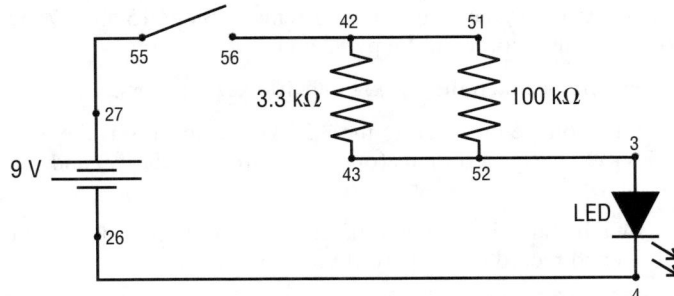

Figure 2

10. Press the switch to make sure that the circuit is complete. Set your meter to the Ω scale. Check the total resistance of the 3.3 kΩ and 100 kΩ resistors connected in parallel as follows. Disconnect one end of the wire that connects the 100 kΩ resistor to the LED at terminal 52 (_____). Insert the ohmmeter test probes into 42 (_____) and 52 (_____). Select the appropriate resistance setting in order to obtain 3 SDs. Read and record the displayed resistance.

    The ohmmeter should display ~3.14 (kΩ) on the 20K scale.

    Is the value less than 3.3 kΩ? If not, check the meter hookup. While the wire between the 100 kΩ resistor and the LED terminal is still disconnected, check the current flowing through the LED by completing Steps 11–12.

11. Insert the black test probe into terminal 3 (_____) at the LED and the red test probe into 52 (_____). Set the selector switch to 200m on the DCA scale.

12. Press the switch. If the ammeter display does not show at least 3 SDs, then select the 20m scale. Read and record the displayed current.

    The ammeter should display ~2.30 (mA).

13. Replace the wire leading from the 100 kΩ resistor to the LED. Measure the current before the two resistors by inserting the test probes into the two terminals of the switch (remember—red to positive). Read and record the displayed current value.

The ammeter should display ~2.30 (mA).

Notice that the current is the same before and after the two parallel resistors.

14. Remove the wire between the switch end of the 3.3 kΩ resistor and the 100 kΩ resistor (42 ____ to 51 ____). Insert the ammeter test probes into these terminals, observing correct polarity.

15. Press the switch. The ammeter display indicates the amount of current flowing through the 100 kΩ resistor. Adjust the scale selection to obtain at least 3 SDs. Read and record the current.

The ammeter should display ~73.2 (μA) on the 200μ scale.

16. Replace the wire between the 3.3 kΩ and the 100 kΩ resistors. Remove the other wire between the two resistors (43 ____ to 52 ____). Return the ammeter selector switch to the 20m position and insert the ammeter test probes into these terminals, observing correct polarity.

17. Press the switch. The display shows that current is flowing through the 3.3 kΩ resistor. Read and record the displayed current.

The ammeter should display ~2.23 (mA) on the 20m scale.

You should observe that nearly all of the current in the circuit flows through the 3.3 kΩ resistor and that very little current flows through the 100 kΩ resistor. Current always takes the path of least resistance. You should also notice that the sum of the currents in Steps 15 and 17 are close to the total current recorded in Steps 12 and 13.

18. Replace the wire between the 3.3 kΩ and 100 kΩ resistors.

19. Determine the voltage drop across the 3.3 kΩ resistor. Insert the test probes into the 3.3 kΩ resistor terminals (observing proper polarity) and select 1000 on the DCV scale.

20. Press the switch and adjust the voltmeter scale setting in order to obtain 3 SDs. Read and record the displayed voltage drop.

The voltmeter should display ~7.25 (V) on the 20 scale.

21. In a similar way, measure the voltage drop through the 100 kΩ resistor. Read and record the displayed voltage.

The voltmeter should display ~7.25 (V) on the 20 scale.

The voltage drop should be the same across both resistors.

22. Remove all of the wires from the Learning Center.

From Theory to Practice with Parallel Circuits

23. Connect the circuit indicated by the solid lines in Figure 3. Notice that there is no LED in this circuit.

Figure 3

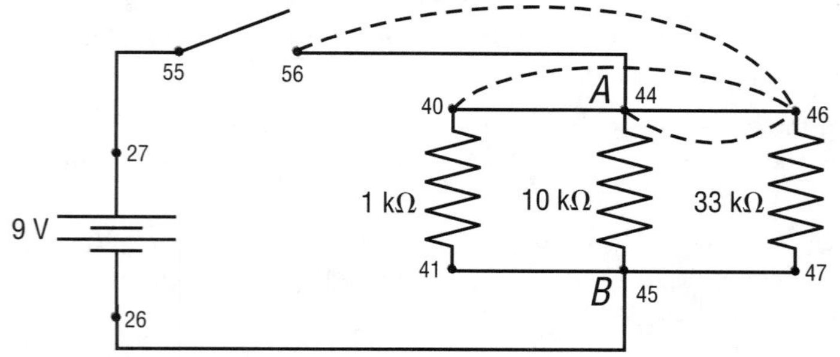

24. Review the procedures for the use of electrical test instruments in Appendix E.

25. Measure resistance, current, and voltage drop for each part of the circuit listed in Table 1. Remember that you should never connect the test leads of an ammeter across the terminals of a battery.

   a. The resistance and the voltage drop for the parallel branch in Table 1 are measured at points *A* and *B*.

   b. The resistance for the total circuit in Table 1 is the same as the parallel branch total resistance.

   c. The total circuit voltage drop in Table 1 is the same as the battery voltage.

   d. Measure the current on the positive side of each component. Measure the current flowing through the 1 kΩ and 33 kΩ resistors first; then switch the wires on the positive side of the resistors in order to make the connections represented by the dashed lines in Figure 3. After making the revised connections, measure the current through the 10 kΩ resistor. Measure total circuit current on the negative side of the battery.

26. Record all measurements in Table 1.

Data

Table 1
Parallel Circuit Resistance, Current, and Voltage Data and Calculations

Circuit Component	Measured Resistance, R_m		Measured Current, I_m		Measured Voltage Drop, V_m		Calculated Current, $I_c = V_m/R_m$		Calculated Voltage Drop, $V_c = I_m R_m$	
1 kΩ	988	(Ω)	9.52	(mA)	9.47	(V)	9.59	mA	9.41	V
10 kΩ	9.80	(kΩ)	972	(μA)	9.47	(V)	966	μA	9.53	V
33 kΩ	32.2	(kΩ)	296	(μA)	9.47	(V)	294	μA	9.53	V
Parallel Branch	874	(Ω)	10.74	(mA)	9.47	(V)	10.84	mA	9.39	V
Total Circuit	874	(Ω)	10.74	(mA)	9.47	(V)	10.84	mA	9.39	V

Data in Table 1 is typical. Actual data and calculations will vary.

Postlab Exercises

1. Calculate the current through each part of the circuit listed in Table 1. Use the measured values for resistance and voltage drop in your calculations. Record the calculated currents in Table 1.

2. Calculate the voltage drop across each of the parts of the circuit listed in Table 1. Use the measured values of resistance and current for each. Record the calculated voltage drops in Table 1.

Postlab Analysis

1. How did the total resistance in the parallel circuit that you connected according to Figure 3 relate to the individual component resistances?

   The total resistance was less than the smallest individual resistance.

2. In the same circuit, how did the current through a particular resistor vary with the value of the resistor?

   The larger the resistor, the smaller the current.

3. How did total voltage drop across the parallel portion of the circuit compare to the individual voltage drops across the resistors?

   The total voltage drop across the parallel portion of the circuit was

   equal to the individual voltage drops across the resistors.

4. Resistors can fail by opening the circuit path like a blown fuse or by shorting so that they act like a segment of low-resistance wire. Assume you are troubleshooting an electrical malfunction in a control circuit. The equipment schematic shows three resistors connected in parallel—a 275 kΩ resistor, a 360. kΩ resistor, and a 450. kΩ resistor. A permanently installed ammeter in the equipment indicates that a 143 μA current is flowing through the parallel resistors. The measured voltage drop across the resistors is 24.0 V. From these indications, you conclude that the resistor must be open rather than shorted. (Why?) You do not have the tools to disconnect the resistors in order to test them individually. Which resistor is bad (open)? Assume that only one resistor has failed.

   The method of solution involves calculating the current resulting from each of the three possible pairs of good resistors. The current that most closely matches the displayed current reveals the good pair of resistors.

   Given: $V = 24.0$ V; $R_1 = 275$ kΩ; $R_2 = 360.$ kΩ; $R_3 = 450.$ kΩ

   Formulas: $I_T = \dfrac{V_T}{R_T}$; $R_T = R_{(a,\ b)} = \dfrac{R_a R_b}{R_a + R_b}$

   Solution:

   Assume that R_1 failed. $R_{(2,\ 3)} = \dfrac{(360.\ \text{k}\Omega)(450.\ \text{k}\Omega)}{360.\ \text{k}\Omega + 450.\ \text{k}\Omega} = 200.\ \text{k}\Omega;$

   $$I_{(2,\ 3)} = \frac{24.0\ \text{V}}{200.\ \text{k}\Omega} = 120.\ \mu\text{A}$$

   Assume that R_2 failed. $R_{(1,\ 3)} = \dfrac{(275\ \text{k}\Omega)(450.\ \text{k}\Omega)}{275\ \text{k}\Omega + 450.\ \text{k}\Omega} \doteq 171\ \text{k}\Omega;$

   $$I_{(1,\ 3)} = \frac{24.0\ \text{V}}{171\ \text{k}\Omega} \doteq 140.\ \mu\text{A}$$

   Assume that R_3 failed. $R_{(1,\ 2)} = \dfrac{(275\ \text{k}\Omega)(360.\ \text{k}\Omega)}{275\ \text{k}\Omega + 360.\ \text{k}\Omega} \doteq 156\ \text{k}\Omega;$

   $$I_{(1,\ 2)} = \frac{24.0\ \text{V}}{156\ \text{k}\Omega} \doteq 154\ \mu\text{A}$$

   According to the data, R_2 has failed.

Name _____

Date _____ Hour _____

PRELAB HOMEWORK

1. What electrical principle or law applies to both series and parallel circuits?

   Ohm's law applies to both series and parallel circuits.

2. Three resistors with the following values are connected in parallel: 50 kΩ, 3 MΩ, and 150 Ω. All resistors have a tolerance of ±5%. The voltage drop across the 50 kΩ resistor is 12 V. What is the voltage drop across the 150 Ω resistor?

   The voltage drop across the 150 Ω resistor is also 12 V.

3. Calculate the current through each of the three resistors in Question 2. Express your answers in units of milliamps or microamps, as appropriate, to 2 SDs.

   Given: $V_1 = V_2 = V_3 = 12$ V; $R_1 = 50$ kΩ; $R_2 = 3$ MΩ; $R_3 = 150$ Ω;

   $I_1 = ?; I_2 = ?; I_3 = ?$

   Formula: $I = \dfrac{V}{R}$

   Solution: $I_1 = \dfrac{V_1}{R_1} = \dfrac{12 \text{ V}}{50 \text{ k}\Omega} = 240 \text{ μA}; I_2 = \dfrac{V_2}{R_2} = \dfrac{12 \text{ V}}{3 \text{ M}\Omega} = 4.0 \text{ μA};$

   $I_3 = \dfrac{V_3}{R_3} = \dfrac{12 \text{ V}}{150 \text{ }\Omega} = 80. \text{ mA}$

4. What is the total current in the parallel portion of the circuit in Question 2?

   The total current is the sum of the currents in each resistor.

   $I_T = 240 \text{ μA} + 4 \text{ μA} + 80\,000 \text{ μA}$

   $I_T = 80\,244 \text{ μA} \approx 80. \text{ mA}$ (precise only to the nearest milliamp)

5. What is the total resistance in the parallel circuit in Question 2? Use Equation (5) and express your answer to 2 SDs.

   Given: $R_1 = 50$ kΩ; $R_2 = 3$ MΩ; $R_3 = 150$ Ω; $R_T = ?$

   Formula: $\dfrac{1}{R_T} = \dfrac{1}{R_1} + \dfrac{1}{R_2} + \dfrac{1}{R_3}$

   Solution: $\dfrac{1}{R_T} = \dfrac{1}{50 \text{ k}\Omega} + \dfrac{1}{3 \text{ M}\Omega} + \dfrac{1}{150 \text{ }\Omega}$

   $\dfrac{1}{R_T} = \dfrac{(3 \text{ M}\Omega)(150 \text{ }\Omega) + (50 \text{ k}\Omega)(150 \text{ }\Omega) + (50 \text{ k}\Omega)(3 \text{ M}\Omega)}{(50 \text{ k}\Omega)(3 \text{ M}\Omega)(150 \text{ }\Omega)}$

   $R_T = \dfrac{(50\,000 \text{ }\Omega)(3\,000\,000 \text{ }\Omega)(150 \text{ }\Omega)}{(3\,000\,000 \text{ }\Omega)(150 \text{ }\Omega) + (50\,000 \text{ }\Omega)(150 \text{ }\Omega) + (50\,000 \text{ }\Omega)(3\,000\,000 \text{ }\Omega)}$

   $R_T = \dfrac{2.25 \times 10^{13} \text{ }\Omega^3}{1.5 \times 10^{11} \text{ }\Omega^2} \approx 150 \text{ }\Omega$ (2 SDs allowed)

6. How does the total resistance in a parallel circuit compare to the individual resistances?

   The total resistance is always less than the value of the smallest resistance.

7. If 200 mA flows into a node connecting four resistors in parallel, what must be the total current flowing through the resistors? What principle does this example illustrate?

   The total current flowing through the resistors must be 200 mA because Kirchoff's

   law states that the sum of the currents flowing into a node equals the sum of the

   currents flowing out of the node.

8. In Step 13, the switch is not shut to read the current flowing into the resistors. Why is this possible?

   The ammeter completes the circuit across the switch (it "jumps" the switch).

   Therefore, the switch is not shut. (If the switch were shut, the ammeter would

   read 0 A.)

9. When measuring voltage or current, what does a negative sign in the meter display indicate?

   A negative voltage or current indicates that the meter is connected with the red

   probe to the negative side of the component and the black probe to the positive

   side.

10. What is the difference in the circuit connections when using a voltmeter and an ammeter?

    A voltmeter is connected in parallel with the component being tested, but an

    ammeter is connected in series with the component.

Name _____

Date _____ Hour ____

SERIES-PARALLEL CIRCUITS

Purpose

This lab combines the principles learned in Labs 4-3 and 4-4. The purpose is to

- provide real-world evidence of theoretical principles.
- practice using electrical test meters.
- gain experience reading electrical schematics.

Prelab Discussion

Review pages 13–14 in the Learning Center manual. Be sure that you understand the material covered on those pages as well as the material discussed in the Prelab Discussion of Labs 4-3 and 4-4 before proceeding with this lab. Also review Appendix E pertaining to test meter usage and safety precautions.

You will combine the information from the previous labs during this exercise. Your ability to connect this circuit and to read the various meters to determine voltage, current, and resistance for each resistor will demonstrate your understanding of the previous lab instructions.

This lab also demonstrates a method for predicting total resistance and current in a complex circuit without actually measuring those quantities. This ability is important when designing electrical and electronic circuits in order to determine what currents will be generated in a circuit and what voltage source is needed to supply the required currents. The technique for determining total currents and resistances in a circuit is called *Thevinizing* or *Nortonizing*. A **Thevinin** circuit is a circuit consisting of a single voltage and current source and a single circuit element (resistive, inductive, or capacitive) equivalent to a more complicated circuit. A **Norton** circuit element is an element equivalent to a more complicated arrangement of elements in a circuit. In this lab you will be required to determine the Norton resistance and the current in a simple series-parallel circuit and then to measure the actual values in order to compare them with your prediction.

Nortonizing a series-parallel circuit is relatively simple, even though some real-world circuits can become very complex. The process is analogous to solving nested parenthetical equations. You begin with the resistances that have the most nodes between them and the main wire to the voltage source. Using the appropriate resistance addition formula for series or parallel resistors, you find the equivalent resistance in each parallel or series branch and then eliminate the branches until you have only series or parallel resistances left. The final set of resistances are combined to find a single resistance. This resistance is the Norton resistance equivalent to all of the original resistors together. Figure 1 demonstrates how this process works.

Prelab Discussion

- Review the prerequisites for Lab 4-5 in the back of this manual.

- This lab provides additional practice measuring resistance, current, and voltages in DC circuits. More importantly, it introduces the concepts of Thevinin and Norton circuit analysis.

- Practice the technique for determining equivalent resistances in class prior to the lab.

Equipment and Setup

- The same Elenco Learning Center and multimeter are used for this lab as for the previous electrical labs.

- Verify that all DC functions work on each multimeter prior to the lab. The fuse protecting the *low-range current scales* can be blown without any indication on the resistance or voltage scales.

Procedure

- It is intended that the students make the connections for the circuit in this lab with a minimum of assistance.

- Spot-check results during the lab to ensure that the students are making the correct measurements.

Home School Notes

- Refer to the Lab 4-2 Home School Notes for information about constructing an electrical breadboard similar to the Elenco Learning Center kit.

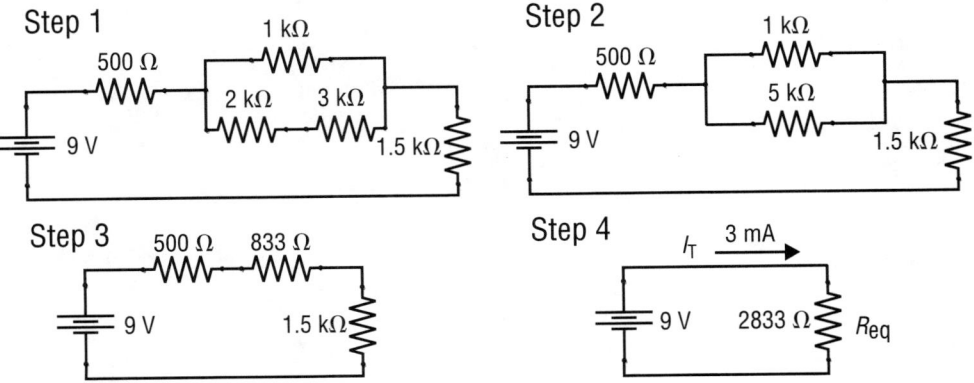

Figure 1

Procedure

1. Connect the following circuit on the Learning Center kit.

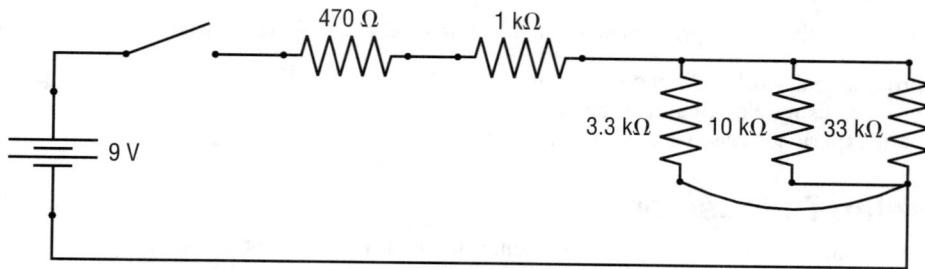

Figure 2

2. Check to verify that the circuit is complete by disconnecting the wire between the battery and the switch. Insert the test probes of the multimeter into these terminals and set the selector switch to the 200m position on the DCA scale. A displayed current when the switch is pressed indicates that the circuit is complete. Disconnect the meter and replace it with the original wire.

3. Test the circuit with the multimeter in order to determine the data for each circuit component or group of components listed in Table 1.

   a. When measuring resistance, remember that at least one end of the resistor must be completely disconnected from the circuit.

   b. Recall that you must pay attention to the path of current flow through parallel resistors when measuring current. The circuit in Figure 2 is connected so that you do not have to change the wiring to measure each of the three resistor currents.

   c. The total circuit current can be measured between the switch and the 470 Ω resistor. The total circuit voltage should be measured at the battery terminals.

4. Nortonize the circuit, using the measured values for each resistor, and determine the equivalent resistance in the circuit, R_{eq}. Record the value in the blank above Table 1.

5. Using the value for equivalent resistance and the measured voltage of the battery in the Learning Center, calculate the total current flowing through the circuit, I_T. Record the value in the second blank above Table 1.

Data

Table 1
Series-Parallel Circuit Data and Calculations

Norton R_{eq} _3.73 kΩ_   Norton I_T _2.56 mA_

Circuit Components	Measured Resistance, R_m		Measured Current, I_m		Measured Voltage, V_m		Calculated Current, $I_c = V_m/R_m$		Calculated Voltage Drop, $V_c = I_m R_m$	
470 Ω	465	Ω	2.56	mA	1.18	V	2.54	mA	1.19	V
1 kΩ	990	Ω	2.56	mA	2.52	V	2.55	mA	2.53	V
470 Ω-1 kΩ Series Combination	1454	Ω	2.56	mA	3.71	V	2.55	mA	3.72	V
3.3 kΩ	3.24	kΩ	1.79	mA	5.80	V	1.79	mA	5.80	V
10 kΩ	9.81	kΩ	591	μA	5.80	V	591	μA	5.80	V
33 kΩ	32.2	kΩ	181	μA	5.80	V	180	μA	5.83	V
3.3 kΩ-10 kΩ-33 kΩ Parallel Combination	2.26	kΩ	2.56	mA	5.80	V	2.57	mA	5.79	V
Total Circuit	3.71	kΩ	2.56	mA	9.54	V	2.57	mA	9.50	V

Data in Table 1 is typical. Actual student data will vary.

Postlab Exercises

Calculate the current and voltage drop for each part of the circuit listed in Table 1. Express your answers with the same units and precision as the measured data. Record the results in the appropriate columns in Table 1.

Name _____

Date _____ Hour ____

MAPPING A MAGNETIC FIELD

Purpose

Magnetism is one of the fundamental forces of nature. The purpose of this exercise is to

- observe and sketch the magnetic field surrounding a bar magnet.
- observe and sketch the interactions of the magnetic fields of two magnets.
- describe the magnetic field around a wire and its dependence on current direction.

Prelab Discussion

A **field** is a three-dimensional region of space where some measurable quantity, usually a force, energy, or a distribution of particles, varies from point to point within the space region. The mathematical study of field theory is an important application of calculus, and complex changing fields require the use of supercomputers to analyze their temporal and spatial behaviors.

A **magnetic field** is the region of magnetic forces surrounding a source of magnetism. From your earlier study of forces, you know that a force is a vector quantity, having both magnitude and direction. The magnetic force at every point in a magnetic field can be represented as an arrow pointing in a certain direction. By convention, the direction of the magnetic field is the direction in which a north magnetic monopole would move under the influence of the field, similar to the definition of an electrostatic field. However, unlike electrostatic charges, a magnetic monopole has not been discovered and is not believed to exist. Therefore, magnetic field force directions are conceptually determined by the orientation of a tiny theoretical test magnet suspended in the field. The north end of the test magnet points in the field direction.

Artificial magnetic fields are, for practical purposes, limited in size and influence, but theoretically, the magnetic field extends indefinitely. The forces within the magnetic field tend to change direction as one moves from point to point within the field. If a small test magnet, such as a lab compass, moves through the field, the orientation of the field can be observed. If a series of test magnets were placed end to end within the field, they would form a continuous curving line, apparently originating at the north pole and ending at the south pole of the source of magnetism. (The lines actually form loops through the magnet.) This imaginary line is called a **magnetic field line.** For this lab exercise, you will use a compass to map field lines around one or more magnets.

There are some artificialities and limitations within this lab exercise that you should be aware of. You should remember that magnetic fields, like electric fields, are not physical objects but rather convenient descriptions of magnetic phenomena. Likewise, this experiment is simply an approximation of the magnetic field because even a small compass needle will distort the field somewhat. Other factors could also be involved. Magnetic fields from the electric wires in the walls and outside the building, as well as the magnetic field of the earth can influence the magnetic field of a magnet. For this reason, we will confine our study to the field very close to the magnet. There the strength of the magnet's field will not be significantly affected by outside magnetic fields. You should also remember that magnetic fields are three-dimensional, but the sketches you will make on a sheet of paper are two-dimensional cross-sections of the field.

Required Equipment

bar magnets, 2
books, 2
cardboard sheet
insulated wire
lab battery
masking tape
metric ruler
small magnetic compass
unlined paper, 4 sheets

Optional Equipment

battery holder
odd-shaped magnets, 2

Prelab Discussion

- Review the prerequisites for Lab 4-6 in the back of this manual.

- It would be helpful to review the characteristics of the various types of magnetic materials in class before assigning the Prelab Homework.

- Note that even a small compass will distort the magnetic field of a magnet. The directions obtained from this method are approximations at best.

Equipment and Setup

- Standard bar magnets and horseshoe magnets from science equipment suppliers are best for this lab.

- Inexpensive soft iron magnets tend to lose their strength with time. Purchase quality alloy magnets that will last for years or obtain a remagnitizer to rejuvenate "tired" magnets.

- The compasses can be the small "button" variety.

- The closer the cardboard is to the magnet, the stronger the field, so the supporting books should be only slightly thicker than the magnet.

- The demonstration of the magnetic field around the wire requires approximately 50 cm of insulated wire and a 1.5 V or 6 V battery. If necessary, provide the battery with a battery holder to facilitate connecting the wire to the battery. A switch used to energize the wire is convenient, but it is not necessary.

- Odd-shaped magnets can be used to demonstrate the characteristic orientation of magnetic fields.

Procedure

- This lab is similar to labs performed in earlier physical science courses; however, students are required to actually trace the field lines, following a procedure.

- The demonstration of field orientation around a current-carrying conductor is intended to prepare students for, or reinforce their understanding of, electromagnetism.

Home School Notes

- Cow magnets may be substituted for bar magnets. Cow magnets are exceptionally strong magnets and may be obtained from many farm and feed stores. These magnets are swallowed by grazing animals to trap nails and other magnetic debris eaten while grazing.

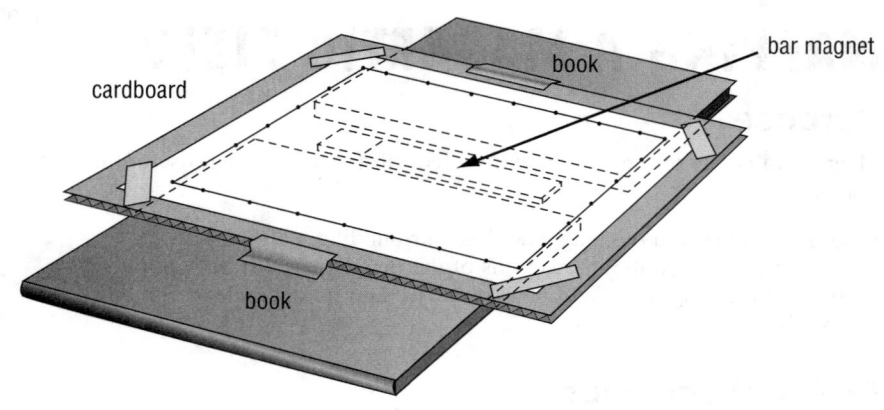

Figure 1

Procedure

One Bar Magnet

1. Place a bar magnet on the tabletop. Set two books of equal thickness on both sides of the bar magnet to support the cardboard. Place the cardboard over the books so that the cardboard is centered over the magnet. Fasten the cardboard to the books with tape so that it cannot move (see Figure 1).

2. Draw a line along all four edges of a sheet of paper, parallel to and about 2 cm from the edges.

3. Mark dots at the four corners where the lines intersect. Mark five evenly spaced dots on the short lines at each end of the paper and seven evenly spaced dots on the line at each side. The dots will be about 3 cm apart (see Figure 2). Tape the sheet of paper to the cardboard.

4. Position the compass so that one of the ends of the compass needle is directly over one of the dots.

5. Mark another dot on the paper on the opposite side of the compass case in line with the needle. Remove the compass. Draw a line connecting the two dots. Place an arrowhead on the line pointing in the direction that the north pole of the compass was pointing.

6. Position the compass at the end of the line that you drew in Step 5 and align the end of the needle with the end of the line on the paper. Mark the paper at the opposite end of the needle (as you did above) and draw another line.

7. Continue making line segments in the same way until the line either runs off the paper or the compass needle becomes jammed because it is pointing downward toward the magnet. If there is room, start at the original dot and extend the line in the same way in the other direction. Your paper should look something like diagram A in Figure 2. When you have connected a dot at the edge of the paper to the magnet with a continuous line, repeat the process for each dot around the perimeter of the paper. The completed project should look like diagram B in Figure 2.

8. Outline the location of the magnet with a dotted line and label the north and south poles.

Opposite-Pole Field Interaction

9. Remove the paper from the cardboard and then remove the cardboard from the books. Place a second magnet in line with the first magnet so that the north pole of one magnet is facing the south pole of the other magnet about 15 cm apart.

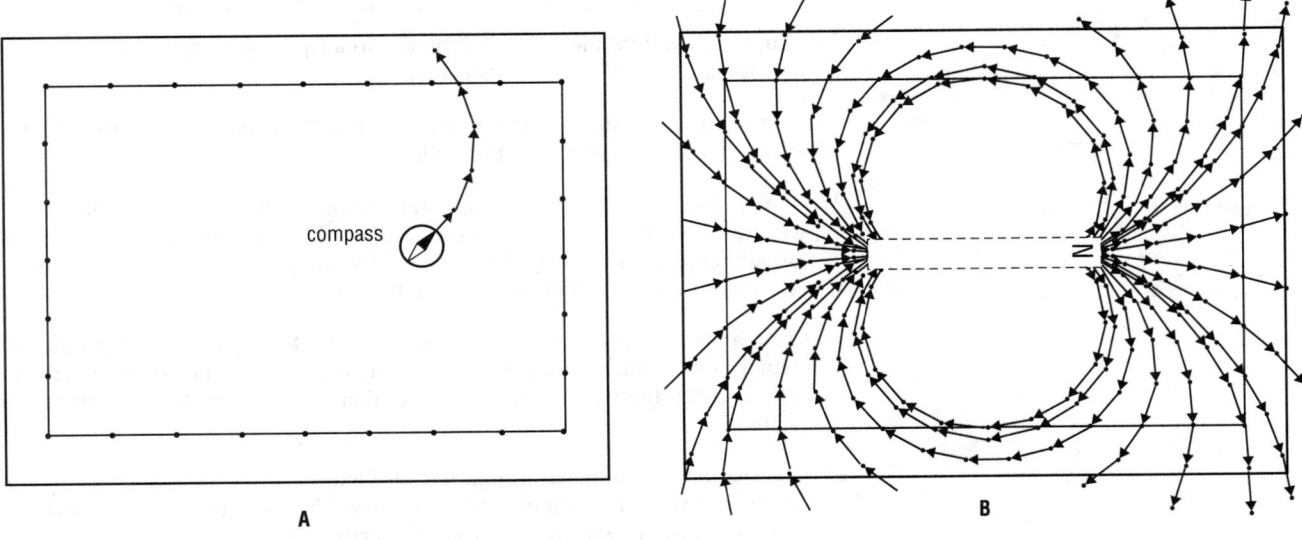

Figure 2

10. Replace the cardboard and tape a clean sheet of paper to the cardboard.

11. Draw a single line across the paper so that it is between the two magnets and perpendicular to their lengths.

12. Mark dots on the line at 2 cm intervals.

13. Starting at the dots, construct the magnetic field lines in both directions as before.

Like-Pole Field Interaction

14. Remove the paper from the cardboard and then remove the cardboard from the books. Reverse one of the magnets so that the north pole of one magnet is about 15 cm from the north pole of the other.

15. Replace the cardboard and tape a clean sheet of paper to the cardboard.

16. Draw two lines on the paper. Both lines will be parallel to the magnets about 2 cm from the long edges of the paper.

17. Mark dots on the lines at 2 cm intervals.

18. Construct the magnetic field lines through the dots as before.

Outside Factors Influencing a Magnetic Field

19. Remove the cardboard and books and place a single magnet on the table. Remove all other magnets to a remote location in the room.

20. Hold the compass in your hand near the south pole of the magnet that is on the table. Rotate the case until the north mark on the compass rose is aligned under the north end of the needle. Move gradually away from the magnet, keeping the north mark pointed at the magnet. Record in the blanks provided the estimated number of degrees the compass needle moves away from the north mark at the specified separation distances.

    a. 15 cm _____   e. 1.5 m _____

    b. 30 cm _____   f. 2 m _____

    c. 60 cm _____   g. 2.5 m _____

    d. 1 m _____   h. 3 m _____

Magnetic Field Around a Current-Carrying Conductor

21. Cut a lightweight piece of cardboard into a square or circle about 15 cm across and punch a hole in its center.

22. Thread the wire through the hole and connect one end to the positive terminal of the battery or the battery holder.

23. One person should hold the wire taut and oriented vertically so that the positive end of the wire enters the cardboard from below. Another person should support the cardboard horizontally and place the compass on the cardboard approximately 4 cm from the wire.

24. Touch the free end (upper end) of the wire to the negative terminal of the battery or the battery holder. Observe the direction of the compass needle. Do not keep the wire energized longer than is necessary for the compass to stabilize.

25. Reposition the compass around the cardboard surface several times and energize the wire for each new position. Note the direction of the compass needle when the wire is energized. Describe your observations.

    According to the right-hand rule for conventional current, the

    magnetic field should be oriented counterclockwise around the wire.

26. Disconnect the lower end of the wire from the positive battery terminal and connect the upper end of the wire in its place. Touch the lower end of the wire to the negative battery terminal to energize the wire.

27. Repeat Steps 24–25 a sufficient number of times to map the magnetic field around the wire with the current flowing in the opposite direction. Record your observations.

    The field is oriented clockwise around the wire.

Postlab Analysis

1. In the magnetic field diagrams, where were the field lines bunched together most closely, relative to the magnet?

   The field lines were bunched most closely at the ends or poles of the

   magnet.

2. What happens to the magnetic field lines that run off the paper? Do they disappear, curve into space, or continue in a straight line?

   Magnetic field lines form loops. Any lines that run off the paper will

   eventually loop back to the magnet. (Some loops can be very large.)

3. _____B_____ Identify the location of the north pole in the magnet in Figure 3.

4. Explain how the compass aligned itself when it was directly above the midpoint of the magnet.

   Answers may vary. The compass should align itself with the north end

   pointing to the south pole. The magnetic flux may be so weak along-

   side the magnet that the compass drifts or aligns itself with the

   earth's field.

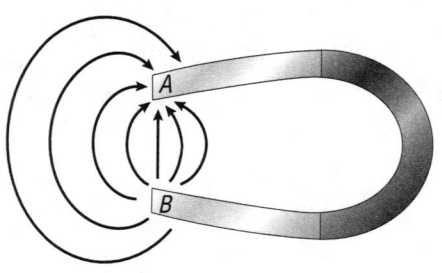

Figure 3

5. Explain your observations when checking for outside magnetic influences. Why did the compass needle drift away from the magnet?

   Since the influence of the magnet quickly drops off, other magnetic

   fields in the room begin to affect the compass. The most significant

   of these other fields is the earth's magnetic field.

6. In what direction does the earth's magnetic field point directly over the magnetic North Pole?

   The earth's magnetic North Pole is a south pole, so the field vector

   will point straight down.

7. Is it possible for magnetic field lines to cross? Explain your answer.

   No, it is impossible because, in that case, the magnetic field vector at

   the point of intersection would have to point in two directions at the

   same time.

8. If a wire is formed into a loop and a current flows through the wire, describe the magnetic field that is produced.

   The circular field surrounding the wire is reinforced in the center of

   the loop, and magnetic poles are formed (according to the right-hand

   rule for solenoids).

Name _____

Date _____ Hour ____

PRELAB HOMEWORK

1. Describe the orientation of a compass needle in a magnetic field.

   The compass needle is parallel to the magnetic field, and the north end points
   toward the south pole of the field.

2. Review the presentation of the source of magnetism in your text. Discuss why it is improbable that a magnetic monopole exists.

   According to the domain theory, magnetic materials are composed of tiny regions
   consisting of magnetic dipoles resulting from characteristic electron structures. It
   appears that magnetism requires the existence of dipoles.

3. Discuss at least three factors that could affect the mapping of a bar magnet's field in this lab exercise.

   The bar magnet's field could be affected by the compass's magnetic field, other
   magnets close by, the magnetic fields generated by electrical circuits in the vicinity,
   or the earth's magnetic field.

4. Discuss at least one method that you could use to demonstrate that a magnetic field around a magnet is three-dimensional.

   Answers will vary. The magnet could be turned on its side and the mapping repeated, a magnetized needle could be suspended by a thread and moved around
   a magnet in all directions, or a magnet could be inserted into a special jar containing iron filings suspended in oil. All of these demonstrate the three-dimensional
   arrangement of a magnetic field.

5. What is the major difference in shape between an electrostatic field line and a magnetic field line?

   An electrostatic field line starts at a positive charge and ends at a negative charge.
   A magnetic field line forms a closed loop that passes out the north pole of a magnet around to the south pole and completes the path through the magnet.

6. One way to view magnetic field strength is to note how close together the magnetic field lines are. Where do you expect the field lines to be closest together?

   Magnetic field lines tend to be closest together at the poles and within materials
   with high magnetic permeability.

7. _____B_____ Which of the following diagrams correctly shows the magnetic field for a horseshoe magnet? Write the letter of the correct diagram in the blank.

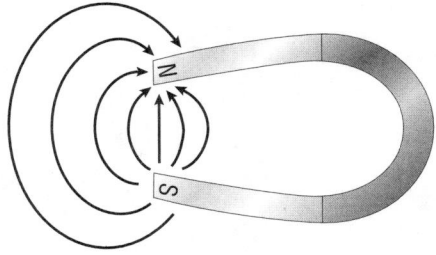

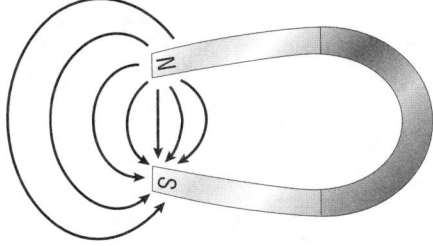

A.   B.

8. The following questions may be answered from reviewing your text or other sources.

   a. Discuss the composition of a lodestone that gives it its magnetic character.

      Lodestone is a form of mineral magnetite that exhibits a magnetic characteristic.
It usually contains two forms of iron oxide. The net magnetic moment resulting
from the imbalance of the two oxides is believed to be responsible for the magnetism of lodestone, making it a ferrimagnetic material.

   b. Describe the orientation of the magnetic flux vector **B** compared to the magnetic field line.

      The magnetic flux vector is tangent to the magnetic field line at all points in the
magnetic field.

   c. Of what class of magnetic material is your magnet most likely to be? Explain why it could not be one of the other classes of magnetic materials.

      A permanent magnet is usually composed of a ferromagnetic or ferrimagnetic
material. Paramagnetic materials are only weakly magnetic, and diamagnetic
materials actually weaken a magnetic field. Neither of the latter two materials
would make good, strong magnets.

9. Describe the orientation of the magnetic field formed by a current flowing through a conductor. Include in your answer some reference to a memory aid that helps identify magnetic field orientation in relation to *conventional* current flow.

   The right-hand rule for current-carrying conductors states that if the right hand is
held so that the thumb points in the direction of conventional current flow in a
conductor, then the fingers curl in the direction of the magnetic field as it wraps
around the conductor.

Name _____

Date _____ Hour _____

ELECTRICAL WORK

Purpose

One of the earliest applications of electricity was the powering of motors to perform useful work. The purpose of this lab is to

- construct an electrical circuit that can perform a practical function.
- observe the relationship between mechanical and electrical work.
- calculate the power generated by an electric motor.
- calculate the efficiency of a motor.

Prelab Discussion

Electric motors have been in use for more than a century, performing numerous beneficial functions. The earliest electric motors were used for driving manufacturing equipment, mine ventilators, irrigation pumps, and elevators. As the technology was refined and domestic electrical service became more widespread, many electrical appliances were developed to take the drudgery out of housekeeping. Today, electric motors are found in nearly every appliance in which mechanical energy must be used, from VCRs to hair dryers to computer disk drives. Electric motors propel vehicles, circulate liquids, and provide ventilation. They lift heavy objects, provide power for numerous industrial processes, and propel many hand tools.

Before energy transformations in an electric motor can be examined, the definitions of work and power should first be reviewed. Recall that **mechanical work** is calculated from the product of force and distance, $W = Fd$. The work to lift an object in a gravitational field is equal to the change in gravitational potential energy of the object, or

$$W = \Delta U_g = mg\Delta h. \tag{1}$$

Mechanical power is defined as the rate of mechanical work, or $P = W/t$.

In a simple DC electrical circuit, you can identify some analogous electrical quantities that permit you to compute the work accomplished in a circuit and the power used. The "force" that moves electrons through an electrical device is often called the **electromotive force,** or **emf.** The term *emf* is often used for the electrical potential difference, or voltage drop (V), across a device. Emf is not really a force; if it were, it would have units of newtons (N). Recall that voltage is defined in units of joules per coulomb (J/C). Current is measured in units of amperes (A), which are coulombs per second (C/s). The product of the voltage across a circuit element and the current flowing through it yields units of joules per second, which is equivalent to watts (W), the unit of power. Therefore, *power supplied by the circuit to an electrical device* can easily be calculated by finding the product of the device's current and voltage ($P = IV$).

The power expended *in an electrical resistance* can be calculated from Ohm's law. If $V = IR$, then $P = IV = I(IR) = I^2R$. This formula permits determining the rate of heat generation in a resistance because a resistance does no mechanical work. This information is needed to determine the net electrical power developed in a motor to do mechanical work. The electrical power delivered to a DC motor by the circuit (P_E) can be determined by measuring the current supplied to the motor (I_m) and the terminal voltage (V_t) at the motor,

$$P_E = I_mV_t. \tag{2}$$

The power lost in the motor due to the resistance of the motor's wires and associated heating (P_h) is calculated from

$$P_h = I_m^2R_m, \tag{3}$$

Required Equipment

electric motor, DC
Elenco M-1000B multimeters, 2
flask clamp
insulated wire
lab battery, 6 V
metric masses
metric measuring tape
potentiometer or rheostat
spool
support stand
switch
test leads with alligator clips, 7
thread

Optional Equipment

ammeter
ohmmeter
voltmeter

Prelab Discussion

- Review the prerequisites for Lab 4-7 in the back of this manual.

- The discussion presents the development of the theory and formulas necessary to complete the lab in a logical order. As with previous labs, a number of new symbols have been included to streamline the discussion. Students may find them confusing, so spend some time defining the variables and their symbols.

- It is very important to emphasize the need to attain constant motor speed during the data trials. Review Question 4 in the Postlab Homework for the background of this concept if necessary.

- Students may question why, when calculating motor efficiency, the ratio of mechanical work (W_M) to energy supplied (W_E) is used instead of the ratio of the calculated electrical work (P_mt) to energy supplied. Motor efficiency can be calculated both ways, but the better method uses mechanical work independently determined with mechanical measurements. Electrical work is derived from the same quantities that are used to determine total energy delivered to the motor. There is less potential for compounding error by using mechanical work obtained from an independent source.

Equipment and Setup

- This experiment uses several items unique to this lab. The motor should be a reasonably good quality DC motor that can run on 1.5 to 9 V. Motors may be obtained from most science or hobby supply companies. Avoid the poorly constructed motors from inexpensive toys if at all possible.

- Some science equipment suppliers sell an electrical work kit that includes a motor, a spool, and masses.

- The potentiometer or rheostat is another device that must be provided and is not easily substituted. See the Home School Notes for other suggestions.

- You may use multimeters such as the Elenco model referenced in previous electrical labs. If your multimeters have autoranging scales, allow the students to rely on them because demonstrating the techniques for measuring electrical quantities is not paramount in this lab.

- The meters may also be standard lab ammeters and voltmeters. Ensure that the meters have the capacity appropriate for this lab (i.e., don't use a microammeter for currents measured in hundreds of milliamps).

- The large lab dry cell batteries are ideal for this lab because they have a large capacity; therefore, terminal voltage should not vary with extended use.

Procedure

- The procedure for this lab is one of the more complex ones with respect to technique. Several students will be required to obtain the data for each trial as discussed in the procedure, and their efforts must be coordinated.

- If meter indications vary widely during a data run, instruct students to check and tighten all electrical connections. Also, note if the string seems to be winding up at one point on the spool. If the effective spool diameter changes during the trial, the current and voltage may vary.

where R_m is the resistance of the motor's field wires (windings). The electrical power actually developed by the motor to do useful work (P_m) is the difference of the power supplied to the motor and internal resistance power losses,

$$P_m = P_E - P_h. \tag{4}$$

Substituting Equations (2) and (3) into Equation (4), the power generated by a motor is

$$P_m = I_m V_t - I_m^2 R_m,$$

which simplifies to

$$P_m = I_m(V_t - I_m R_m). \tag{5}$$

Recall that in a DC motor, as the windings rotate through the magnetic field of the fixed magnets (stator), a voltage is induced in the windings that opposes the voltage producing the rotation (Lenz's law). This voltage is known as **back emf** (**ℰ**). You can account for back emf in the motor voltage expression

$$V_t = I_m R_m - ℰ, \tag{6}$$

where $I_m R_m$ is the voltage drop in the motor windings (V_m). Solving Equation (6) for ℰ, you obtain

$$ℰ = I_m R_m - V_t. \tag{7}$$

Notice that the right side of Equation (7) is numerically equal to the expression in parentheses in Equation (5) but negative in sign. The reason for this equality is that back emf acts in opposition to terminal voltage. Electrical power delivered by a motor can then be calculated by the formula

$$P_m = I_m ℰ, \tag{8}$$

the product of motor current and back emf, which is equivalent to Equation (5).

To determine the energy supplied or work accomplished in a given time interval, the power (in joules per second) is multiplied by the time (in seconds). The product has units of joules, the units of energy and work. This relationship is summarized in the equation

$$W_m = P_m t. \tag{9}$$

If the experiment is carefully conducted, the net electrical work of the motor (W_m) should equal the mechanical work actually accomplished (W_M).

It is essential that the speed of the motor be controlled so that it is constant throughout the time that work is being done; otherwise the power delivered by the motor is not constant, and the work formula cannot be used. The speed of the motor is controlled using a variable resistance, such as a potentiometer or a **rheostat,** connected in series with the motor. A rheostat is a variable resistor that is used to control electrical loads. The rheostat adjusts the voltage available to the motor terminals so that just enough power is produced to lift the mass and overcome the friction in the system in order to maintain a constant speed.

You know that no process in nature is 100% efficient, and that principle holds true for energy conversions. When converting electrical energy to mechanical energy, some energy is lost in the form of heat generated in the conductors of the motor, friction in the shaft bearings, wind resistance as the rotor turns, and eddy currents generated in the magnets. The most significant loss in an otherwise well-designed motor is from conductor heating (I^2R losses). The efficiency of any process is the ratio of the work out and the work in ($\eta = W_{out}/W_{in}$). For a motor, its efficiency is the ratio of mechanical work actually accomplished and the electrical work supplied by the circuit to the motor:

$$\eta = \frac{W_M}{W_E} \times 100\%. \tag{10}$$

In this experiment electrical work is converted into mechanical work as a mass is lifted through a vertical distance by a motor. The mechanical work accomplished can be calculated from Equation (1). The net electrical power available for doing work can be calculated from either Equation (5) or (8) as long as the mass is lifted at a constant speed. The work performed by the motor's net electrical power can be calculated using Equation (9). You will measure the mass, height, time, terminal voltage, motor resistance, and motor current in order to determine mechanical work and electrical work accomplished. Then you will compare the results. You will also calculate the electrical energy supplied to the motor and determine the efficiency of the motor.

- Motor winding resistance will be very small. The ohmmeter should be set to its lowest scale.

Postlab Analysis

- The questions in this assignment not only cover the concepts in this lab but also tie together many other ideas from earlier units.

Procedure

1. Assemble the apparatus according to Figure 1 with the exception of attaching the thread to the spool. Position the support stand next to the edge of the table and clamp the motor nearly horizontally so that the spool extends beyond the edge and the spool-end is tilted *slightly* with respect to the floor. The incline will allow the thread to wind up evenly. A typical setup is shown in Figure 2. Ensure that the switch is initially open and that the potentiometer is set to the middle of its range.

2. If you are using multimeters, you will need two for each setup—one that will be permanently connected in the circuit as an ammeter and a second to measure motor terminal voltage. The second meter may be shared among several lab teams, if required. The voltmeter should be clipped to the terminals of the motor. Set the ammeter to its highest scale for current. Set the voltmeter to a scale that will accommodate the voltage source.

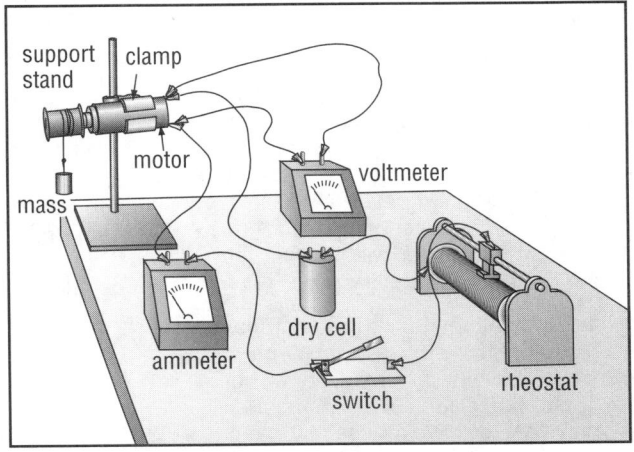

Figure 1

3. Tie the thread to the higher end of the spool. If the thread slips, place a spot of white glue or hot glue on the thread to fasten it to the spool. The thread should be 10 to 15 cm longer than the distance to the floor. Tie a loop in the lower end of the thread. Hook a 10 g mass onto the end of the thread. Start the motor and wind the thread evenly onto the spool. Stop the motor when the thread is completely wound onto the spool.

4. Allow the mass to slowly descend to the floor. Rotate the spool to take up the slack in the thread. Measure the distance from the center of the mass to the center of the spool shaft. Record this distance as Δh in Table 1.

Collecting data for this experiment is best accomplished by at least three individuals—one to monitor the time required to raise the mass, one to monitor amperage and operate the switch, and a third to monitor the motor voltage during a trial. Perform Steps 5–6 as many times as necessary in order to establish the proper conditions to collect data. This will require coordinating the stopwatch, adjusting the potentiometer for constant motor speed, selecting the correct meter scales, and reading the data during the operation.

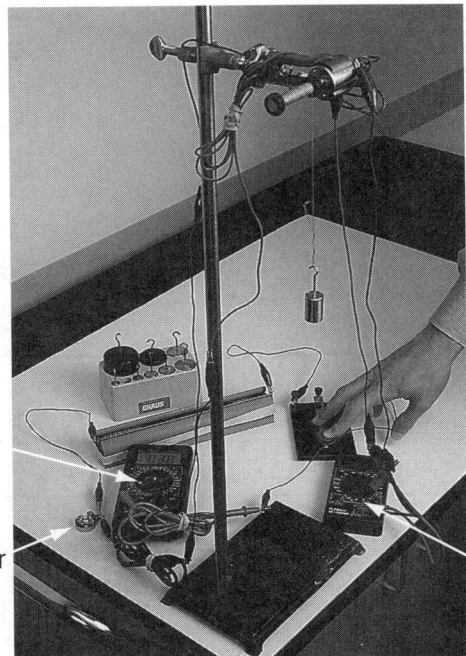

Figure 2

Prelab Homework

- This exercise is fairly sizable. It is suggested that you either split the assignment or allow the students to begin it in class.

Home School Notes

- Small DC motors may be obtained from discarded remote control toys. Other potential local sources are drive motors from discarded VCRs, video cameras, computer cooling fans, and computer printers. Some of these may require modifications in order to run on dry cell batteries.

- DO NOT use AC motors or any motor that has an electrical plug that connects it directly to a wall outlet. There is no great personal hazard if such a motor is connected to a battery, but the motor will not run and the battery will quickly discharge.

- The potentiometer or rheostat may be substituted by a light dimmer switch obtained from a home improvement store. The resistance may be excessive for use in this lab. You may have to use a group of batteries connected in series in order to obtain sufficient voltage.

- A variable resistor similar to the one included in the Elenco Learning Center may be useful. Variable resistors (potentiometers) can be purchased in a range of resistance values from electronics stores such as Radio Shack.

5. Shut the switch and adjust the potentiometer as necessary in order to obtain a slow but constant motor speed. Open the switch just as the mass touches the spool. Allow the mass to descend and repeat as necessary until the mass rises at a constant speed. The person timing the ascent should practice starting and stopping the stopwatch when the motor is started and stopped. The switch operator should audibly mark these events to assist the individual who is timing. The current and voltage readings should remain constant. If the current is fluctuating during the ascent of the mass, then the motor is not running at a constant speed.

6. While performing Step 5, team members should note the readings on the two meters and verify that the scales are set as necessary in order to obtain the proper displays. Review Appendix E for the proper use of voltmeters and ammeters. If the voltmeter test leads cannot be clipped to the motor terminals, touch the probes to the terminals to obtain the voltage reading. If a negative reading is obtained, swap the probes. The displays should be stable or at least not changing rapidly while the motor is running.

7. When the motor speed has been adjusted correctly, the individual with the stopwatch has practiced measuring the time interval, and the meters are set to the correct scales, you are ready to collect data. Shut the switch and observe the time that the mass requires to travel from the floor to the spool. Also note the terminal voltage and motor current while the motor is running. Report the voltage when the mass is at the midpoint of its ascent. Record these values in Table 1 for Trial 1.

8. Perform four additional trials with the 10 g mass according to Step 7 and record the results in Table 1.

9. After collecting the dynamic data for the 10 g mass, immediately disconnect the wires from the motor and measure the motor winding resistance (R_m) with an ohmmeter or multimeter set to the smallest resistance scale. The measurement is taken *after* loading the motor because current flow heats conductors and resistance rises with temperature in a conductor. Record the resistance in the blank at the top of Table 1. When finished, reconnect the motor.

10. Repeat Steps 4–9 with a 20 g mass. The motor speed will have to be readjusted for the larger mass. Record Δh, t, V_t, I_m, and R_m for the five trials with the 20 g mass in Table 2.

Data

Table 1
Electrical Work Data for 10 g Mass
Motor resistance, R_m _____ 1.8 _____ Ω

Trial	Height, Δh	Time, t	Voltage, V_t	Current, I_m
1	1.486 m	3.15 s	0.708 V	0.26 A
2		2.66 s	0.695 V	0.26 A
3		2.65 s	0.711 V	0.26 A
4		2.54 s	0.705 V	0.27 A
5		2.40 s	0.717 V	0.29 A
Average		2.68 s	0.707 V	0.27 A

Table 2
Electrical Work Data for 20 g Mass
Motor resistance, R_m _____ 1.8 _____ Ω

Trial	Height, Δh	Time, t	Voltage, V_t	Current, I_m
1	1.480 m	1.62 s	1.100 V	0.45 A
2		1.53 s	1.060 V	0.47 A
3		1.60 s	1.163 V	0.48 A
4		1.65 s	1.095 V	0.45 A
5		2.06 s	1.002 V	0.47 A
Average		1.69 s	1.084 V	0.46 A

Data in Tables 1 and 2 are typical. Actual student data will vary.

11. Repeat Steps 4–9 with a 50 g mass. Record Δh, t, V_t, I_m, and R_m for the five trials with the 50 g mass in Table 3. (Lifting the 50 g mass may require a 9 V battery or two series-connected 6 V batteries.)

12. When all trials are complete, disassemble the apparatus, disconnect all wires, remove the thread and spool, and return all components to their designated locations. Turn off the multimeters.

Table 3
Electrical Work Data for 50 g Mass
Motor resistance, R_m _____ Ω

Trial	Height, Δh	Time, t	Voltage, V_t	Current, I_m
1	m	s	V	A
2		s	V	A
3		s	V	A
4		s	V	A
5		s	V	A
Average		s	V	A

Postlab Exercises

1. Calculate the averages for t, V_t, and I_m in Tables 1, 2, and 3. The change in height, Δh, is assumed to be the same for all trials with a given mass.

2. Assume that the metric masses are accurate to 1 g. Calculate the mechanical work accomplished for each mass, using Equation (1). Record calculated mechanical work performed on each mass in Table 4.

3. For each mass, calculate the voltage drop in the motor windings, using the *average* motor current (I_m) and motor resistance (R_m). Record these values in Table 4.

4. Use Equation (5) to calculate the electrical power (P_m) produced by the motor, using the *average* values of I_m and V_t and the motor voltage drop (V_m) calculated in Step 3. Record the results in Table 4.

5. Calculate the net electrical work accomplished by the motor (W_m) by finding the product of the net electrical power developed by the motor (P_m) and the *average* time (t), using Equation (9). Record the electrical work results in Table 4 for each mass.

6. Determine the percent difference between mechanical work (W_M) and electrical work performed by the motor (W_m) for each mass. Record the results in Table 4.

7. Calculate the electrical power delivered to the motor by the circuit (P_E) by finding the product of the *average* value for motor terminal voltage (V_t) and *average* motor current (I_m). Enter the result for each mass in Table 4.

8. Calculate the total work or energy (W_E) delivered by the circuit to the motor by multiplying the electrical power delivered by the circuit by the average time for each mass. Enter these values in Table 4.

9. Finally, calculate the efficiency of the motor for each mass, using Equation (10). Record the results in Table 4.

Table 4
Calculations

Mass	W_M $(mg\Delta h)$	V_m $(I_m R_m)$	P_m $[I_m(V_t - I_m R_m)]$	W_m $(P_m t)$	W_M and W_m Percent Difference	P_E $(I_m V_t)$	W_E $(P_E t)$	Efficiency, η
10 g	0.15 J	0.49 V	0.60 W	0.16 J	6.5 %	0.19 W	0.51 J	29 %
20 g	0.29 J	0.83 V	0.12 W	0.30 J	3.4 %	0.50 W	0.85 J	34 %
50 g	J	V	W	J	%	W	J	%

Results in Table 4 are typical. Student results will vary.

Postlab Analysis

1. What was the average efficiency of the motor used by your lab team? According to your data, how is efficiency related to the size of the load on a motor?

   Efficiencies of the motors and conclusions will vary. Theoretically, the

   efficiency of a DC motor should decrease as it becomes increasingly

   loaded because higher motor currents will increase I^2R power losses

   in the windings due to heating.

2. Explain why a motor turns faster as more current is supplied to it. Include in your discussion appropriate references to motor theory.

   More current flowing through the motor windings produces a stronger

   magnetic flux, which interacts with the permanent magnets, produc-

   ing greater torque on the rotor shaft. This unbalanced force couple

   causes the shaft to accelerate until back emf increases enough

   (Lenz's law) to produce an opposing torque, which eventually estab-

   lishes an equilibrium of torques on the shaft. The motor then runs at a

   higher constant speed.

3. Draw an electrical schematic of the circuit used for this experiment. Include the test meters connected at the appropriate points. Use a circle containing the letter "M" to represent the motor.

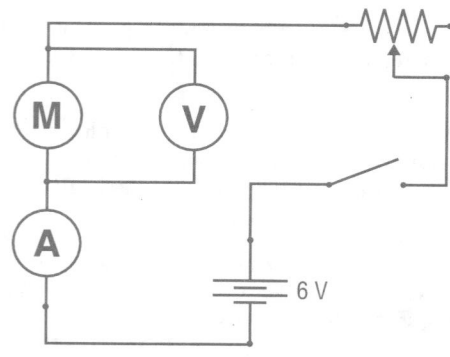

4. Figure 3 is a graph of power vs. time. Refer to the diagram when answering the following questions.

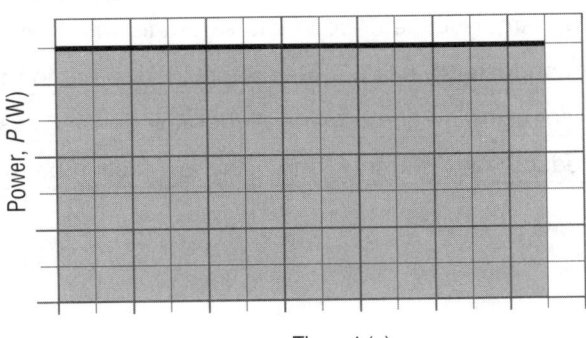

Figure 3

Time, t (s)

a. Describe how power varies with time in the graph—is it increasing, decreasing, or remaining constant?

Power remains constant with time.

b. What is the shape of the shaded area under the graph?

The shaded area is a rectangle.

c. What is the appropriate formula for calculating the area of the geometric shape in Question 4b?

$A = wl$

d. Write a formula for calculating the area under the line, using P and t for the width and length, respectively.

$A = Pt$

e. Review the Prelab Discussion. What quantity is the shaded area calculated in Question 4d equivalent to?

The quantity Pt is equivalent to work accomplished at power P in time t.

f. Based on your response to Question 4e, make a general statement about the significance of the area under a power-time graph during a specified time interval.

The area under a power-time graph is equivalent to the work accomplished during the specified time interval.

g. If the graph were a sloped line or a curve, what would be happening to power during the time interval?

A sloped line or curve indicates that power was changing during the time interval.

h. Discuss the effects of changing power on the ease of determining work accomplished during the associated time interval.

When power varies with time, work can no longer be calculated by the product Pt. If power varies at a constant rate, the area under the curve could be calculated using the formula for a triangle or trapezoid. If power varies with a changing rate (producing a curve), more advanced math techniques (integration) are required to determine the work accomplished.

5. Discuss three changes that would make the motor more efficient.

Answers will vary. Students should consider reducing winding electrical resistance, (larger-diameter conductors, metals with lower resistivity, shorter conductors), using more streamlined rotors to reduce wind resistance, using magnets with a higher flux density, designing magnets to reduce eddy currents, and using low-friction bearings.

Name _____

Date _____ Hour ____

PRELAB HOMEWORK

1. Symbols for physical quantities are often defined by a textbook for a particular discussion, but many variables are standardized throughout science. Write the symbol specified in this exercise for the following quantities.

   a. back emf ___ε___

   b. net electrical power *from* motor ___P_m___

   c. motor current ___I_m___

   d. resistance power loss ___P_h___

   e. electrical energy *to* motor ___W_E___

   f. electrical power *to* motor ___P_E___

   g. motor winding resistance ___R_m___

   h. terminal voltage ___V_t___

2. ___3.68 J___ Calculate the mechanical work accomplished when lifting a 500. g mass 75.0 cm.

   Given: m = 500. g = 0.500 kg; Δh = 75.0 cm = 0.750 m; W_M = ?

   Formula: $W_M = \Delta U_g = mg\Delta h$

   Solution: W_M = (0.500 kg)(9.81 $\frac{m}{s^2}$)(0.750 m) $\doteq$ 3.68 J

3. ___0.93 W___ If 3.7 J of work takes 4.0 s to accomplish, how much power is being developed?

   Given: W = 3.7 J; t = 4.0 s; P = ?

   Formula: $P = W/t$

   Solution: $P = \dfrac{3.7\ J}{4.0\ s} \doteq 0.925\ \frac{J}{s} \approx 0.93\ W$ (2 SDs allowed)

4. Why is the voltage drop across an electrical circuit component sometimes called *emf* (refer to your textbook discussion)?

   In the past, scientists believed that a "force" similar to the electrostatic force caused the movement of electrons within a conductor, and this force was called the electromotive force (emf). Present theory states that electrical potential differ-ence (voltage drop) is the cause of current flow.

5. ___225 W___ How much power is lost as heat in a 100. Ω resistor when a 1.50 A current passes through it?

   Given: R = 100. Ω; I = 1.50 A; P_h = ?

   Formula: $P_h = I^2R$

   Solution: P_h = (1.50 A)²(100. Ω) = 225 W

6. ___0.17 W___ While performing this experiment, students measured the current in a small DC motor at 650. mA. The winding resistance of the motor was 0.40 Ω. What was the power loss due to electrical heating in the motor windings?

   Given: R_m = 0.40 Ω; I_m = 0.650 A; P_h = ?

   Formula: $P_h = I_m^2R_m$

   Solution: P_h = (0.650 A)²(0.40 Ω) = 0.169 W $\approx$ 0.17 W   (2 SDs allowed)

7. ___0.774 W___ During the same experiment in Question 6, students also measured the motor terminal voltage at 1.45 V. Calculate the net electrical power developed by the motor, using Equation (5).

   Given: V_t = 1.45 V; I_m = 0.650 A; R_m = 0.40 Ω; P_m = ?

   Formula: $P_m = I_m(V_t - I_mR_m)$

   Solution: P_m = (0.650 A)[1.45 V − (0.650 A)(0.40 Ω)] = (0.650 A)(1.45 V − 0.26 V)

   = 0.7735 W $\approx$ 0.774 W   (3 SDs allowed)

8. __−1.19 V__ What is the back emf generated in the motor in Question 6?

   Given: $V_t = 1.45$ V; $I_m = 0.650$ A; $R_m = 0.40$ Ω; $\mathcal{E} = ?$

   Formula: $\mathcal{E} = I_m R_m − V_t$

   Solution: $\mathcal{E} = (0.650$ A$)(0.40$ Ω$) − 1.45$ V $= −1.19$ V

9. __0.943 W__ Calculate the power (in watts) delivered to the motor in Question 6.

   Given: $V_t = 1.45$ V; $I_m = 0.650$ A; $P_E = ?$

   Formula: $P_E = I_m V_t$

   Solution: $P_E = (0.650$ A$)(1.45$ V$) \doteq 0.943$ W

10. __0.90 W__ Assuming that a small DC motor uses 1.00 W of electrical power and loses 0.10 W to electrical heating in its windings, how much electrical power is delivered by the motor to do mechanical work?

    Given: $P_E = 1.00$ W; $P_h = 0.10$ W; $P_m = ?$

    Formula: $P_m = P_E − P_h$

    Solution: $P_m = 1.00$ W $− 0.10$ W $= 0.90$ W

11. How is back emf related to the electrical work delivered by a motor?

    Electrical work can be calculated from the product of back emf and motor current.

12. Discuss how a potentiometer or rheostat controls the speed of a DC motor.

    The sum of the voltage drops in a circuit equals the voltage supplied by the voltage source. The larger the voltage drop across one circuit element, the less voltage available to the other elements. A potentiometer is a variable resistor. As the resistance of the potentiometer increases, the voltage drop across the potentiometer increases, resulting in less voltage delivered to the terminals of the motor. The result is that the motor has less energy to perform work.

13. Why should you wait to measure motor winding resistance to determine voltage drop in the motor until *after* performing the trials for a particular mass?

    Current used by the motor under load is greater than when the motor is not loaded. The current flowing through the motor causes heating of the windings. As the temperature of the wires increases, their resistance increases. To determine the total voltage drop in the motor windings under load, the resistance of the windings after warming will provide a more representative value.

14. __67.2%__ After completing this lab, a student determines that a motor performed 0.638 J of work while lifting a 50 g mass. If the electrical energy delivered to the motor was 0.950 J, what was the efficiency of the motor?

    Given: $W_{in} = W_E = 0.950$ J; $W_{out} = W_M = 0.638$ J; $\eta = ?$

    Formula: $\eta = \dfrac{W_{out}}{W_{in}} = \dfrac{W_M}{W_E} \times 100\%$

    Solution: $\eta = \dfrac{0.638 \text{ J}}{0.950 \text{ J}} \times 100\% \doteq 67.2\%$

Name _____

Date _____ Hour _____

CAPACITORS, DIODES, AND TRANSISTORS

Required Equipment
Elenco Learning Center kit
Elenco M-1000B multimeter

Purpose

Most electronic circuits consist of various combinations of capacitors, diodes, and transistors in addition to resistors. The purpose of this exercise is to

¥ demonstrate the electrical characteristics of capacitors and their ability to collect, deliver, and store charge.
¥ demonstrate the one-way characteristic of diodes.
¥ connect transistors to function as switches, amplifiers, and diodes.
¥ describe practical uses for these components.

Prelab Discussion

In previous electrical labs you have examined the properties of basic electrical circuits, using mostly resistors and LEDs to determine the characteristics of the circuits. Many electrical circuits and most electronic circuits contain many other elements and devices to shape and control voltage and current in order to perform specific functions. Three common elements discussed at some length in your textbook are the subject of this lab: capacitors, diodes, and transistors; however, they are by no means the only other electrical components.

Capacitors are devices that store electrical charge by developing an electrical potential between two plates separated by an insulator or dielectric. In some circuits they function to reduce or eliminate voltage variations; in others they function as a rechargeable battery, supplying essential power to digital memory during periods of power loss. **Capacitance** is measured in farads (F), but this unit is so large that most electronics capacitors are rated in microfarads (μF). Connecting capacitors in *parallel* effectively increases the plate area exposed to a particular voltage drop. The total capacitance is equal to the sum of the
individual capacitors and is thus greater than any individual capacitor value. Connecting capacitors in *series* produces a total capacitance that is less than any individual capacitor. This effect is analogous to the total resistance of parallel resistors. Capacitance is inversely proportional to the number of voltage drops required to store a certain amount of charge. The more voltage drops (capacitors) there are, the smaller the total capacitance. The relationship can be expressed by

$$\frac{1}{C_\text{T}} = \frac{1}{C_1} + \frac{1}{C_2} + ... + \frac{1}{C_n}. \tag{1}$$

Diodes are semiconductor devices that allow current to flow in only one direction. The symbol for a diode indicates the allowed direction of flow for *conventional current* through the diode. If the positive voltage source is connected to the pointed end of the arrow in the symbol, the diode is **reversed-biased,** and no current will flow. Some diodes convert electrical energy into other forms of energy such as thermal energy and visible light. A light-emitting diode (LED), with which you are already familiar, is such a device.

Transistors are another class of semiconductor devices that are used to switch current on and off, amplify current, and block current when required. The transistors included in the Elenco Learning Center are the *NPN* type. The semiconductor theory behind transistors is discussed in greater depth in your textbook. A transistor consists of a base (indicated in the symbol by the single line) that

Prelab Discussion

• Review the prerequisites for Lab 4-8 in the back of this manual.

• Students often have difficulty making sense of the total capacitance of series-connected capacitors. Recall that $C \equiv Q/V$. The total charge that is stored on each series-connected capacitor is equal because the positive charge on one plate induces an equal negative charge on the adjacent plate, and so on down the line of capacitors. The charge stored by the *circuit* then is $Q = C_n V_n$, where n refers to any capacitor in the string. The voltage drop across each capacitor is determined by its capacitance; therefore, the smallest capacitor will have the largest voltage drop to store a given amount of charge. This voltage drop across the smallest capacitor is less than it would be if the capacitor were connected to the battery by itself. Consequently, the amount of charge stored per volt (capacitance) for the circuit is less than the smallest capacitor's capacitance.

Equipment and Setup

• The same Elenco Learning Center and multimeter are used for this lab as for the previous electrical labs.

Procedure

• It is intended that the students make the connections for the circuit in this lab with a minimum of assistance.

• Students need to carefully read each step in order to obtain maximum benefit. Encourage them to predict the behavior of the circuit before actually performing the step.

Home School Notes

- Refer to the Lab 4-2 Home School Notes for information about constructing an electrical breadboard similar to the Elenco Learning Center kit.

other two lines on the opposite side of the symbol are the collector and the emitter (with the arrowhead). When approximately 0.7 V exists between the base and the emitter, a small current flows into the transistor through the base, and this process causes a much larger current to flow through the collector-emitter connections. The emitter current is the sum of the collector and base currents. As base current increases over a narrow range, the emitter current increases proportionally. Once base current exceeds a certain value, no further increase of emitter current occurs, and the transistor is said to be **saturated.** As with a diode, if the voltage between the emitter and the base opposes the direction of conventional current flow through the transistor (indicated by the arrow), the transistor is reversed-biased, and the transistor will not conduct or switch on.

In this lab you will observe how capacitors, diodes, and transistors function. For most demonstrations, questions may be answered with comparative descriptions (i.e., slower, faster, fastest). When numerical information must be measured or calculated, include the correct number of SDs in your answer.

Procedure

Capacitors

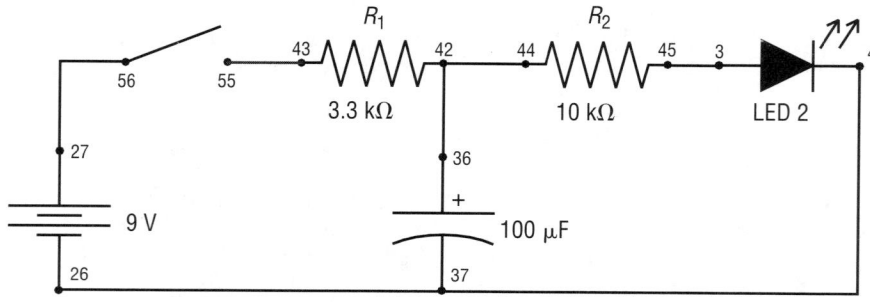

Figure 1

1. Connect the circuit shown in Figure 1.

2. Press the switch and note comparatively how long it takes the LED to reach full brightness.

   The LED should reach full brightness fairly quickly.

3. How does the time for the LED to go out compare to the time it took to light up?

   The LED should take considerably longer to go out than it did to light up.

   When the switch is pressed, the closed circuit allows current to flow to both the capacitor and the LED. Consequently, the LED may take a little longer to reach full brightness than if the capacitor were not in the circuit. It should be obvious that the LED takes a lot longer to go out when the switch is released. The reason for the longer time is that the capacitor discharges through the LED. Notice from the schematic that the capacitor charges through the 3.3 kΩ resistor and discharges through the 10 kΩ resistor.

4. Experiment with different combinations of charging and discharging resistors by substituting the resistors listed in Table 1 for the resistors labeled R_1 and R_2 in Figure 1. Note the relative speed with which the LED attains full brightness and goes out for each set of resistors in Table 1.

Table 1
Changing R_1 While Keeping R_2 Constant

R_1	R_2	Time On	Time Off
1 kΩ	33 kΩ	fast	very slow
3.3 kΩ	33 kΩ	slower	very slow
10 kΩ	33 kΩ	slowest	very slow

Answers in Table 1 may vary. Speeds shown are typical.

5. What effects did you observe as R_1 increased?

   Increasing R_1 should cause the LED to attain maximum brightness

   more slowly. The time required to go off should not be significantly

   affected.

6. Reconnect the 3.3 kΩ resistor as R_1 and vary R_2 according to Table 2.
   Record the relative speed with which the LED attains full brightness and
   the relative brightness as well as the time required to go out completely in
   Table 2.

Table 2
Changing R_2 While Keeping R_1 Constant

R_1	R_2	Time On	Brightness	Time Off
3.3 kΩ	1 kΩ	fast	bright	slow
3.3 kΩ	10 kΩ	fast	medium	slower
3.3 kΩ	33 kΩ	fast	dim	slowest

Answers in Table 2 may vary. Properties shown are typical.

7. What effects did you observe as R_2 increased?

   Increasing R_2 should reduce the brightness of the LED (because

   more voltage is dropped across the resistor in series with the LED),

   and the time to go off should increase. The time required to light up

   should not be significantly changed.

8. Connect the circuit shown in the schematic in Figure 2.

9. Are the capacitors connected in series or parallel?

   The capacitors are connected in series.

10. Would you expect the total capacitance of the two ca-
    pacitors to be greater than or less than 10 μF?

    The total capacitance of the capacitors connected

    in series should be less than the value of the

    smaller capacitor.

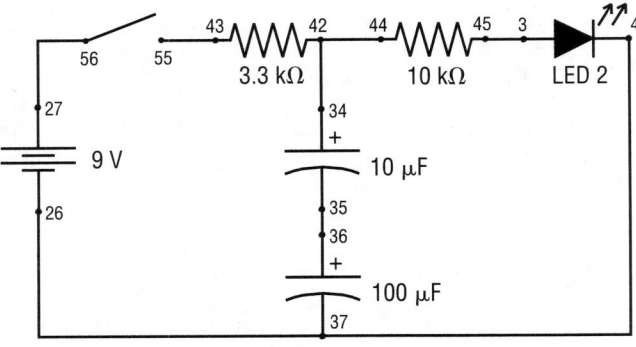

Figure 2

11. Calculate the total capacitance of the two capacitors. Assume that all of the digits in the capacitor values are significant.

Given: $C_1 = 10. \ \mu F; \ C_2 = 100. \ \mu F; \ C_T = ?$

Formula: $\dfrac{1}{C_T} = \dfrac{1}{C_1} + \dfrac{1}{C_2} \Rightarrow C_T = \dfrac{C_1 C_2}{C_1 + C_2}$

Solution: $C_T = \dfrac{(10. \ \mu F)(100. \ \mu F)}{10. \ \mu F + 100. \ \mu F} = \dfrac{1.0 \times 10^3 \ \mu F^2}{110. \ \mu F} \doteq 9.1 \ \mu F$

If the capacitance is less than that of the smaller capacitor, it should take less time for the capacitors to charge and discharge. If it is greater, the charge and discharge times should be longer.

12. How should the times required for the LED to illuminate and go out compare to the times for the circuit shown in Figure 1?

The LED in this circuit should take less time than in the circuit in

Figure 1.

13. Test your prediction and record your observations.

The LED illuminated and extinguished noticeably faster with the

capacitors in series.

14. Connect the capacitors in parallel according to the schematic in Figure 3.

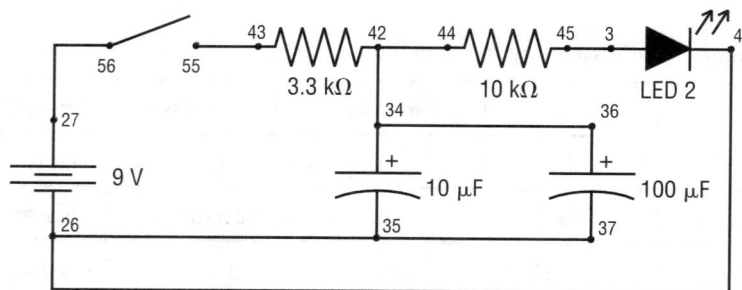

Figure 3

15. Would you expect the total capacitance of the two capacitors to be less than or greater than 10 μF? Calculate the total capacitance for the parallel capacitors.

The total should be greater than 10 μF. Parallel capacitors produce a

capacitance that is the sum of the individual capacitances. The total

capacitance should be 110 μF.

16. How should the times for the LED to illuminate and go off compare to the times for the first circuit (in Figure 1)?

The times should be significantly longer.

17. Test your prediction and record your observations.

The LED took noticeably longer to illuminate and extinguish than the

circuit in Figure 1.

Diodes

18. Connect the circuit shown in the schematic in Figure 4. Note that the shaft of the arrow of the diode symbols are connected to the positive terminal of the battery. (In conventional current flow, the positive terminal is the source of electrical current.)

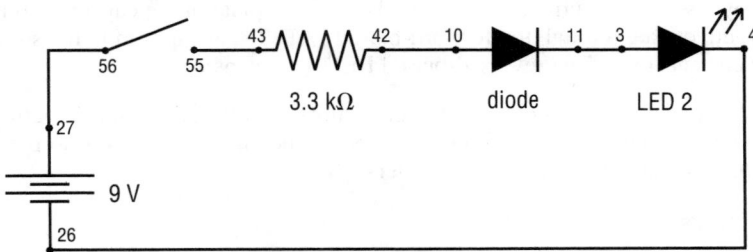

Figure 4

19. Press the switch and observe that LED 2 lights up.

20. Reverse the wires connecting the diode (at terminals 10 _____ and 11 _____).

21. Press the switch and report your observations.

   The LED does not illuminate.

   Like the diode, the LED will allow current to flow in only one direction. The arrow in the symbol points in the direction of conventional current flow. Connecting the LED terminals with the opposing polarity will prevent the LED from lighting.

The schematic in Figure 5 will further demonstrate the current-blocking function of the diode. In this circuit, there are two diodes connected in parallel, but with opposite biasing. One will illuminate as current flows in one direction, and the other will illuminate as current flows in the opposite direction.

22. Connect the circuit shown in Figure 5. Note that you will not be using the switch for this experiment.

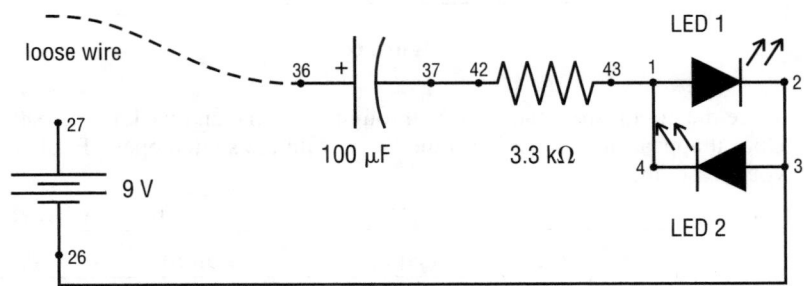

Figure 5

23. Touch the end of the loose wire to the positive terminal of the battery and describe what happens.

   LED 1 illuminates briefly, then goes out.

   The flow of current in the circuit is from the positive battery terminal toward the positive plate of the capacitor. Since current flows in the entire circuit, the current flows through the forward-biased LED 1, and it lights up until the capacitor is fully charged. LED 2 is reversed-biased under these conditions and remains dark.

24. Touch the end of the wire to the negative terminal of the battery and describe what happens.

   LED 2 comes on briefly, then goes out.

   When the wire is touched to the negative terminal of the battery, the capacitor is "grounded," or discharged, to the lowest (or ground) potential. The capacitor then becomes the source of potential in the circuit because the battery is bypassed, and current flows from the positive plate of the capacitor to its negative plate through the forward-biased LED 2, causing it to light as long as current flows. The reversed-biased LED 1 remains dark.

Pairs of opposing diodes connected to capacitors are often used in alternating current (AC) circuits to produce electrical resonance in subcircuits or to produce DC from an AC signal (AC rectifiers).

Transistors

Observe the shape of the transistors installed in the Elenco Learning Center. If you hold the transistor so that the flat surface is facing you and the electrode wires point down, the left wire will be the emitter, the center wire will be the base, and the right wire will be the collector. Note that these electrodes are arranged in the same relationship in the schematic symbol—the base is always in the middle, even though the sides occupied by the emitter (indicated by the arrow) and the collector may vary, depending on the location of the symbol in the schematic.

25. Connect the schematic in Figure 6.

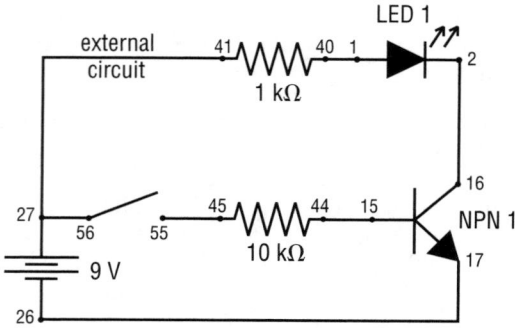

Figure 6

26. Trace the circuit from the battery, through the LED, and back to the battery. Does it appear that the LED should be on with the switch open? Explain your reasoning.

    Yes. There is a continuous path from the battery through the 1 kΩ

    resistor, the LED, and the transistor back to the battery.

27. Give an explanation that might explain why the LED does *not* illuminate with the switch open.

    The circuit appears to be open at the transistor.

28. Press the switch and describe what happens.

    The LED illuminates.

29. Set the multimeter to read current by selecting 20m on the DCA scale. Remove the wire between the 10 kΩ resistor and the base of the transistor. Insert the red test lead probe into terminal 44 (____) and the black probe into 15 (____).

30. Press the switch and record the base current displayed.

    Data will vary, but base current should be ~0.90 (mA).

31. Remove the multimeter probes and reconnect the wire removed in Step 29.

32. Remove the wire between the 1 kΩ resistor and the LED. Insert the probes of the multimeter into the terminals, observing proper polarity.

33. Press the switch and record the current flowing into the collector of the transistor.

   Data will vary, but collector current should be ~6.60 (mA).

34. Remove the multimeter and reconnect the wire removed in Step 32.

35. Remove the wire between the emitter of the transistor and the battery. Connect the multimeter to the terminals as before.

36. Press the switch and record the emitter current.

   Data will vary, but emitter current should be ~7.50 (mA), the sum of

   Steps 30 and 33.

   The 10 kΩ resistor allows only a small current to flow in the base circuit, but that current is sufficient to "switch on" the transistor to permit the much larger current to flow in the main circuit through the LED. Although there is a mechanical switch in the circuit controlling the operation of the transistor, the switch could be replaced by a current source such as a magnetic coil. Induced current from the coil could turn on the transistor, causing it to function as a switch. The transistor output could then control many other electronic devices.

37. Transistors are also used as amplifiers. Connect the circuit shown in the schematic in Figure 7. **Note:** Connect the wires from terminals 18 (_____) and 51 (_____) to the end of the variable resistor that is *actually* 0 Ω, either 48 (_____) or 50 (_____).

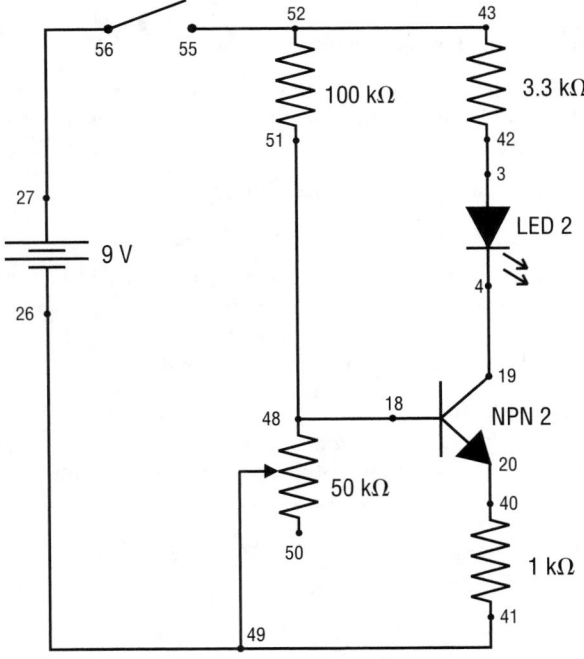

Figure 7

38. Press the switch and rotate the variable resistor both clockwise and counterclockwise. Record your observations.

   As the resistance decreases, the LED illuminates and increases in

   brightness. It dims and goes out when resistance increases.

Imagine what would happen if the 100 kΩ resistor were replaced by a source of a small variable current such as a microphone or antenna. The variations in the flow of the small current would be duplicated in the external circuit but at a much higher current level. If a speaker and its necessary supporting circuit elements replaced the LED, the resulting circuit could function as an audio amplifier.

One other consideration in the design of the amplifier circuit is the need for a sufficient forward bias on the base of the transistor to allow it to amplify even in the presence of very small signal currents. Recall that the *NPN* transistors provided with the Learning Center require approximately 0.7 V to switch on the transistor. If the signal current flowing into the transistor base is not sufficient to generate this voltage, the transistor stays off and no amplification occurs. The variable resistor can set the amount of current flowing into the base so that even very small signal currents added to that current are able to turn on the transistor and obtain the desired amplification. At the same time, the variable resistance can be lowered within certain limits to prevent saturating the transistor.

39. Remove the wire between the collector and LED 2. Set the multimeter to display current as in Step 29 and insert the probes into the terminals.

40. Press the switch, rotate the variable resistor back and forth, and record your observations. Discuss collector current indicated on the meter compared to the resistor position.

    The collector current increases as resistance decreases, and it

    decreases as resistance increases. The current reaches a

    maximum before the resistor reaches minimum resistance.

41. While pressing the switch, carefully adjust the resistor to reduce collector current to 0 mA but no further. Release the switch.

42. Remove the multimeter and reconnect the wire removed in Step 39.

43. Set the multimeter to display voltage by selecting 2000m on the DCV scale. Insert the red test lead into the terminal at the transistor base (18 ____) and the black test lead into the emitter terminal (20 ____).

44. Press the switch and measure the base voltage.

    Data will vary, but base voltage should be ~700 (mV).

    Although the expected reading based on transistor design should be approximately 700 mV or 0.7 V, the actual voltage will vary somewhat, so your reading could be as low as 500 mV or as high as 900 mV. This is the voltage at which the transistor functions as a switch.

You have seen the transistor function as a switch and as an amplifier. You can also use the transistor in place of a *diode*. This application is common in integrated circuit technology; many transistors are manufactured into a single silicon chip for the purpose of limiting the *direction* of current flow.

45. Disconnect the wires from the previous experiment. Connect the circuit shown in the schematic in Figure 8.

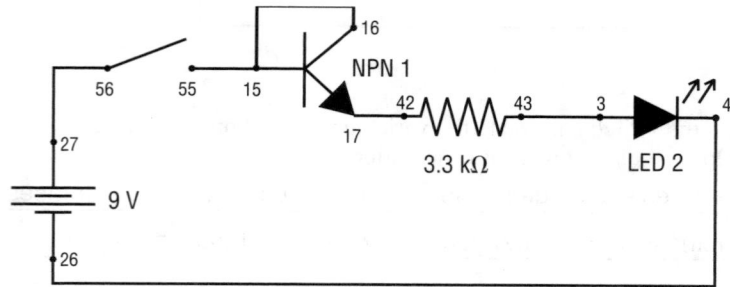

Figure 8

46. Press the switch. Does the LED illuminate?

    yes

47. Swap the long wires between the emitter and the base. Notice that the battery voltage is being supplied to the transistor's emitter.

48. Press the switch. Does the LED still illuminate? Explain the results.

    No. The transistor base is reversed-biased (the voltage is higher at the emitter than at the base), so the transistor is off.

Laboratory Activity ━━━━━━━━━━━━━━━━━━━ **4-8**

Name _____

Date _____ Hour ____

PRELAB HOMEWORK

1. According to your text, what are the variables associated with the structure of a capacitor, and how does capacitance vary with each?

   The variables associated with a capacitor's structure are the plate area (A), the distance between the plates (d), and the type of dielectric. Capacitance varies directly with the plate area and the dielectric constant (ϵ), and inversely with the distance between the plates.

2. Why does the schematic symbol for a capacitor show a space between the positive and negative plates?

   An insulator separates the two plates of a capacitor so that there is no conducting path through the capacitor.

3. Explain how current can flow through a capacitor. Include in your discussion the conditions under which current flow occurs and what limits the duration of current flow.

   When a voltage drop occurs across a capacitor, charges flow into the capacitor, repelling the like charges on the opposite plate. Those charges flow out the other side of the capacitor, and it appears that current is flowing through the capacitor. Charges will continue to flow until the internal voltage drop across the plates equals the external voltage drop across the capacitor; then current stops flowing.

4. How is the total capacitance of two or more capacitors connected in a circuit related to the way in which they are connected?

   The total capacitance of capacitors connected in parallel is the sum of the individual capacitances. The *reciprocal* of total capacitance of capacitors connected in series is the sum of the *reciprocals* of the individual capacitances.

5. What is the total capacitance of 50. μF and 200. μF capacitors connected in parallel? In series?

   Given: $C_1 = 50.\ \mu F$; $C_2 = 200.\ \mu F$; $C_T = ?$

   Parallel Formula: $C_T = C_1 + C_2$

   Solution: $C_T = 50.\ \mu F + 200.\ \mu F = 250.\ \mu F$

   Series Formula: $\dfrac{1}{C_T} = \dfrac{1}{C_1} + \dfrac{1}{C_2} \Rightarrow C_T = \dfrac{C_1 C_2}{C_1 + C_2}$

   Solution: $C_T = \dfrac{(50.\ \mu F)(200.\ \mu F)}{50.\ \mu F + 200.\ \mu F} = \dfrac{1.0 \times 10^4\ \mu F^2}{250.\ \mu F} = 40.\ \mu F$

6. According to your text, how many doped semiconductor regions are there in a typical diode?

   There are two doped semiconductor regions in a diode.

7. What is the result of applying a very high reverse bias to a diode?

   Applying a reversed bias that is too high can permanently damage the diode.

8. What is the primary function of diodes in electronic circuits?

   Diodes are used to control the direction of current in a circuit by allowing only one-way flow.

9. How many doped semiconductor regions are there in the type of transistors used in this lab? What are they called?

The transistors used in this lab contain three doped regions. They are called the base, the collector, and the emitter.

10. When a transistor in a circuit operates only in either a reversed-biased state or a saturated state, it is functioning as a(n) _____switch_____.

11. When a transistor in a circuit produces a large emitter current proportional to the small base current and the signal pattern supplied to the base is duplicated at the emitter, it is operating as a(n) _____amplifier_____.

12. If the positive voltage of a transistor is higher at the emitter than at the base, the transistor is _____reversed-biased_____ and it (will/will not) conduct in this state. (Circle the correct choice.)

Name _____

Date _____ Hour _____

SPECIAL TRANSISTOR APPLICATIONS

Required Equipment
Elenco Learning Center kit
Elenco M-1000B multimeter

Purpose

The preceding labs have introduced most of the basic components found in electrical and electronic circuits. The purpose of this lab is to

- experiment with inductors, transformers, and miscellaneous devices.
- provide practice reading more complicated electronic schematics.
- experiment with various combinations of devices in order to observe some of the functions possible with electronics.

Prelab Discussion

This lab exercise consists of a variety of experiments and demonstrations that will expand on the foundation of knowledge you have gained after completing the earlier labs dealing with electricity and electronics.

Time will not permit you to make every circuit connection included in this exercise within your normal class schedule, but it would be helpful for you to connect each of the circuits in the Learning Center manual on your own time. Rather than just making the connections, you should study the circuit diagrams and determine for yourself what is taking place. Remember that most of the circuits in the manual are not actual circuits that you could go out and purchase as an electronic device but are just a simple part of more complicated circuits. Once you determine how these circuits work, you will be able to connect them in order to make a practical piece of equipment. Also, keep in mind that most electronic devices today are not made by connecting individual circuit components, as you are doing here, but through the fabrication of special semiconductor chips that have many transistor circuits etched into them during a complex multilayer manufacturing process. These circuits are called integrated circuits, or **ICs.** Nevertheless, designers of ICs must begin with the basic diagrams that you will refer to and then design the IC to duplicate on a smaller scale the results you will observe.

Several new components are introduced in this lab. They are inductors, transformers, and antennas. Each of these devices contains one or more coils of wire. As the magnetic field surrounding a coil of wire changes, back emf is generated in the coil according to Faraday's law. Review the discussion of Faraday's law in your text. Back emf opposes the change in the magnetic field by generating a current in the conductor that tends to sustain the original field. This effect is called self-inductance, or simply **inductance.** Inductance can be amplified by winding a conductor into a series of coils. Such a device is called an **inductor.** As current flow changes in an inductor, inductance tends to resist the change in current. **Transformers** are devices that magnetically link two or more inductors together. The changing magnetic field formed by changing current in one inductor generates a current in an adjacent inductor wound on the same iron core. If the two inductors have the same number of coils, the input voltage and the induced output voltage should be the same. If the output inductor has fewer coils than the input inductor, the output voltage will be lower and vice versa. Review transformer theory in your textbook. **Antennas** are special-purpose inductors that detect electromagnetic signals and convert the miniscule magnetic field into a voltage that can be amplified in an electronic circuit. Applications of each of these devices will be seen in the following experiments.

Prelab Discussion

- Review the prerequisites for Lab 4-9 in the back of this manual.

- Ensure that students are familiar with inductive theory prior to assigning the Prelab Homework and performing this lab.

- References to the function of capacitors requires that Lab 4-8 be completed prior to this lab.

- If you want your students to connect circuits having an audio output, you will need to introduce the schematic symbol for a speaker.

Equipment and Setup

- This lab is based on the Elenco Learning Center and multimeter.

Procedure

- There is more explanatory material in the Procedure section for this lab than in previous labs because of the more complex nature of the circuits.

- Encourage students to check voltages and current at various points in the circuits that they build. Also, they should experiment by changing the values of resistors and capacitors in order to observe their effect on the circuits.

- Encourage students to build some of the other circuits during free time in order to help them understand some of the other configurations discussed in the Learning Center manual.

Home School Notes

- Refer to the Lab 4-2 Home School Notes for information about constructing an electrical breadboard similar to the Elenco Learning Center kit.

Procedure

Transistor Applications

A. Darlington Configuration

The circuit in Figure 1 contains a combination of transistors called a _Darlington configuration_. In this arrangement, the output (emitter current) of one transistor controls the base current of another. The base current of the first transistor is therefore amplified twice. This process may be repeated many times to produce very large currents. In this circuit, the LED cannot light until transistor NPN 2 turns on. This will occur only after the base-to-emitter voltage for each transistor exceeds approximately 0.7 V, or a total of 1.4 V from the base of NPN 1 to the emitter of NPN 2.

1. Connect the circuit shown in the schematic in Figure 1.

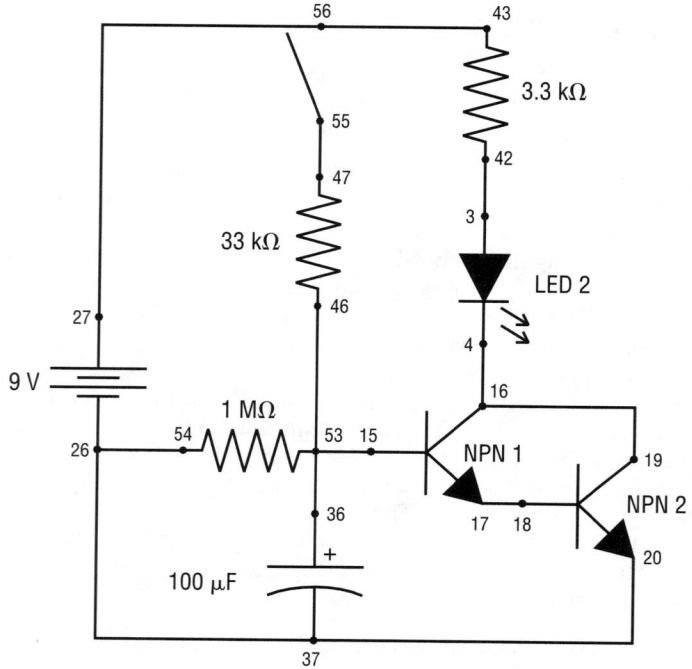

Figure 1

2. Using a stopwatch, measure the time required for the LED to reach full brightness after the switch is pressed and the time required for the LED to completely extinguish after the switch is released.

   a. Time to full brightness _____1 to 2 s (Ans. vary.)_____

   b. Time to completely extinguish _____~23 s (Ans. vary.)_____

Note that the voltage required to turn on both transistors will be available only after the capacitor has charged up via the 33 kΩ resistor. After the switch is opened, the transistors will continue to conduct (indicated by the lit LED) until the capacitor voltage drops below about 1.4 V as it discharges through the 1 MΩ resistor and the transistor bases.

   c. Did the LED reach full brightness slowly or nearly instantaneously? Explain.

   The LED remained dark until NPN 2 turned on like a switch. Then

   full current flowed through the LED with little observable transition.

B. Voltage Regulator

You may have noticed in your house that when a large electrical load such as a refrigerator or washing machine starts running that the house lights dim briefly. This is caused by the appliance drawing current from the house circuit, which momentarily drops voltage to the lights. This is not a problem for simple electrical equipment, but sophisticated electronic devices contain components that require power to be supplied with very tight specifications for voltage and current. These devices usually contain special circuits that deliver nearly constant voltage even though the supply voltage varies widely. Circuits that perform this function are called **voltage regulators** or **regulated power supplies.**

1. Connect the circuit in Figure 2. Do not connect the wire to the positive battery terminal (27 _____) until you are ready to begin Step 2. Use a long wire from the kit for the "loose wire" specified in the schematic.

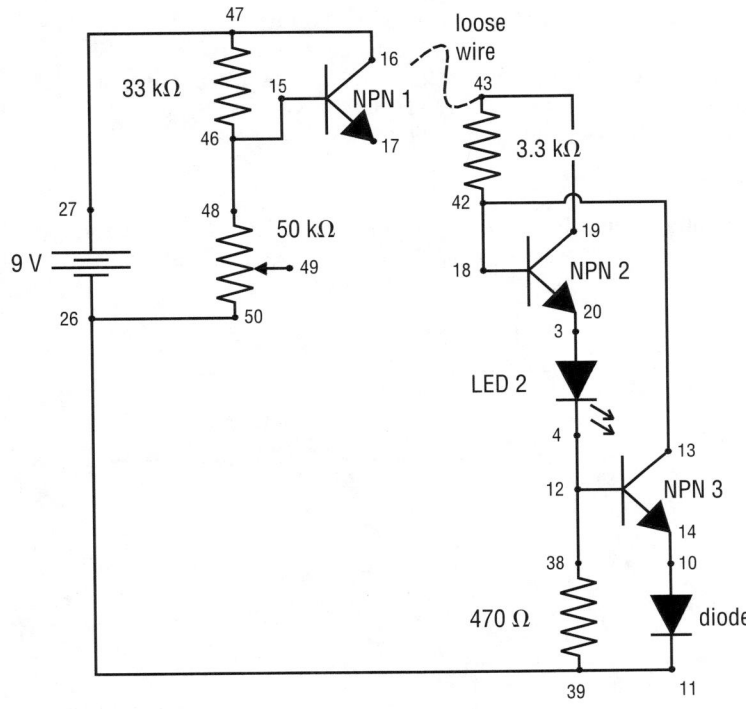

Figure 2

2. Touch the loose wire to the NPN 1 collector. Then touch the loose wire to the NPN 1 emitter. Did you notice any difference in LED brightness?

   There should be no discernable difference in brightness.

3. Connect the free end of the loose wire to the NPN 1 emitter (17 _____). The LED should light up.

4. Set the multimeter to 20 on the DCV scale and insert the red test probe into the NPN 1 emitter terminal (17 _____) and the black probe into the negative battery terminal (26 _____). Record the displayed voltage.

   ~4.9 V (Ans. vary.)

5. Measure the voltage across the LED, observing proper polarity.

   ~2.6 V (Ans. vary.)

6. Remove the loose wire from 17 (____) and connect it to the NPN 1 collector (16 ____). Measure the voltage between the NPN 1 collector and the negative battery terminal as in Step 4. Record the displayed voltage.

~9.4 V (Ans. vary.)

7. Measure the voltage across the LED.

~2.5 V (Ans. vary.)

The left half of the circuit in Figure 2 supplies two different voltages to the right half—approximately 4.7 V at the emitter of NPN 1 and approximately 9 V at the collector. Notice that the voltage drop across the LED is essentially the same for both voltage supplies. The right half of the circuit functions as a voltage regulator.

C. Differential Transistor Pairs

You probably will not have time to examine the **differential pair** transistor configuration discussed in the Learning Center manual on pages 36–39 during the regular class time. However, if you have the opportunity outside class to read and complete Experiments 21, 22, and 23, you will find your time well spent. Always refer to the line schematics when connecting the circuits.

Inductors

The schematic symbol for an inductor looks like a spring. The Learning Center kit does not have a separate inductor but uses one of the windings of the transformer instead.

1. Connect the circuit shown in the schematic in Figure 3.

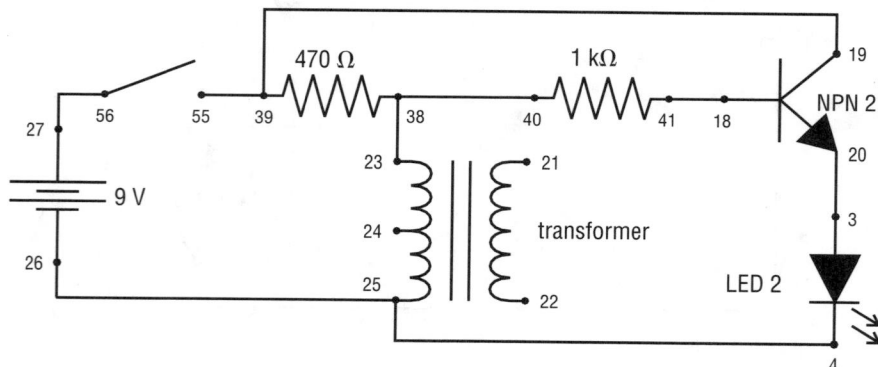

Figure 3

2. Press the switch; hold it; then release it. Describe what happens.

The LED blinks briefly when the switch is pressed.

You should consider why this takes place. Reread the textbook material regarding *self-induction*. As you follow the schematic in Figure 3, you will notice that when the switch is shut, the collector of the NPN 2 transistor is connected to the positive terminal of the battery with no resistor between. You might expect the current to flow through the LED by taking that path. However, in order for that to happen, the transistor must be turned on, which means that the transistor's base current must exceed the threshold value. Follow the circuit through the 470 Ω resistor. The current could flow through either the 1 kΩ resistor or the inductor. If you measure the resistance of the inductor, you will find that it is less than 100 Ω. Therefore, the most probable path for current flow is through the 100 Ω inductor rather than the 1 kΩ resistor.

When the switch is closed, many things happen in a fraction of a second. The increasing flow of current through the inductor creates an expanding magnetic field that induces back emf in the inductor. The back emf produces a momentary voltage spike large enough to provide the necessary bias current through the 1 kΩ resistor to turn on the transistor and light the LED. However, as soon as the current flowing through the inductor rises to a constant value, the magnetic field stops changing ($\Delta\phi/\Delta t = 0$), the back emf disappears, the current through the 1 kΩ resistor stops, the transistor turns off, and the LED goes out. When the switch is opened, the current rapidly decreases to zero, collapsing the magnetic field in the inductor. This induces a back emf with a polarity opposite to the switch-on polarity that maintains the original current flow. The back emf reverse-biases the transistor as well as the LED, and the LED does not light at all.

Notice that inductors allow DC current to pass but oppose changing currents (such as AC). This is the opposite of the way that a capacitor works; capacitors block DC but allow AC potentials to pass. Thus, inductors could be viewed as "anticapacitors."

Transformers

The transformer is essentially two inductors magnetically linked together. The primary inductor or winding, which is located between terminals 21 (____) and 22 (____) of the transformer provided in the Learning Center kit, has fewer turns than the secondary winding, which is located between terminals 23 (____) and 25 (____).

1. Connect the circuit according to the schematic in Figure 4. Note that the *antenna* connected between the battery and the transformer provides a small amount of resistance (~10 Ω) so that the battery is not short-circuited.

2. Press the switch; wait a few seconds; then release the switch. Record your observations.

   <u>When the switch was pressed, LED 1</u>

   <u>blinked on and off. When the switch was</u>

   <u>released, LED 2 blinked on and off.</u>

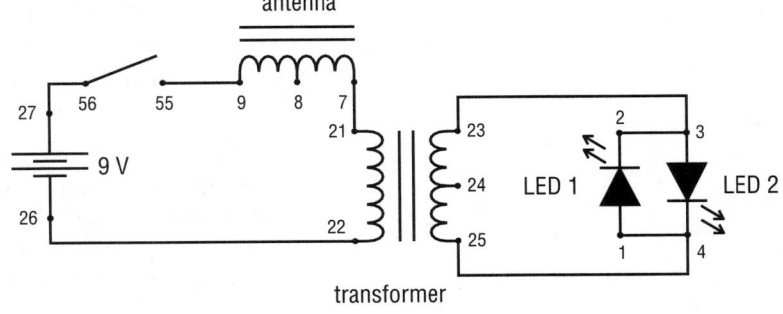

Figure 4

When the switch is closed, the following events occur concurrently and in a very short amount of time. Current begins to flow from the battery through the primary side of the transformer. As the current increases to its final value, the magnetic field around the primary winding expands, which cuts across the secondary coils. This induces a brief voltage spike in the secondary winding that is larger than the primary side voltage because there are more turns on the secondary side ($V_i = -N\Delta\phi/\Delta t$). The voltage spike forces current through LED 1 while reverse-biasing LED 2. When the current reaches its full value in the primary winding, the magnetic field stops changing, the induced voltage in the secondary disappears, and LED 1 goes out. When the switch is opened, the primary current begins decreasing. As the primary magnetic field collapses, the voltage induced in the secondary winding has opposite polarity to the switch-on voltage. This polarity reverse-biases LED 1 but forward-biases LED 2, and LED 2 blinks on briefly.

Oscillating Circuits

A. Blinking Lights

1. Connect the circuit according to the schematic in Figure 5. Press the switch and record your observations.

   <u>The LED blinks on and off.</u>

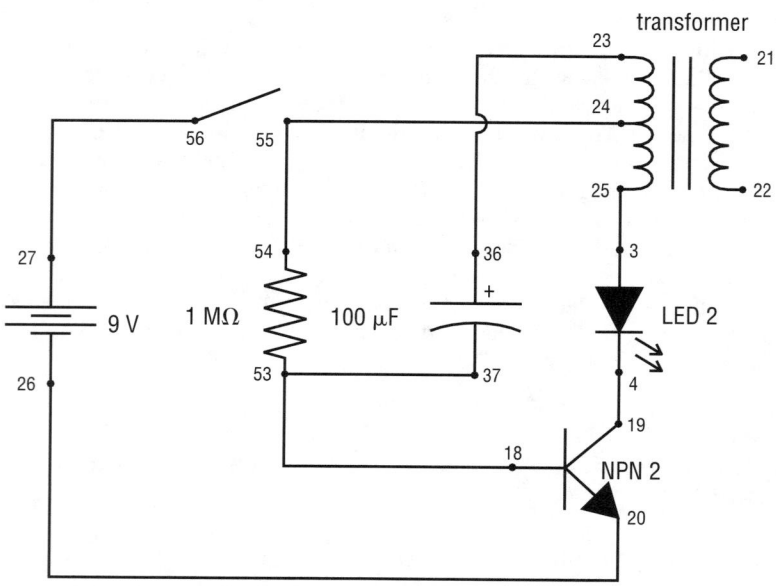

Figure 5

2. Move the wires from the 1 MΩ resistor to the 100 kΩ resistor (51 ____ and 52 ____). Press the switch and describe what happens.

The LED blinks more slowly.

3. Move the wires from the 100 kΩ resistor to the 50 kΩ variable resistor (48 ____ and 49 ____). Adjust the variable resistor from maximum to minimum and describe what happens.

The speed at which the LED blinks can be varied.

4. Set the variable resistor so that the light blinks as slowly as possible. Now move the wires from the 100 μF capacitor to the 10 μF capacitor (34 ____ and 35 ____). Press the switch and record your observations.

The LED blinks more rapidly.

B. Electronic Tone Generator

Audio oscillators are the principal sources of synthetic sounds. Perform Experiment 27 in the Learning Center manual. Describe the sound quality for as many of the circuits as you have time to connect on a table similar to the one on page 46. Do not write in the Learning Center manual.

Radio Receiver

The circuit schematic on page 61 of the Learning Center manual is a simple AM radio receiver. If you connect the circuit meticulously and listen carefully while tuning the variable capacitor, you may be able to receive one or more radio stations. You may need to go outside to obtain any radio reception. The Learning Center manual also suggests connecting the negative terminal of the battery to a well-grounded object, such as a metal water pipe.

Computer Circuits

The Elenco Learning Center manual contains several experiments that illustrate the operation of basic computer circuits, such as flip-flops and NOR, AND, and NAND gates. Take the opportunity to complete Experiments 47, 48, 49, and 50. Obviously, you will not be able to make a complete, functional computer, but these circuits will help you understand how computer circuits work. After observing how bulky discrete components are, you will have a better appreciation for the efficiency of the large-scale integration of modern computer chips.

Name _____

Date _____ Hour ____

PRELAB HOMEWORK

1. Review Faraday's law in your textbook. Write the expression representing induced voltage in a *single coil of wire*. Identify each of the variables and explain the significance of the negative sign.

   $V_i = -\Delta\phi/\Delta t$, where $\Delta\phi$ is the change in magnetic flux and Δt is the change in time (in other words, the rate of change of the magnetic flux). The negative sign indicates that the induced voltage is opposite to the change in flux.

2. How does the formula in Question 1 change for a wire with *N* coils?

   The induced voltage in a wire with *N* turns is $V_i = -N\Delta\phi/\Delta t$.

3. Induced voltage is also called back emf ($\mathcal{E}$). Back emf in an inductor is directly proportional to the rate of change of current in the inductor. What is the proportionality constant in this relation called? What units are associated with this quantity?

   The proportionality constant is called inductance (*L*). Inductance is measured in henrys (H).

4. If four NPN transistors were connected in a Darlington configuration, what would the total base-to-emitter voltage drop have to be in order to turn on all four transistors?

   Each transistor requires approximately 0.7 V across the base to turn on, so a total voltage drop of 2.8 V would be required.

5. What is the purpose of a regulated power supply circuit?

   A regulated power supply circuit provides a nearly constant output voltage even though the input voltage may vary significantly.

6. What is the relative magnitude of the resistance in an inductor?

   Inductors usually have low resistance, similar to a standard wire.

7. A circuit that changes its output back and forth based on feedback from the output is called a(n) _____oscillator_____. (Review Experiment 26 in the Learning Center manual.)

8. If the primary windings in a transformer have more turns than the secondary windings, it is considered to be a step-____down____ transformer.

9. Explain why the following statement is false: A step-up transformer can generate a secondary voltage higher than the primary voltage, which means that more power can be produced by a step-up transformer.

   The statement can be shown false by at least two methods. The student can discuss that voltage is higher and that current is proportionately lower in the secondary of a step-up transformer, based on the discussion in the textbook. Or he may argue from a conservation of energy position that increasing the rate of output energy compared to the rate of input energy violates energy conservation principles.

Name _____

Date _____ Hour ____

PLANE MIRROR REFLECTIONS

Purpose

The fact that light propagates in straight lines is a basic property that can be used to evaluate optical principles. The purpose of this lab is to

- determine and compare the angle of incidence and angle of reflection of a light ray.
- determine and compare the image distance to the object distance.
- evaluate the properties of the image compared to the object.

Prelab Discussion

One of the fundamental postulates of Euclidean geometry is that two points determine a straight line. Geometrically, any point that lies between these two determining points must be on the same line (they must be collinear). Surveyors use this principle by assuming that light travels in a straight line (a reasonable assumption) when they align fence posts and corners for house foundations. Navy pilots landing on an aircraft carrier use an optical landing aid that shows a series of lights that are aligned when the aircraft is on the correct approach path but are out of alignment if the pilot is above or below the approach path.

This simple geometric concept is used in the study of reflection and refraction. In optical science, the path of a photon of light is said to be a **ray,** and the geometric principle of light propagation is called the **ray theory.** For a light ray moving through a uniform medium in a low gravitational field, its path is essentially a straight line. Every point on an object emits innumerable rays of light, and every point in an image consists of many rays of light intersecting at that point.

In this experiment you will place several pins in line with an image point in order to define one of the rays passing through the image. After determining two or more image lines that pass through the same point, you can locate the image point by finding the intersection of the lines. The image is reflected from a plane mirror, so the image line is also the **reflected ray.** The rays of light that form the image seen in the mirror must follow a straight line from the object to the mirror, reflect off the mirror's surface, and follow a straight line to your eye. The point where the image line intersects the mirror's surface must be the point where the ray from the object was incident on the mirror. This point and the location of the object itself determine the **incident ray.** Using a protractor, you can determine the angles of the incident and reflected rays referenced to the **normal line,** which is perpendicular to the mirror's surface at the point of reflection.

Reflected images usually have many of the same visual properties as their associated objects, but under certain circumstances these properties are different. You will evaluate the size and orientation (upright or inverted and left or right) of the image in comparison to the object.

Mirrors can be manufactured in several different ways, depending on their use. Mirrors that are not required to provide critical optical performance and that are subject to abrasion, such as bathroom mirrors and automobile rearview mirrors, usually have the mirrored surface on the back surface of a transparent material such as glass or Plexiglas. These are called back-surface or **second-surface mirrors.** Light must travel twice through the clear material as it is reflected. This results in distortion of the image, and multiple images are often produced by internal reflection of the light. Mirrors that must provide distortion-free optical performance and that are not subject to abrasion or weathering are usually mirrored on the front surface so that light does not have to travel through the substrate glass or Plexiglas. These are called **first-surface mirrors.** They are found in optics labs, astronomical telescopes, headlight reflectors, and precision optical instruments.

Required Equipment

corrugated cardboard
masking tape
metric ruler
plane mirror
protractor
semicircular dish (or other support)
sewing pins, round-headed
unlined paper, 2 sheets

Prelab Discussion

- Review the prerequisites for Lab 4-10 in the back of this manual.

- Ray optics is the basis for studies in future optics labs, so be sure to perform this introductory lab in order to demonstrate the principles.

Equipment and Setup

- The recommended semicircular dish and mirror come from the optics experiment kit available through BJUP. Note that the mirrors supplied in this kit are second-surface mirrors.

- See the Home School Notes for alternative sources and substitute materials.

- If you do not want to etch a line in the mirror's reflective surface, you can use a water-soluble marker to mark the point of incidence on the edge of the mirror.

- Round-headed sewing pins are more visible than standard sewing pins. Use a different colored pin for the object pin to make it easy to differentiate from the others.

Procedure

- Students sometimes have difficulty understanding the alignment necessary to obtain the image lines. If this occurs, walk them through the first trial; then let them do the second on their own.

- The procedure is brief enough that all of the analysis can also be completed in the same class period.

Postlab Analysis

- The answer to Question 7 states that something able to perceive a visual image is necessary for a virtual image to be recognized. You may want to point out that this does not necessarily require a mind because robotic sensors can be programmed to recognize visual patterns.

Home School Notes

- First-surface mirrors can be obtained from almost any science supplier. These may be harder to obtain locally.

- Plexiglas and glass mirrors can be obtained through local glaziers and cut to size.

- The mirror support can be simply a block cut from a wooden 2 × 4.

Procedure

1. Inspect the mirror you will be using for the experiment. There should be a 1 cm line etched through the reflective surface perpendicular to one long edge.

2. Use a loop of masking tape to fasten the back of the mirror to the semicircular dish so that the edge with the etch mark is at the bottom.

3. Draw two perpendicular lines on the paper to divide the sheet into fourths. Use a protractor to ensure that the angular separation of the lines is exactly 90°.

4. Tape the paper to the cardboard at the corners. Write *Trial 1* in one corner.

5. Place the mirror and its support on the paper so that the reflective surface coincides with the short line on the paper and the etched mark is on the long line perpendicular to the mirror. The short line is called the **mirror line,** and the long line is called the **center line** (see Figure 1).

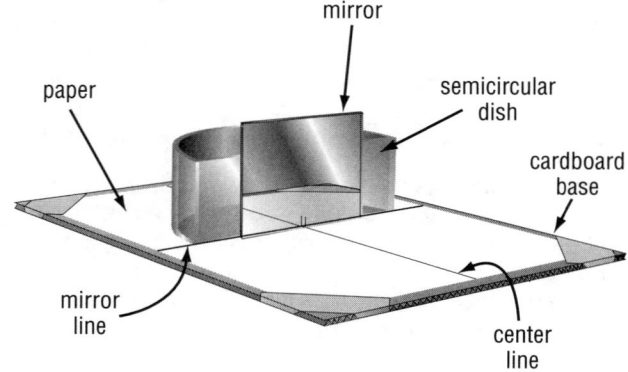

Figure 1

6. Place a pin about 5 cm in front of the mirror and about 2 cm to the left of the center line. This will be referred to as the *object*. Write the letter *O* on the paper next to the pin.

7. Use one eye to look into the mirror from the opposite side of the center line. Move your head left or right until the etch mark is lined up with the image of the object pin (which seems to be behind the mirror). Insert a second pin in line with your eye and the etch mark. This pin should cover the etch mark and the image of the object pin in the mirror (see Figure 2). Label this *pin 2* on the paper.

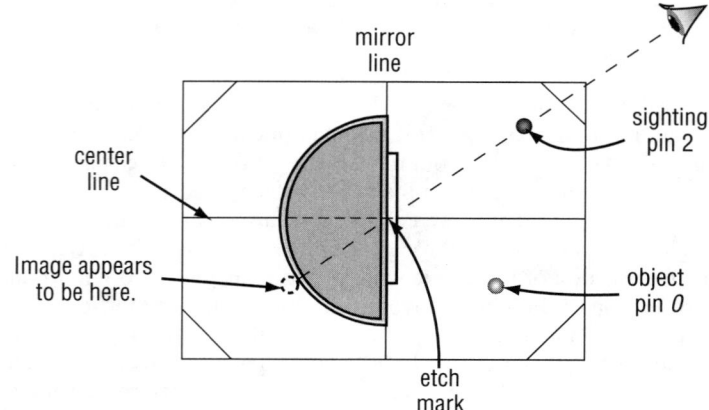

Figure 2

8. Look into the mirror from the same side of the center line as the object. Move left or right until the object pin is lined up with its image in the mirror. Insert another pin in line with your eye and the object pin. This pin should cover the object pin and the image of the pin in the mirror (see Figure 3). Label this *pin 3* on the paper.

9. Evaluate the image.

a. Where is the image located—behind the plane of the mirror, at the mirror, or in front of the mirror? ___behind the mirror___

b. What is the orientation of the image? (upright or inverted) ___upright___

c. How does the size of the image seem to compare to the object? Consider perspective in making your determination. ___about the same size___

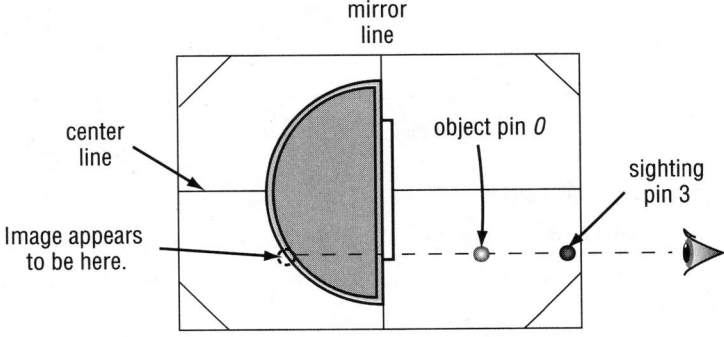

Figure 3

10. Remove the mirror and its support from the paper. Remove the pins from the paper. Using a ruler or straightedge, draw a line from pin 2 through the intersection of the two perpendicular reference lines (the location of the etch mark) and extend the line all the way to the edge of the paper (see Figure 4). This will be called *image line 1*.

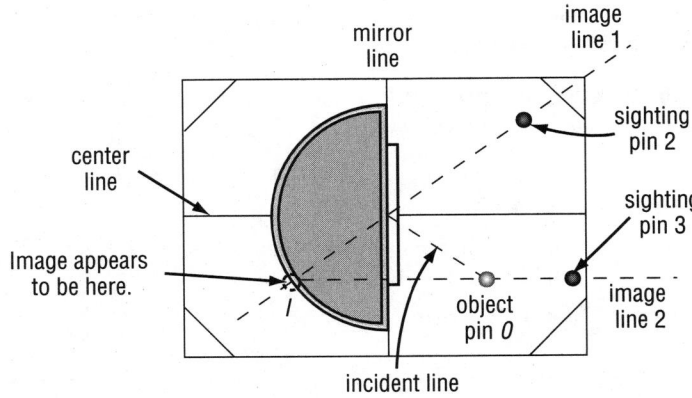

Figure 4

11. Draw a second line from object pin *O* to the intersection of the two perpendicular lines. This will be called the *incident line*.

12. Draw a line from pin 3 through the position of object pin *O,* and extend the line several inches beyond the mirror line so that it crosses image line 1 (see Figure 4). This is *image line 2*. Label the intersection of image lines 1 and 2 point *I*.

13. Label the angle of incidence θ_i and the angle of reflection θ_r.

14. Carefully remove the sheet of paper from the cardboard.

15. Label a new sheet of paper *Trial 2* and repeat Steps 3–14, placing the object pin in a different location. Do not place the pin on the center line.

Data

Table 1
Object, Image, and Reflection Data and Calculations

Trial	Angle of Incidence, θ_i	Angle of Reflection, θ_r	θ_i and θ_r Percent Difference	Object Distance, d_o	Image Distance, d_i	d_o and d_i Percent Difference
1	°	°	%	cm	cm	%
2	°	°	%	cm	cm	%

Plotting Sheets for Trial 1 and Trial 2 (attached)

Postlab Exercises

Complete the following steps for both trials.

1. Measure the angles of incidence and reflection with your protractor and record the values in Table 1.

2. Measure the distance along image line 2 from the object pin to the mirror line. Record the object distance (d_o) in Table 1.

3. Measure the distance along image line 2 from point *I* to the mirror line. Record the image distance (d_i) in Table 1.

4. Calculate the percent differences between the angles of incidence and the angles of reflection. Record the results in Table 1.

5. Calculate the percent differences between the object distances and the image distances. Record the results in Table 1.

6. Hand in the two sheets of paper attached to your lab report. These are the plotting sheets mentioned in the Data section.

Postlab Analysis

1. Describe the difference in the relationship of the paths of the light rays forming virtual images and those forming real images.

   A virtual image is formed by diverging light rays, but a real image is

   formed by converging light rays.

2. Look at yourself in a mirror. Raise your right hand. If your image were an actual person, which hand would your image appear to raise?

   The image appears to raise its left hand.

3. On which side of the reflection is the raised hand as you look at it?

   The raised hand is on the right side.

4. Many people say that in plane mirrors, images are reversed compared to the objects. Is this correct? Explain your answer.

No. A reversed image would show your left side on the right side of the reflection and vice versa. What actually occurs is that your right side is reflected in the right side of the image and your left in the left. This is called a *mirror image*.

5. How does the image distance compare to the object distance in a plane mirror reflection?

The image distance is equal to the object distance.

6. A parabolic mirror can reflect an image of the sun in such a way that its image can burn a hole in paper or be recorded on film. Are these effects true for the reflection of the sun in a plane mirror? Explain.

No. The rays of the sun are always diverging, even after reflecting off the mirror, so they will never come together to form an image.

7. What must exist in order for a virtual image to be recognized?

Something that can perceive a visual image must exist in order to recognize a virtual image.

Name _____

Date _____ Hour _____

PRELAB HOMEWORK

1. A line drawn to represent the path of a light photon is called a(n) ____ray____.

2. Describe the path of a light ray in a single medium in a normal gravitational field.
   A ray of light travels in a straight line under these conditions.

3. Light rays that bounce off the surface of an object are said to be ____reflected____.

4. An imaginary line perpendicular to a reflecting surface at the incident point of a ray of light is called a(n) ____normal____.

5. The angle of incidence is the angle between the ____normal____ and the ____incident ray of light____.

6. The angle of reflection is the angle between the ____normal____ and the ____reflected ray of light____.

7. The law of reflection states that the angle of incidence equals the angle of reflection and that the incident ray, the normal, and the reflected ray are in the same plane.

8. A reflection from a polished surface produces rays of light reflected in a predictable pattern. This type of reflection is called regular (or specular) reflection.

9. What kind of image is produced in a plane mirror reflection?
   The image is virtual.

10. Based on the location of the mirrored surface, which kind of mirror produces less distortion of the light ray?
    A first- or front-surface mirror produces less distortion.

11. What mirror construction is used for precision optical instruments and astronomical telescopes?
    First-surface mirrors are used for these applications.

12. What relationship does the center line have to the reflected ray in this exercise?
    The center line is the normal at the point of reflection.

Name _____

Date _____ Hour _____

CURVED MIRROR REFLECTIONS

Purpose

In the previous lab you verified the law of reflection in a plane mirror. Now you will extend that concept to reflections in curved mirrors. The purpose of this lab is to

- demonstrate the relationship between the properties of an object and the properties of its reflection in a curved mirror.
- determine the focal length of a concave mirror.
- determine the theoretical magnification for a given combination of object and image and compare it with the actual magnification for a concave mirror.

Prelab Discussion

A surface of a curved mirror is usually either a portion of the surface of a sphere or *paraboloid* (a curved surface that is formed by the rotation of a parabola around its axis), but it can have any curvature, depending on its use. A spherical mirror is the easiest curved mirror to discuss because there is a distinct center of curvature—the center of the sphere forming the mirror's surface. If the mirror surface is on the inside of the sphere, a concave mirror is formed. If the outer surface of the sphere is reflective, a convex mirror is formed.

The concepts of reflection for plane mirrors can be applied to curved mirrors, but the normals to a curved mirror are not parallel the way they are for a plane mirror. Consequently, in a beam of parallel light rays shining on a curved mirror, the angles of incidence are different throughout the beam. The reflection will either converge to a point somewhere in front of a concave mirror or apparently diverge from a point behind a convex mirror.

In order to study the characteristics of reflection from a curved mirror, you need to review the important concepts associated with this topic. Refer to Figure 1 during this discussion. The **center of curvature (C)** for a spherical mirror is equidistant from all points on the mirror's surface. The distance from the center of curvature to the mirror is the mirror's **radius (R)**. The geometric center of the mirror is called the **vertex (V)**, and the line passing through the center of curvature and the vertex is called the **principal axis.** Light rays parallel to the principal axis reflect off a concave spherical mirror and intersect the principal axis at a point called the **principal focus,** or **focal point (F).** The distance from the focal point to the vertex is called the **focal length (f),** and it is approximately one-half the radius. It is *approximately* half because light rays parallel to the principal axis cannot reflect to a single point due to a phenomenon called *spherical aberration*. The light rays incident near the edges of a concave spherical mirror focus at a point slightly nearer the mirror than those incident near the center of the mirror. Parabolic mirrors correct this problem. For relatively flat spherical mirrors, the effects of spherical aberration are negligible, and you can assume that $f = R/2$.

Real images are formed by the intersection of multiple reflected rays originating from the same point on the

Prelab Discussion

- Review the prerequisites for Lab 4-11 in the back of this manual.

- The discussion deals primarily with concave mirrors but briefly refers to convex mirrors when necessary. Emphasize that convex mirrors always produce virtual images no matter where the object is, while concave mirrors produce real images except when $d_o < f$. Students should be able to deduce this from the results of the lab.

- It is important to understand the sign conventions of the variables. Positive object and image distances indicate that the object or image is in front of the reflective surface. The focal length, f, is positive for a concave mirror. A negative image distance implies that the image lies behind the mirror; therefore, a convex mirror has a negative f. The signs of magnification indicate the orientation of the image—positive

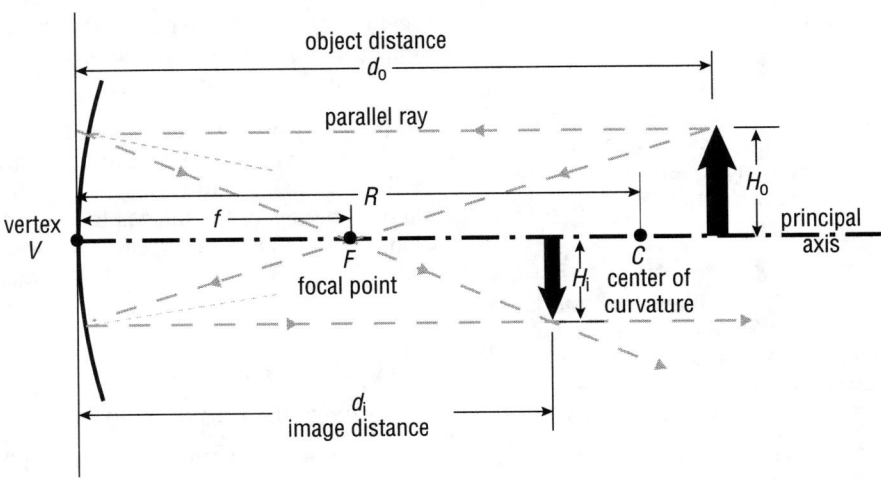

Figure 1

for an inverted real image and negative for an upright virtual image.

Equipment and Setup

- The recommended equipment includes standard optical bench components and a good-quality spherical or parabolic concave mirror. The larger the mirror, the brighter the image and the more accurate the data.

- See the Home School Notes for minimum equipment and substitutions.

- For best results, make the room as dark as possible, but leave a working light on in a corner so that students can see well enough to write and move around.

Procedure

- Students should not have any problems with the procedure except possibly in the following areas:

  1. The object distance for Trial 1 will be unknown unless you have measured the distance to the object outside the building.

  2. In Trial 5, the image produced when $d_o < f$ is virtual. Students will not be able to project an image, so they will not be able to measure the image distance for this trial.

- It is suggested that you measure the distances with a second meter stick or a metric tape measure because the pointers on the mirror and screen supports may not be accurate, and because the object, mirror, and screen may not be set in the center of the holders.

- Measuring the height of an image may be difficult because the images tend to be dim. Shining a bright flashlight on the candle may make it more visible in the reflected image.

Postlab Analysis

- The exercise leads the students through several self-discovery questions that reveal the properties of images at several object distances not evaluated in the lab.

- An "infinite" image distance is used in the answer for Question 5, but you should remind students that this result actually means "does not

object. The location of a real image can be determined by analyzing the paths of certain predictable light rays that are incident on or reflected from a concave mirror. There are four kinds of rays that can be located easily:

1. Incident rays that are parallel to the principal axis are reflected through the principal focus.

2. Incident rays that pass through the principal focus are reflected parallel to the principal axis.

3. Incident rays that pass through the center of curvature, C, are reflected straight back through C.

4. Rays that are incident at the vertex are reflected symmetrically about the principal axis.

The focal length of a curved mirror can be calculated by using an equation that relates object distance, d_o, image distance, d_i, and focal length, f. It is assumed that d_o is always in front of the mirror and is positive. The variables d_i and f are positive if they are in front of the mirror's surface, and they are negative if they appear to lie behind the mirror's surface. The traditional formula relating these quantities is

$$\frac{1}{d_o} + \frac{1}{d_i} = \frac{1}{f}. \tag{1}$$

This formula is sometimes called the **spherical mirror equation.** To make this formula more useful for finding focal length, Equation (1) can be rewritten in terms of f to yield

$$f = \frac{d_o d_i}{d_o + d_i}. \tag{2}$$

The magnification, M, of an image compared to the object is equal to the ratio of the image height, h_i, and the object height, h_o.

$$M = \frac{h_i}{h_o} \tag{3}$$

The magnification for a particular arrangement of an object and its image formed by a curved mirror can also be determined using object distance and image distance. The applicable formula to use is

$$M = \frac{d_i}{d_o}. \tag{4}$$

If M is positive, the image is inverted compared to the object, a property of all real images. If M is negative, the image is an upright, virtual image. The magnitude of magnification should be expressed by a positive number followed by the symbol $\times$, as in $2\times$.

In this lab you will approximate the focal length of a concave mirror by focusing a distant image on a screen and measuring the image distance. Then you will experiment with various object distances in order to determine the location and properties of the images formed, if any. You will also calculate the focal length of the mirror by measuring object and image distances, using Equation (2). Finally, you will determine the magnification of the images, using Equations (3) and (4).

Procedure

Approximate Focal Length by Direct Measurement

1. Assemble the mirror, mirror support, meter stick, screen, and screen support according to Figure 2. This assembly is called an **optical bench.** The mirror should be positioned at one end of the meter stick with the concave surface facing the screen.

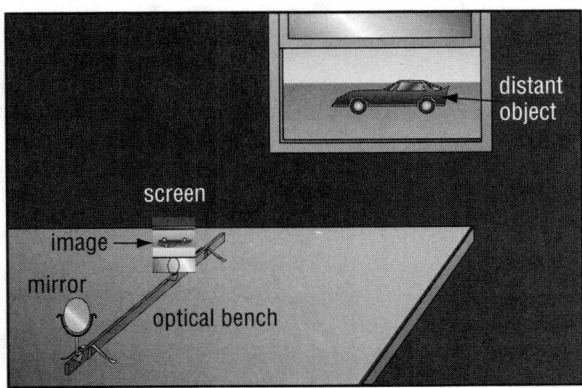

Figure 2

2. Darken the room by closing all but one shade and turning out the lights. Aim the apparatus at a distant, bright, distinct object, preferably outside at least 30 m away.

3. Slowly move the screen back and forth along the meter stick until a reflection image is formed. You may have to realign the meter stick or the mirror in its holder several times until you find the image.

4. Adjust the screen position until the image is at its sharpest focus. Measure the distance from the center of the mirror to the position of the screen and record the image distance in Table 1 for Trial 1. Move the screen out of focus; then perform the procedure three additional times. Record these values in Table 1 for Trials 2–4. Average the four values and enter the result in both Table 1 and Table 2 as d_i for Trial 1. The average of these image distances is the focal length found by direct measurement, f_m.

5. Compare the image to the object. Note the relative size of the image as well as its orientation (upright or inverted) and record these observations in Table 2.

Comparison of Object to Images

6. Calculate the approximate value of R from f_m. Recall that $f = R/2$, so $R = 2f$. Write this value in the blank above Table 2.

7. If not already done, darken the room as much as possible. Place a light source, such as a candle or minilamp, at a position somewhat greater than R from the mirror and just far enough from the side of the meter stick so that the focusing screen will not block illumination of the mirror (see Figure 3).

8. Move the screen back and forth until a sharp image of the light source appears on the screen. Measure the distances of the light source and the image from the mirror, using a second meter stick. The distances should be measured from the center of the mirror to the center of the light source and the surface of the screen. Record the object and image

exist." Students may recognize the trend that d_i rapidly increases without limit as d_o approaches f.

- Similarly, as d_o approaches f, the image size rapidly increases (Question 6).

Home School Notes

- The minimum equipment required is a concave mirror, a candle, and a meter stick or metric tape measure.

- The spherical mirror should be obtained from a science supply company, but the parabolic mirror from a reflector telescope will also work well. Avoid touching or scratching the surface of a coated mirror.

- Optical bench hardware is not required. The meter stick or tape measure can be taped in place, the mirror can be mounted on a mound of clay, and the candle can be mounted in a short candleholder. The screen can be just a piece of card stock held by hand or supported with clay.

Figure 3

distances for Trial 2 in Table 2. Note the relative size of the image and its orientation and record in Table 2.

9. If the image is bright enough, measure its height by using the millimeter scale printed along the edge of the screen card or by using a metric ruler. Measure the corresponding height on the light source itself. For candles, measuring from the support to the top of the wick gives the best results. Record the object and image heights for Trial 2 in Table 2. If the image is not bright enough, omit these measurements.

10. Move the light source to the distance R from the mirror. Repeat Steps 8–9 at this position and record your data in Table 2 for Trial 3. If you are using a candle, be sure to measure the object height for each trial because the candle will burn down as the lab period progresses.

11. Place the light source at a position between f and R for Trial 4 and place the light source between the mirror and f for Trial 5. Record object and image data according to Steps 8–9 for both trials in Table 2. Remember that you will not be able to directly measure a virtual image's distance.

12. If an image cannot be formed on the screen, you should remove the screen from the optical bench and look into the mirror in order to see the image.

Data

Table 1
Direct Measurement of Focal Length

Trial	Image Distance, d_i
1	cm
2	cm
3	cm
4	cm
Average ($= f_m$)	cm

Data in Table 1 will vary.

Table 2
Image Data and Calculations
Radius, R _____Ans. vary._____ cm

Trial	Object Position	Object Distance, d_o	Image Distance, d_i	Relative Image Size	Image Orientation	Object Height, H_o	Image Height, H_i	Magnification, M
1	$d_o \gg R$		cm	smaller	inverted			
2	$d_o > R$	cm	cm	smaller	inverted	cm	cm	×
3	$d_o = R$	cm	cm	smaller	inverted	cm	cm	×
4	$f < d_o < R$	cm	cm	larger	inverted	cm	cm	×
5	$0 < d_o < f$	cm	cm	larger	upright	cm	cm	×

Numerical data in Table 2 will vary, but image size and orientation should be as stated.

Postlab Exercises

1. Calculate the magnification for each trial in which you obtained height measurements for the object and image. Use Equation (3) and enter your results in Table 2.

2. Write the focal length (f_m) determined in Table 1 in Table 3.

3. For every trial that yielded a real image, calculate the focal length of the mirror, f_c, using Equation (2). Record the results in Table 3.

4. Calculate the percent difference between f_m and the average value of f_c.

Table 3
Calculation of Focal Length

Trial	Measured Focal Length, f_m	Calculated Focal Length, f_c	f_m and f_c Percent Difference
1	cm		
2	cm	cm	%
3	cm	cm	%
4	cm	cm	%
5	cm	cm	%
Average		cm	%

Data and calculations in Table 3 will vary.

5. Complete Table 4 by indicating whether the image for each trial was real or virtual.

Table 4
Image Evaluation

Trial	Image Type
1	real
2	real
3	real
4	real
5	virtual

Observations in Table 4 are the expected results.

6. Calculate the magnification of the image for each trial that produced a real image, using Equation (4). Record your results in Table 5.

Table 5
Calculated Magnification

Trial	Magnification, M
1	unknown*
2	Ans. vary.
3	Ans. vary.
4	Ans. vary.
5	Ans. vary.

*assumes that object size is not known

Postlab Analysis

1. _____Ans. vary._____ Using the calculated value of f for your mirror, what will the image distance be for an object at distance R from the mirror?

   The following solution will be calculated in terms of f and R. Students should use the actual numerical values for their mirrors.

   Given: f; $d_o = R = 2f$; $d_i = ?$

   Formula: $d_i = \dfrac{d_o f}{d_o - f}$

   Solution: $d_i = \dfrac{(2f)(f)}{2f - f} = \dfrac{2f^2}{f} = 2f = R$

   The image will be the same distance from the mirror as the object.

2. Image height is found by multiplying the object's height by the magnification. How does the height of the image compare to the height of the object in Question 1? Justify your answer, using Equation (4).

   The image is the same size as the object.

   Given: $d_o = d_i$; $M = ?$

   Formula: $M = \dfrac{d_i}{d_o}$

   Solution: $M = \dfrac{d_i}{d_o} = \dfrac{d_o}{d_o} = 1\times$

3. Review your data and the conclusions from Questions 1–2. Make a general statement that describes the relative size, location, and orientation of the image compared to the object as the object moves from greater than R from the mirror to a point between f and R.

   An object greater than R from the mirror will produce a smaller,

   inverted image located between f and R. When the object distance

   is R, the image is the same size, inverted, and located at a distance

   of R from the mirror. When the object distance is between f and R,

   the image is larger than the object, inverted, and located at a

   distance greater than R from the mirror.

4. Continuing with the analysis of image properties in the preceding questions, what is the image distance when the object is located at the focal point, *F?* Justify your answer, using the formula from Question 1.

   The image distance is a very large, undefined distance away.

   Given: $f; d_o = f; d_i = ?$

   Formula: $d_i = \dfrac{d_o f}{d_o - f}$

   Solution: $d_i = \dfrac{(f)(f)}{f - f} = \dfrac{f^2}{0}$ (The result does not exist.)

5. What is the theoretical size of the image in Question 4? Justify your answer.

   The magnification is indefinitely large; therefore, the image size is also indefinitely large.

   Given: $d_o = f; d_i \Rightarrow \infty; M = ?; h_i = ?$

   Formulas: $M = \dfrac{d_i}{d_o}; h_i = h_o M$

   Solution: $M = \dfrac{\infty}{f} \Rightarrow \infty$; therefore, $h_i \Rightarrow \infty$

6. Using your calculated focal length and the object distance for Trial 5 $(0 < d_o < f)$, determine the location of the image, its magnification, and its orientation.

   Answers will vary. The solution shown assumes that $d_o = \dfrac{f}{2}$.

   Given: $f; d_o = \dfrac{f}{2}; d_i = ?$

   Formulas: $d_i = \dfrac{d_o f}{d_o - f}; M = \dfrac{d_i}{d_o}$

   Solution: $d_i = \dfrac{(f/2)f}{(f/2) - f} = \dfrac{f^2/2}{(f - 2f)/2} = \dfrac{f^2}{-f} = -f$

   The negative image distance indicates that the image is located behind the mirror.

   $M = \dfrac{d_i}{d_o} = \dfrac{-f}{f/2} = -2\times$

   The negative sign indicates that the image is upright, which implies that it is a virtual image. The magnification is $2\times$.

Name _____

Date _____ Hour _____

PRELAB HOMEWORK

1. For a curved mirror, what do the center of curvature, the principal focus, and the vertex of the mirror have in common?

   All of them lie on the same line—the principal axis.

2. How can spherical mirrors be constructed so that the spherical aberration is minimized?

   Spherical mirrors that are relatively flat have little spherical aberration.

3. In what direction will a light ray that passes through the focal point of a spherical concave mirror be reflected?

   The light ray will be reflected parallel to the principal axis of the mirror.

4. Write the spherical mirror equation and define each of the variables.

   $\dfrac{1}{d_o} + \dfrac{1}{d_i} = \dfrac{1}{f}$, where d_o is the object distance (the distance from the mirror to the object), d_i is the image distance, and f is the focal length.

5. In optics design work, an engineer is often interested in knowing where the image will be formed for a given mirror. Rewrite Equation (1) by solving for d_i.

   $\dfrac{1}{d_o} + \dfrac{1}{d_i} = \dfrac{1}{f} \Rightarrow \dfrac{1}{d_i} = \dfrac{1}{f} - \dfrac{1}{d_o} \Rightarrow \dfrac{1}{d_i} = \dfrac{d_o - f}{d_o f} \Rightarrow d_i = \dfrac{d_o f}{d_o - f}$

6. __−29 cm__ The spherical mirror equation applies to both concave and convex mirrors. If a *convex* mirror has a focal length of −50. cm, what will be the virtual image distance of an object that is 70. cm in front of the mirror? (Remember that virtual images have *negative* image distances.)

   Given: $f = -50.$ cm; $d_o = 70.$ cm; $d_i = ?$

   Formula: $d_i = \dfrac{d_o f}{d_o - f}$

   Solution: $d_i = \dfrac{d_o f}{d_o - f} = \dfrac{(70.\text{ cm})(-50.\text{ cm})}{(70.\text{ cm}) - (-50.\text{ cm})} = \dfrac{-3500\text{ cm}^2}{120.\text{ cm}} \doteq -29\text{ cm}$

7. Derive the focal length formula, Equation (2), from the spherical mirror equation, Equation (1).

   $\dfrac{1}{d_o} + \dfrac{1}{d_i} = \dfrac{1}{f} \Rightarrow \dfrac{d_i + d_o}{d_o d_i} = \dfrac{1}{f} \Rightarrow \dfrac{d_o d_i}{d_o + d_i} = f$

8. __32.7 cm__ What is the focal length of a concave mirror if an object 120. cm in front of it produces an image at a distance of 45.0 cm?

   Given: $d_o = 120.$ cm; $d_i = 45.0$ cm; $f = ?$

   Formula: $f = \dfrac{d_o d_i}{d_o + d_i}$

   Solution: $f = \dfrac{(120.\text{ cm})(45.0\text{ cm})}{(120.\text{ cm}) + (45.0\text{ cm})} = \dfrac{5400\text{ cm}^2}{165\text{ cm}} \doteq 32.7\text{ cm}$

9. __0.375×__ What is the magnification of the image in Question 8?

   Given: $d_o = 120.$ cm; $d_i = 45.0$ cm; $M = ?$

   Formula: $M = \dfrac{d_i}{d_o}$

   Solution: $M = \dfrac{45.0\text{ cm}}{120.\text{ cm}} = 0.375\times$

Name _____

Date _____ Hour _____

REFRACTION

Purpose

Refraction occurs whenever a wave transits different media. The purpose of this lab is to

- measure the angles of incidence and refraction in a liquid and a solid.
- determine the index of refraction of water (a liquid) and compare it to the accepted value.
- determine the critical angle of the water-air interface and compare it to the accepted value.
- determine the index of refraction of glass (a solid) and compare it to the accepted value.

Prelab Discussion

From your reading and your experience, you know that light rays bend as they pass from one medium into another. Corrective lenses and the illusion of a broken pencil in a glass of water are common examples. Wave bending occurs at the boundary, also called the **interface,** between two media. The bending of any wave as it transits a media interface is called **refraction.** Refraction occurs not only at media interfaces, but also within nonuniform media. The atmosphere, for example, changes in composition, in temperature, and in density with altitude. As the light from a star passes through the atmosphere, it is bent repeatedly. This is the cause of twinkling. Another example of refraction in a nonuniform medium is sound propagation in the ocean. Salinity and temperature change with depth and horizontal distance. These factors vary water density, and sound moving through seawater is significantly refracted in the deep ocean basins, near river mouths, and under ice caps.

The physical constant that indicates the *refractivity* of a substance is its **index of refraction (*n*).** The index of refraction is the ratio of the speed of light in a vacuum to the speed of light in the substance. Since the wavelength of light can be measured more precisely than its speed, *n* is often expressed as the ratio of the wavelength of light in a vacuum to its wavelength in the substance.

As a light ray passes from one medium to a denser medium, it bends *toward* the normal at the point of incidence. If the ray passes out of the denser medium, it will bend *away* from the normal. Similar to reflection, the angles of incidence (θ_i) and refraction (θ_r) are measured from the normal at the media interface (see Figure 1). Snell's law is the principle that relates the indexes of refraction and the angles of incidence and refraction. The formula is

$$n_i \sin \theta_i = n_r \sin \theta_r, \qquad (1)$$

where n_i is the index of refraction for the media containing the incident ray and n_r is that of the medium containing the refracted ray. Notice that there are four variables in the Snell's law formula. If any three of the variables are known, the fourth can be calculated. For example, an unknown index of refraction for a material may be determined experimentally if the index of refraction of the other material at the interface is known and the angles of incidence and refraction are measured.

An interesting optical phenomenon occurs when a light ray passes from a denser medium (with a larger *n*), such as water, to a less dense medium (with a smaller *n*), such as air. As the angle of incidence (in the water) increases, the refracted ray (in the air) bends away from the normal until the angle of refraction equals 90°. At this angle, the light ray lies on the interface surface between the two media. The angle of incidence that produces this effect is called the **critical angle, θ_c.** If the angle of incidence is increased further, the light ray is *reflected*

Required Equipment

corrugated cardboard
glass square (crown glass)
masking tape
metric ruler or straightedge
plane mirror
protractor
semicircular dish (or other support)
sewing pins, round-headed
unlined paper, 3 sheets
water

Prelab Discussion

- Review the prerequisites for Lab 4-12 in the back of this manual.

- The discussion reviews the salient points of the textbook presentation of refraction, index of refraction, and critical angle. Ensure that the students are familiar with this material prior to performing this lab.

- Alert students that they must always keep in mind where the incident and refracted rays are located.

- The notation for indexes of refraction presented in this manual may vary from other texts you have

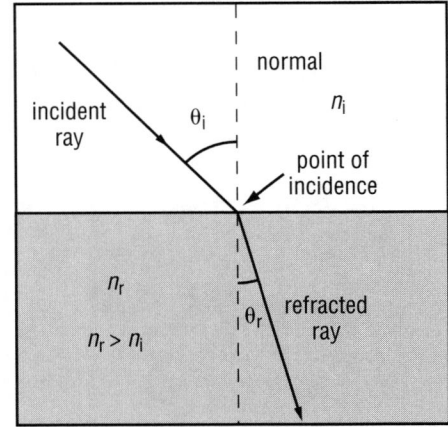

Figure 1

used. The symbols n_i and n_r will promote less confusion than n_1 and n_2, respectively, because they are clearly associated with the incident ray and the refracted ray for any given situation.

- There are no standard significant digit rules associated with trigonometric ratios. This manual uses ratios expressed to 4 decimal places, thereby ensuring precision of 3 SDs for the sines of most angles.

Equipment and Setup

- The semicircular dish and mirror are the same ones used in Lab 4-10 from the optics materials kit available through BJUP.

- Round-headed sewing pins are ideal for visibility.

Procedure

- You should make the etch mark on the dishes prior to class. If you do not want any marks etched on the dish, you can use a water-soluble marker to make a temporary mark

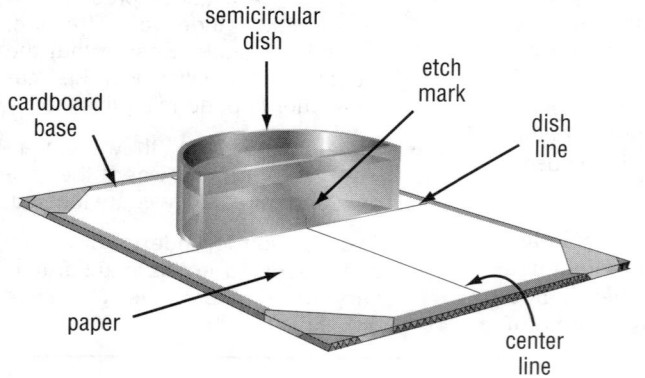

semicircular dish

cardboard base

etch mark

dish line

paper

center line

Figure 2

or use a pin as suggested in the crown glass experiment.

- In the critical angle experiment, the critical angle obtained is actually for a water-plastic-air interface. Polystyrene's index of refraction (1.58) is greater than that of water, so the minimum angle of total internal reflection (which defines the point where the image pin can become visible) will be slightly smaller than the accepted critical angle value for a water-air interface alone.

- In lieu of the water-air critical angle experiment, you may want to determine the crown glass-air critical angle, using the same procedures.

- The mirror is placed facedown in order to allow the coating on the

at the interface, and **total internal reflection** occurs. You may have observed this effect underwater in a swimming pool. The sky and other objects above the pool are visible within a circular area above your head, but outside the circle you can see only the reflection of the interior of the pool. The Snell's law equation can be rewritten to easily determine the critical angle, assuming the less dense medium is air ($n = 1.000$).

$$\frac{\sin \theta_i}{\sin \theta_r} = \frac{n_r}{n_i} \Rightarrow \frac{\sin \theta_i}{\sin 90°} = \frac{1.000}{n_i} \Rightarrow \frac{\sin \theta_i}{1} = \frac{1}{n_i} \Rightarrow \sin \theta_i = \frac{1}{n_i} \qquad (2)$$

Equation (2) shows that the critical angle of a medium in contact with air is the angle of incidence whose sine is the reciprocal of the index of refraction for the medium.

There are three separate experiments in this lab. In the first experiment, you will determine the index of refraction for water. The air will contain the incident ray of light, and the water will contain the refracted ray. The angles of incidence and refraction will be measured at the air-water interface. In the second experiment, the critical angle of a light ray refracted at a water-air interface will be determined. In this case, the water contains the incident ray, and the air contains the refracted ray. The third experiment is the same as the first except that the index of refraction of crown glass will be determined.

Procedure

Index of Refraction for Water

1. Inspect the semicircular dish and verify that there is a 1 cm etch mark exactly in the center of the flat side at the lower edge. If not, your teacher will give you alternate instructions for providing a reference mark at that location.

2. Fill the dish about two-thirds full of water.

3. Draw two perpendicular lines on a piece of paper, using a protractor to divide the sheet into quarters. The angles between the lines must be exactly 90°.

4. Fasten the paper to the cardboard base with tape at the corners.

5. Place the water-filled dish so that the flat side is on the short line and the etch mark lies on the long line. The short line will be referred to as the **dish line,** and the long line will be called the **center line** (see Figure 2).

6. Place a pin about 4 cm from the flat surface of the dish on the center line. This pin will be referred to as the *object*. Label the pin O_1.

7. Close one eye and sight through the opposite side of the dish. Move left or right until you observe the etch mark lined up with the object pin. Insert a second pin at the side of the rounded portion of the dish in line with your eye and the etch mark. This image pin should block the view of the etch mark and the object pin (see Figure 3). Label the pin I_1. Both I_1 and O_1 should be located on the center line.

8. Repeat Steps 6–7 for three other positions of the object in the same quadrant of the paper. Label the object positions O_2, O_3, and O_4. Determine where I_2, I_3, and I_4 will have to be placed in order to mark the rays where the object and the etch mark line up in each trial. Label each pin position on your paper accordingly.

9. Remove the dish and pins from the paper. Connect each object pin position to the intersection of the dish line and center line (where the etch mark was located). Then extend the line to the associated image pin position.

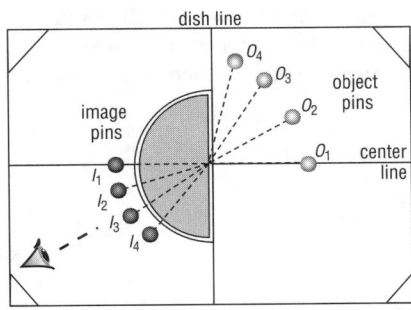

Figure 3

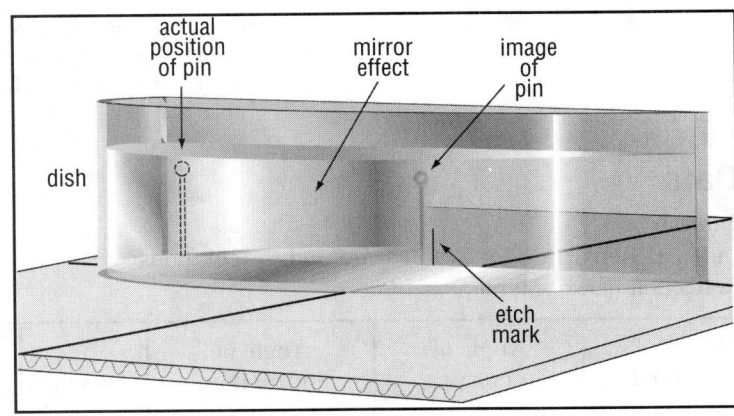

Figure 4

10. Use a protractor to measure the angle of incidence (θ_i) and the angle of refraction (θ_r). Consider the ray to be originating at O and traveling toward I.

11. Record your data in Table 1.

Critical Angle at the Water-Air Interface

The objective of this experiment is to find the object position (on the water side of the interface) that will produce a refracted ray that lies along the flat face of the dish. Unfortunately, attempting to see rays refracted at the critical angle by sighting along the dish face would be fruitless. To solve this dilemma, you will use a principle of ray optics whereby a light ray will follow the same optical path in both directions. You will place a pin representing the image (the *image pin*) on the dish line where your eye would have to be in order to see the image. This pin intersects the ray known to be refracted at an angle of 90° when the incident ray is at the critical angle. You will then sight along the path of the incident ray through the curved side of the dish toward the etch mark until the image pin becomes barely visible and the interior dish surface just begins to appear mirrorlike. The incident angle that produces these results is the critical angle, θ_c. Since the dish does not have sharp corners and the light ray must pass through a layer of plastic, it may not be possible to place the image pin exactly on the dish line in order to see it.

12. Draw two perpendicular lines on a second sheet of paper. Tape the sheet to the cardboard base and place the water-filled dish on the dish line as before.

13. Place a pin on the dish line at the location shown in Figure 4. Label this image pin I.

14. Sight through the curved portion of the dish toward the etch mark and the quadrant that contains the image pin. Move your head from side to side until you can barely see the image pin (before the flat surface loses transparency). If you cannot see the pin, move the pin a short distance away from the dish line and repeat the sighting. Continue making small adjustments to the position of the image pin until it is just visible.

15. Place a pin in line with the etch mark and the image pin at the curved surface of the dish. Label this object pin O.

16. Remove the dish and pins from the paper. Connect the object pin position to the intersection of the dish line and the center line where the etch mark was.

17. Measure the critical angle for the object and record your result in Table 2.

Index of Refraction for Crown Glass

If you place the mirror facedown on a flat surface, you can look from edge to edge through the glass portion to the opposite side of the mirror. Use the mirror back surface to darken the transmission path of light passing through the glass and in order to eliminate objectionable reflections from the mirror.

Postlab Analysis

• The students should sketch out Question 5 before they attempt to solve it. Note that the ray traverses two optical interfaces in this problem.

Prelab Homework

• Require students to show entire solutions for their work.

as you did the dish of water in the first experiment. An etch mark will not be present on the edge of the mirror, so place a pin in the center of the mirror's edge to serve as the reference mark. Perform Steps 3–10 and record the data in Table 3.

Data

Table 1

Index of Refraction for Water Data and Calculations

Refraction index of air, $n_{air} = 1.000$

Trial	Angle of Incidence, θ_i	Angle of Refraction, θ_r	$\sin \theta_i$	$\sin \theta_r$	Refraction Index of Water, n_{water}	n_{water} Percent Error
1	°	°				%
2	°	°				%
3	°	°				%
4	°	°				%
Average						%

Data and calculations in Table 1 will vary.

Table 2

Critical Angle Data and Calculations

Object	Measured Critical Angle, θ_{c_m}	Refraction Index of Water, n_{water}	$1/n_{water}$	Calculated Critical Angle, θ_{c_c}	θ_{c_m} and θ_{c_c} Percent Difference
O_1	°			°	%

Data and calculations in Table 2 will vary.

Table 3

Index of Refraction for Crown Glass Data and Calculations

Refraction index of air, $n_{air} = 1.000$

Trial	Angle of Incidence, θ_i	Angle of Refraction, θ_r	$\sin \theta_i$	$\sin \theta_r$	Refraction Index of Glass, n_{glass}	n_{glass} Percent Error
1	°	°				%
2	°	°				%
3	°	°				%
4	°	°				%
Average						%

Data and calculations in Table 3 will vary.

Postlab Exercises

1. The accepted value for the index of refraction for water at room temperature is 1.333 for yellow light, which is representative of daylight and indoor lighting. Complete the calculations for the experimental index of refraction for water in Table 1. Record the sines of the angles, rounding to four decimal places. Calculate the percent error between the experimental value for each trial and the accepted value. Find the average of the experimental values and determine the percent error between the average and the accepted value.

2. In the second experiment, calculate the theoretical critical angle for a water-air interface, using Equation (2), and determine the percent error between the experimental angle and the calculated value. Complete Table 2.

3. The accepted value for the index of refraction for crown glass is 1.517 for yellow light. Complete the calculations in Table 3 for the index of refraction for crown glass.

Postlab Analysis

1. Review the results of the first experiment. Did you note any pattern in the percent errors between the experimental index of refraction and the accepted value as angle of incidence increased? If so, what may have caused this?

   Answers will vary. Students may notice an increasing trend in percent error with larger angles of incidence due to refraction within the wall of the plastic dish in the light path at the water-air interface.

2. In the critical angle experiment, you noticed that the flat surface of the dish became mirrorlike for angles of incidence greater than the critical angle. The internal reflection is nearly 100%—better than most mirror coatings. Give three applications of optical internal reflection.

   Answers will vary. Possible responses include prisms in optical instruments, fiber optics, and diamond brilliance.

3. Would you anticipate the critical angle for crown glass to be larger or smaller than the critical angle for water? Justify your answer.

   The index of refraction for crown glass is greater than the index of refraction for water. Accordingly, the sine of the critical angle in Equation (2) will be smaller; therefore, the critical angle will be smaller in crown glass.

4. Which direction will a light ray bend as it passes from water into crown glass?

   The ray will bend toward the normal because glass has a higher index of refraction than water.

5. A light ray from a fish in water is incident on the side of a glass fish tank at an angle of 28.0°. The light passes from the water, through the glass, and into the air. Answer the following questions. Show all of your work.

   a. _____38.8°_____ What is the angle of refraction of the ray as it exits the side of the fish tank?

   b. _____10.8°_____ How many degrees is the ray bent from its original path?

Given: $\theta_{i_{water}} = 28.0°$; $n_{water} = 1.333$; $n_{glass} = 1.517$; $n_{air} = 1.000$

Formula: $\sin \theta_r = \dfrac{n_i \sin \theta_i}{n_r}$ from Equation (1)

Solution (a): Find θ_{r_1} from water to glass.

$$\sin \theta_{r_1} = \frac{(1.333)(\sin 28.0°)}{1.517} = \frac{(1.333)(0.4695)}{1.517} = 0.4126$$

$$\theta_{r_1} = \sin^{-1} 0.4126 = 24.4°$$

To find θ_{r_2} from glass to air, note that $\theta_{i_2} = \theta_{r_1}$.
(If parallel lines are intersected by a transversal, then the alternate interior angles are congruent.)

$$\sin \theta_{r_2} = \frac{(1.517)(\sin 24.4°)}{1.000} = (1.517)(0.4131) = 0.6267$$

$$\theta_{r_2} = \sin^{-1} 0.6267 = 38.8°$$

Solution (b): $|\theta_{r_{air}} - \theta_{i_{water}}| = |38.8° - 28.0°| = 10.8°$ change in direction
(The absolute value signs are not essential but are included for completeness.).

Name _____

Date _____ Hour ____

PRELAB HOMEWORK

1. As a light ray moves into denser medium, it is refracted _____toward_____ the normal.

2. Solve Snell's law equation for the index of refraction for the medium containing the refracted ray, n_r.

   $$n_i \sin \theta_i = n_r \sin \theta_r \Rightarrow n_r = n_i \frac{\sin \theta_i}{\sin \theta_r}$$

3. The index of refraction for air (to 4 SDs) is ____1.000____.

4. The index of refraction for water (to 4 SDs) is ____1.333____.

5. ____48.6°____ Calculate the critical angle (θ_c) for a light ray passing from water to air.

   Given: $n_i = 1.333$; $\theta_c = ?$

   Formula: $\sin \theta_c = \dfrac{1}{n_i}$

   Solution: $\sin \theta_c = \dfrac{1}{1.333} = 0.7502 \Rightarrow \theta_c = \sin^{-1} 0.7502 = 48.6°$

6. True/~~False~~ When determining the angle of incidence in this lab, the angle is measured from the incident ray to the dish line.

7. ~~True~~/False If the critical angle is exceeded, the light ray will be reflected.

8. ____26.8°____ If the angle of incidence for a ray of light passing from air into water is 37°, what is the angle of refraction? Express your answer to the nearest tenth degree.

   Given: $\theta_i = 37.0°$; $n_i = 1.000$; $n_r = 1.333$; $\theta_r = ?$

   Formula: $n_i \sin i = n_r \sin r$

   Solution: $\sin \theta_r = \dfrac{n_i \sin \theta_i}{n_r} = \dfrac{(1.000)(\sin 37.0°)}{1.333} = \dfrac{0.6018}{1.333} \doteq 0.4515$

   $\theta_r = \sin^{-1} 0.4515 = 26.8°$

9. ____1.356____ In the determination of n_{water}, if the angle of incidence is 32.0° and the angle of refraction is 23.0°, what is the experimental value for the index of refraction for water? Express your answer to 4 SDs.

   Given: $\theta_i = 32.0°$; $\theta_r = 23.0°$; $n_i = 1.000$; $n_r = ?$

   Formula: $n_r = n_i \dfrac{\sin \theta_i}{\sin \theta_r}$

   Solution: $n_r = 1.000\left(\dfrac{\sin 32.0°}{\sin 23.0°}\right) = \dfrac{0.5299}{0.3907} \doteq 1.356$

10. ____+1.73%____ Calculate the percent error for the result in Question 9. Express your answer to 3 SDs.

    Given: experimental $n_{water} = 1.356$; accepted $n_{water} = 1.333$; percent error $= ?$

    Formula: percent error $= \dfrac{(\text{experimental value} - \text{accepted value})}{\text{accepted value}} \times 100\%$

    Solution: percent error $= \dfrac{1.356 - 1.333}{1.333} \times 100\% \doteq +1.73\%$

Name _____

Date _____ Hour _____

REFLECTED DIFFRACTION

Purpose

The interference of waves from diffraction reveals much about the nature of waves. The purpose of this lab is to

- observe the interference patterns generated by reflected diffraction.
- perform a measurement using an indirect method.
- determine the distance between adjacent data tracks on a compact disc (CD).
- compare the experimental value for track distance with the actual value.

Prelab Discussion

Diffraction is a basic property of all kinds of waves. As a wave passes by an object or through an opening, some of the energy wraps around the edge and deflects at an angle to the original direction. This is one reason that a sound source can be heard from around a corner and that ocean waves wrap around a breakwater into a harbor. The fact that wave energy exhibits diffraction is most conveniently explained by **Huygens's principle** for wave propagation. This rule states that every point on a wave itself becomes a source of new wavelets. The imaginary line tangent to these wavelets coincides with the new wave front. Since the wavelets move away from the points radially in all directions, it is easy to understand how energy bends around an object. The amount of bending depends on both the wavelength and the size of the object or opening. In general, the longer the wavelength in relation to the object or opening, the more bending, or diffraction, occurs.

Light also displays the property of diffraction, but the wavelengths of visible light are so short that diffraction is not noticeable under normal circumstances except around microscopic objects. Diffraction of light was not generally understood until the early 1800s when an English scientist named Thomas Young used another property of waves, interference, in order to demonstrate the existence of diffraction.

From your study of wave theory, you know that two or more waves passing through each other will interfere either constructively or destructively. With light, constructive interference results in increased intensity or brightness, and destructive interference results in a significant reduction in brightness or even complete darkness. If a light beam illuminates an opaque barrier containing two narrow slits close together, the two beams emerging on the other side can interfere with each other through diffraction as they spread out. When projected on a screen, the combination of the two beams produces bands or spots of light separated by dark regions. The bright spots represent points where the beams interfere in phase (the interfering waves are whole numbers of wavelengths apart). The center of the dark regions represent points where the beams interfere out of phase (the interfering waves are odd multiples of half of a wavelength apart). See Figure 1. The **interference pattern** consists of a very bright central band surrounded on both sides by successively dimmer parallel spots. This is the essence of the double-slit experiment that Thomas Young performed in 1801.

The **order number (*n*)** of the spots is significant. The central spot ($n = 0$) is produced from the constructive interference of two waves that have no displacement. The *first-order* spots ($n = 1$) on either side are produced from waves differing by one wavelength, the *second-order* spots ($n = 2$) are from waves

Required Equipment

compact disc, standard-sized
corrugated cardboard screen
felt-tipped marker
laser pointer (or other laser source)
masking tape
meter stick
protractor
unlined paper
wood blocks, 2

Prelab Discussion

- Review the prerequisites for Lab 4-13 in the back of this manual.

- Students will find the information that is essential to understand this lab in the discussion, but it will be helpful if they have studied wave propagation, reflection, and diffraction prior to the lab.

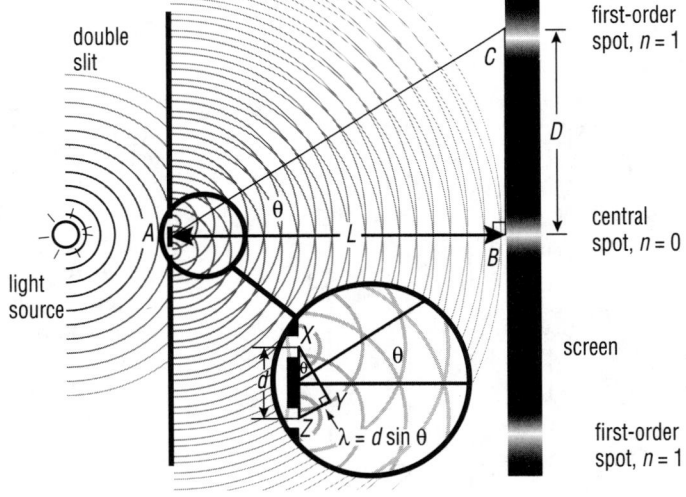

Figure 1

- Interested students can find further information regarding CD manufacturing and technology in the book *The Compact Disc: A Handbook of Theory and Use* by Ken C. Pohlmann (Madison, Wis.: A-R Editions, 1992).

Equipment and Setup

- The equipment and materials should be available locally.

- Almost any laser pointer can be used, including the key-chain variety. Some configurations may be more difficult to mount and aim than others. If you have access to a laboratory-grade laser, you are likely to obtain more precise results by obtaining the wavelength of light from credible documentation.

- The mounting blocks of wood for the pointer and CD can be cut square from a 2 × 4. The pointer support block should have an accurate center line drawn parallel to the long axis of the block on the top and on two ends so that the block can be aligned at the center line on the paper. The support block for the CD should be sawed perfectly square so that the CD will be perpendicular to the table when it is taped to a side. These cuts can be easily made on a table saw.

- The screen should be made from a stiff, flat material such as corrugated cardboard. It should be

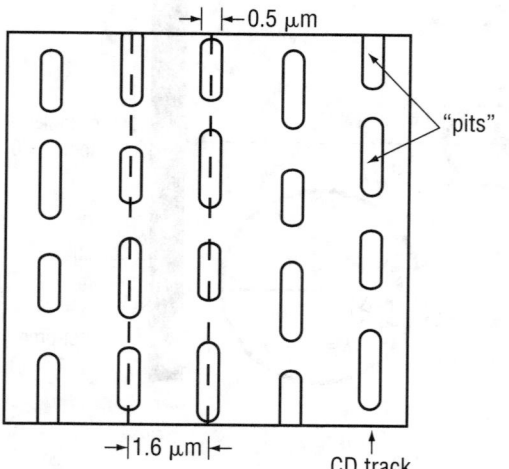

Figure 2

at least 60 cm long but only 10 to 20 cm high.

- The alignment of the laser, the CD, and the screen is essential to the success of this experiment. The CD must be parallel to the screen, the screen and the CD must be perpendicular to the table, and the

differing by two wavelengths, and so on. The phase displacement is caused by the **angle of diffraction (θ).** As the diffraction angle increases in either direction from the central band, one of the waves of light must travel a longer distance than the other from its slit to the screen. When the difference in path length equals an integer multiple of the light's wavelength, constructive interference occurs, and a bright band appears. In Figure 1, *AB* is the distance (*L*) between the double slits and the screen, and *BC* is the distance (*D*) between the central band and the interference band. The length *YZ* is an integer multiple of the laser wavelength ($n\lambda$) needed to produce a bright interference band at *C,* and *XZ* is the distance between slits (*d*). You can prove that ΔABC and ΔXYZ are similar, so the diffraction angle θ exists in both triangles. Trigonometrically,

$$n\lambda = d \sin \theta, \tag{1}$$

where *n* is the order of the interference band. Equation (1) is an important relationship; if the wavelength of light forming the interference pattern is known and the diffraction angle of an interference band can be determined, then the distance between the slits can also be calculated. You will be using this concept in this experiment to find the track spacing on a CD.

When you have been required to measure a quantity in this course, you have used the appropriate instrument and measured directly. In many situations, however, the quantity to be measured is too small, too large, or immeasurable using standard laboratory instruments. Scientists and engineers must often resort to imaginative methods to obtain the required measurements *indirectly.* **Indirect measurements** can be obtained from geometric relationships or from other properties that can be measured. Some examples of quantities found by indirect measurements are the distances between atoms in a crystal lattice, using X-ray diffraction, and the distances to remote astronomical bodies, using spectroscopic red shifts. To measure the track spacing on a CD directly would require a high-powered microscope. Using the indirect method discussed above, you will easily be able to perform this measurement in your classroom.

A standard compact disc, or CD, is a polycarbonate disc approximately 120 mm in diameter and 1.2 mm thick with a center hole 15 mm in diameter. Digital data is encoded on a reflective surface embedded within the polycarbonate during the manufacturing process. The data is recorded as a continuous string of "pits" formed in a spiral pattern beginning at the inner margin of the digital medium. The binary information is encoded so that the *ends* of the pits represent 1 and the flat spots ("lands") within and between the pits represent 0. Each pit is approximately 0.5 μm (micrometer) wide and from 0.83 μm to 3.56 μm long. The distance between the center lines of adjacent tracks is 1.6 μm (see Figure 2). The discs are manufactured so that their pits open toward the CD label; therefore, the CD player laser actually senses the boundaries of "mounds" on the underside of the disc. As laser light reflects off adjacent CD tracks, the effect is identical to that of light transmitted through the slits in Young's experiment. When the reflected light is diffracted, it produces interference spots. In polychromatic light, such as incandescent lighting, the varieties of new wavelengths produced by the interference appear as the rainbow colors typical of CDs.

In this experiment you will illuminate a standard CD with a laser pointer or other laser source. The reflected light will fall on a screen, and interference spots will form. You will measure the distance between the screen and the CD and find the average distance between the central interference band and each band of higher order. From these measurements, the diffraction angle for each order of interference band can be determined (θ = $\tan^{-1} D/L$). The wavelength of the laser light will be determined from either the technical documentation provided with the laser or a reasonable assumption for the wavelength. Using Equation (1), you can then determine the CD track spacing, *d,* from the data for each order of interference band. You can then average the calculated values of *d* and compare that average to the actual value of 1.6 μm.

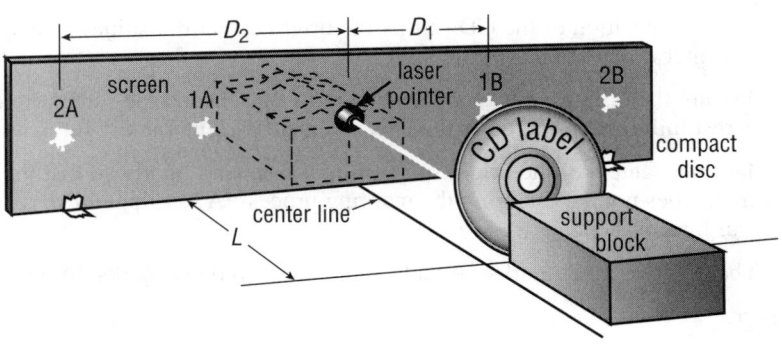

Figure 3

Procedure

1. Refer to Figure 3 as you set up this experiment. Draw a straight line on a legal-sized sheet of paper, using a meter stick or some other straightedge. This line will be referred to as the *center line*. Tape the paper to the table so that the center line is parallel to the edge of the table.

2. Obtain the wavelength of the light emitted by your laser. This information may be printed on a label on the instrument or noted in a specifications sheet in the box, or your teacher may have the information. If you cannot find the actual wavelength, you may assume that a *red* laser's wavelength is 655 nm. Write the wavelength in the blank above Table 1.

3. Place the laser pointer parallel to and on top of the line on the long side of the block marked with the center line on three sides. Tape the emitter end of the laser pointer to the block of wood. Set the block on the paper so that the lines marked on the ends of the block coincide with the center line on the paper. Tape the block in this position.

4. Position the long cardboard screen so that the laser emitter is centered in the hole and the cardboard rests against the block of wood. Tape the screen to the table and the block of wood. Use a protractor to verify that the screen is perpendicular to the center line on the paper and also perpendicular to the table. Adjust the screen as necessary to meet these conditions.

5. Place the other block of wood on the table. Position the CD with its edge on the table and its label against the block. Tape it in place.

6. Position the CD and block assembly so that the center line on the paper intersects the CD within the data portion of its surface to the right or left of the central hole.

Caution: Avoid looking directly into an energized laser, regardless of the size or source.

Trial 1

7. Switch on the laser. You may have to place a piece of tape over the switch to keep the laser energized. Verify that the beam shines in line with the center line. Adjust the free end of the laser pointer as necessary to align it; then tape it in place.

8. Place the CD and support assembly about 15 cm from the screen. Slide the assembly toward the screen until you see five bright dots in a line on the screen. The line of dots should be nearly horizontal, but a small inclination is acceptable. If the pattern is excessively tilted, adjust the laser to shine on the CD at a point where the CD tracks run vertically. Use the protractor to ensure that the CD is perpendicular to the center line on the paper and

laser beam must be perpendicular to the screen and the CD. The height of the support block for the laser needs to be adjusted so that the laser shines horizontally and strikes the CD 60 mm above the table surface.

- Precut the hole in the screen(s) prior to the lab.

Procedure

- Caution students about shining lasers into their eyes. Although brief exposure to typical laser pointers may not be hazardous, prolonged exposure to any laser is potentially injurious, and following precautions promotes good laboratory practices.

- Discuss the importance of equipment alignment.

- The only data that must be obtained during the lab period are the distance between the CD and the screen, the distances between the pairs of interference spots, and the wavelength of light.

- You may want the students to attempt to find the third-order spots by directing the laser reflection toward the wall. If you are using a red laser, you cannot obtain third-order spots, no matter where the assembly is positioned. See Question 3 in the Postlab Analysis.

Prelab Homework

- The optional proof in Question 7 is based on the theorems and logic presented in *GEOMETRY for Christian Schools,* Second Edition, published by BJUP. The proof includes all of the necessary steps, but not every possible step is included for the sake of brevity. Students may find other legitimate ways to prove the statement.

adjust the position of the CD so that the bright center dot shines exactly on the center of the emitter of the laser.

9. Measure the distance between the surface of the CD and the screen (to the nearest millimeter) and enter this measurement as *L* in Table 1 for Trial 1.

10. Mark the centers of the bright spots of light, pressing lightly so that the screen does not move during the marking process. A felt-tipped marker is ideal for this step.

11. Label the two inner marks 1A and 1B and the two outer marks 2A and 2B.

Trial 2

12. Slide the CD and support assembly away from the screen so that there are only three spots visible on the screen. After realigning the center dot and ensuring that the CD is perpendicular to the center line, measure the distance between the CD and the screen and record this measurement in Table 1 for Trial 2. Label the two dots 1A′ and 1B′.

13. Turn off the laser pointer and disassemble all of the materials.

14. Measure the distance from point 1A to 1B. Record this value in Table 1 for Trial 1. Also measure the distance from point 2A to 2B and record in Table 1 for Trial 1. Finally, measure the distance between 1A′ and 1B′ and record in Table 1 for Trial 2 (in the 1A to 1B column).

Data

Table 1
Diffraction Angle Data and Calculations
Laser source wavelength, λ _____650_____ nm

Trial	*L*	1A to 1B	D_1	θ_1	2A to 2B	D_2	θ_2
1	147 mm	134 mm	67 mm	24.5 °	438 mm	219 mm	56.1 °
2	507 mm	471 mm	236 mm	25.0 °			

Data and answers in Table 1 will vary. Data and answers shown are typical.

Table 2
Track Spacing Calculations

Trial	Diffraction Angle		Order Number, *n*	*n*λ	Track Spacing, *d*	Percent Error
1	θ_1	24.5 °	1	650 nm	1.57 μm	−1.9 %
	θ_2	56.1 °	2	1300 nm	1.57 μm	−1.9 %
2	θ_1'	25.0 °	1	650 nm	1.54 μm	−3.8 %
Average					1.56 μm	−2.5 %

Data and answers in Table 2 will vary. Data and answers shown are typical.

Postlab Exercises

1. Determine the average distance from the center spot to the diffraction spots by dividing the "A to B" distances by 2. Enter the results for the first-order spots under D_1 and the results for the second-order spots under D_2 in Table 1.

2. Calculate the diffraction angles for the first-order spots (θ_1 and θ_1') by finding the arctangent ($\tan^{-1} x$) of the ratio of D_1 and L for each trial. Record the angles for Trials 1 and 2 in Table 1. Find the diffraction angle for the second-order spots (θ_2) for Trial 1, using D_2 and L, and record the result in Table 1.

3. Copy the respective values of θ_1 and θ_2 for each trial into Table 2.

4. Write the order number for each diffraction angle, 1 or 2 as applicable, in Table 2.

5. Multiply the wavelength of the laser light in nanometers (10^{-9} m) by the order number and record in the $n\lambda$ column in Table 2.

6. Calculate the distance between CD tracks, using Equation (1) for each diffraction angle, and record the result in micrometers (10^{-6} m) in the d column in Table 2.

7. Find the percent error between your experimentally determined values of track spacing and the actual value of 1.6 μm. Also find the average value of experimental d and determine the percent error. Enter all results in Table 2.

Postlab Analysis

1. Discuss the difference(s) between the central spot, the first-order spots, and the second-order spots.

   As the order of the spot increases, the brightness diminishes.

2. Why was there no illumination between the spots?

   The waves that reflected off the CD tracks interfered destructively in

   those regions.

3. Using this experimental setup, can you obtain a third-order spot, assuming the light source is 655 nm and the CD track spacing is 1.6 μm? Justify your answer.

   Given: $n = 3$; $\lambda = 655$ nm; $d = 1.6$ μm; $\theta = ?$

   Formula: $n\lambda = d \sin \theta \Rightarrow \theta = \sin^{-1}\left(\dfrac{n\lambda}{d}\right)$

   Solution: $\theta = \sin^{-1}\left[\dfrac{3(655 \times 10^{-9} \text{ m})}{1.6 \times 10^{-6} \text{ m}}\right] = \sin^{-1} 1.2281 \Rightarrow$ The angle

   does not exist. Therefore, there is no third-order spot for this wavelength.

4. Describe some specific errors that might be introduced if the CD is not parallel to the screen.

   The CD must be parallel to the screen because the reflected diffraction angles will be affected by the orientation of the CD. A nonparallel CD will produce spot distances (D) that are longer or shorter than they should be; the result will be incorrect calculations for diffraction angles.

5. If you had used a different CD, do you think that your results would be different? Explain your answer.

   The track spacing would be approximately the same. CDs must be played on equipment from many different manufacturers, so the track spacing must be standardized to ensure compatibility.

6. Does accuracy of your value of track spacing increase or decrease as you move the CD farther from the screen?

   Based on the limited data of this experiment, accuracy decreases.

7. If the flat cardboard screen were replaced by a curved screen with a radius of *L*, what advantages and disadvantages would this configuration bring to this experiment?

   Answers will vary but may include the following statements. The curved screen would more closely match the circular propagation of the wave fronts from the CD surface, so a more accurate position of the interference spots would be obtained. The key disadvantage would be the difficulty in calculating the diffraction angle because the similar triangle relationships would not exist.

8. What could you change in order to obtain a third-order or higher interference spot in this experiment?

   The CD track spacing is fixed, so the only possible change is to shorten the wavelength of the light source. The wavelength would have to be less than 1.6 μm/3 (<520 nm) in order to obtain a visible third-order spot.

Name _____

Date _____ Hour ____

PRELAB HOMEWORK

1. Explain in your own words how a straight wave front can wrap around an object or the edge of an opening in its path.

   According to Huygens's principle, every point on a wave front is itself the source

   for new wavelets that proceed radially from that point. As the wave front passes

   an object, the new wavelets tend to move into the region shadowed by the object.

   Thus the wave appears to bend, or diffract, around the object.

2. What experiment conclusively demonstrated the wave nature of light?

   Thomas Young's double-slit interference experiment in 1801 demonstrated the

   wave nature of light.

3. Describe a double-slit interference pattern and explain how it is formed.

   The interference pattern consists of a bright central band surrounded on both

   sides by a symmetrical pattern of parallel, successively dimmer bands of light.

   The interference bands are formed by the diffracted waves of light from the two

   slits constructively interfering at the screen.

4. What would be the order number of the third interference band from the central band? How much farther must the waves that follow the longer path from the slits travel compared to the waves traveling the shorter path to form this band?

   The order number is $n = 3$. The waves that follow the longer path must travel 3λ

   farther.

5. ____23.8°____ While conducting the experiment, a student measured the distance between the CD and the screen and found it to be 138 mm. The distance between the two first-order spots was 122 mm. What is the diffraction angle of the first-order spots in this experiment?

   Given: L = 138 mm; 1A to 1B = 122 mm; D = ?; θ = ?

   Solution: $D = \dfrac{122 \text{ mm}}{2} = 61$ mm; $\theta = \tan^{-1}\left(\dfrac{D}{L}\right) = \tan^{-1}\left(\dfrac{61 \text{ mm}}{138 \text{ mm}}\right) \doteq 23.8°$

6. ____1.62 μm____ Assuming the wavelength of the laser light in Question 5 was 655 nm, what is the calculated CD track spacing?

   Given: θ = 23.8°; λ = 655 nm; n = 1; d = ?

   Formula: $n\lambda = d \sin \theta \Rightarrow d = \dfrac{n\lambda}{\sin \theta}$

   Solution: $d = \dfrac{(1)(655 \times 10^{-9} \text{ m})}{\sin 23.8°} = \dfrac{(655 \times 10^{-9} \text{ m})}{0.4035} \doteq 1.62 \times 10^{-6} \text{ m} = 1.62 \text{ μm}$

7. (Optional) Prove that $\triangle ABC$ and $\triangle XYZ$ in Figure 1 are similar given that $\overline{YZ} \parallel \overline{AC}$, $\overline{AB} \perp \overline{XZ}$, $\overline{AB} \perp \overline{BC}$, and $\overline{AC} \perp \overline{XY}$ from the geometric definition of the experiment.

   Given: $\overline{YZ} \parallel \overline{AC}$; $\overline{AB} \perp \overline{XZ}$; $\overline{AB} \perp \overline{BC}$; $\overline{AC} \perp \overline{XY}$

   Prove: $\triangle ABC \sim \triangle XYZ$

   1. Label the intersection of $\overline{XY}$ and $\overline{AB}$ point P; label the intersection of $\overline{XY}$ and

   $\overline{AC}$ point Q.

2. $\triangle ABC$ is a right triangle because $\angle ABC$ is a right angle.

3. $\angle XYZ \cong \angle XQA$ because corresponding angles of parallel lines cut by a transversal are congruent. $\therefore \angle XYZ$ is a right angle, and $\triangle XYZ$ is a right triangle.

4. $\overline{AQ}$ is an altitude to the right angle of $\triangle AXP$; therefore, the two smaller triangles formed are similar to the larger triangle and to each other (Theorem 13.4 in GEOMETRY *for Christian Schools,* Second Edition).

5. $\angle PAQ \cong \angle PXA$ because corresponding angles of similar triangles are congruent. $\therefore \angle BAC \cong \angle YXZ$.

6. $\triangle ABC \cong \triangle XYZ$ because if an acute angle of one right triangle is congruent to the acute angle of another, then the two triangles are similar (AA Similarity Postulate).

Name _____

Date _____ Hour _____

RADIOACTIVE DECAY SIMULATION

Purpose

Having knowledge of the decay of radioactive materials is important to understanding many subjects, including medical and nuclear materials technology. The purpose is to

- review the modes of radioactive decay.
- define radioactivity and the properties of radioactive decay.
- simulate the radioactive decay of a hypothetical nuclide, develop a graph of the decay, and analyze the characteristics of decay curves.

Prelab Discussion

The vast majority of atoms in the universe are essentially stable. That is, they show little tendency to change by emitting particles or rays or splitting apart. The spontaneous emission of nuclear particles or rays is called **nuclear decay,** while the splitting of a nucleus into relatively large chunks is called **nuclear fission.** Fission is usually accompanied by the emission of one or more neutrons. This lab will concentrate primarily on spontaneous nuclear decay, which includes the emission of gamma rays, alpha particles, and beta particles. Gamma ray emission leaves the nucleus physically unchanged while reducing the total energy of the nucleus. Alpha particle emissions reduce the atomic number by two and the mass number by four. Beta emissions may be in the form of either negative electrons (β^-) or positive electrons (β^+, positrons). A negative beta emission increases the atomic number by one, and a positive beta decay decreases the atomic number by one. Beta decay does not change the mass number.

An **isotope** of an element is one of two or more forms of an element that have the same number of protons but a different number of neutrons. A **nuclide** refers to one atom or a collection of atoms of a particular isotope. An isotope is **radioactive** if it exhibits spontaneous nuclear decay. Every element has at least one radioactive isotope. Radioactivity appears to be associated with one of three conditions: (1) the nucleus is physically too large for stability; (2) it has a neutron-to-proton (n/p) ratio that is either too large or too small for stability; or (3) the nucleus has excessive energy. A nucleus that is too large will decay by alpha emission. A nucleus with an n/p ratio that is too large or too small will decay by either positive or negative beta emission. A nucleus with excessive energy will emit one or more gamma rays until the nucleus is stable. Gamma emission may be associated with a particle emission or may occur alone. Your textbook shows a diagram of the belt of stable isotopes on a graph of neutron number vs. proton number.

The tendency for a given nuclide to decay appears to be completely unaffected by external conditions such as temperature, pressure, or the chemical state of the atom. In addition, the decay of any one atom in a sample of an isotope is totally independent of the decay of any other like atom. In other words, if you start with two identical nuclide atoms, there is no guarantee that they will decay at the same time. All radioactive nuclides have a characteristic average lifetime due to the inherent instability of their nuclei. Nuclear physicists have developed a method for determining the decay rate for nuclides, using the concept of **half-life ($t_{1/2}$).** The half-life of a nuclide is the time required for half of the atoms in a statistical sample to decay to another kind of atom. If a sample originally contains 1000 atoms, approximately 500 will decay during the first half-life. During the second half-life, an additional 250 will decay, leaving 250. Approximately 125 atoms will remain after the third half-life, and so on until no original atoms are left. The half-life of a nuclide is a measurable characteristic of its particular isotope. Some radioactive isotopes have extremely short half-lives approaching 10^{-16} s, while other isotopes that are essentially stable have half-lives estimated to be billions of years.

Prelab Discussion

- Review the prerequisites for Lab 5-1 in the back of this manual.

- Students should be conversant with the concepts of atomic structure, isotopes, and nuclear changes prior to performing this lab.

- This lab can be used to lead into discussions on statistical principles, exponential functions, the details of nuclear decay, radioactive decay product buildup, radiometric dating techniques, calculus concepts, and many other topics.

- Radioactive daughter products were not addressed in order to keep this lab discussion fairly simple. The total activity of a sample of radioactive material is the sum of the activities of all of the radioactive parent nuclides and their radioactive daughter nuclides. Depending on the original nuclide, it may experience a series of decays before it attains stability.

Equipment and Setup

- Ask the students to bring their own bags of M&M's candies to school for this lab. They may also supply the boxes.

Procedure

- Consider using a larger number of candies. Starting with 128 candies will produce an easily plotted curve.

- An error graph may not be a familiar graphing technique. It is used to show the variation of data when a mean value is plotted. Scientists use this technique to evaluate the validity of the graph of the mean values and to determine the "enve-lope" of possible results. Due to the small numbers of items involved in this experiment, the error plots probably will not be very significant.

Postlab Analysis

• Question 6 is a multiple-part exercise that may cause some difficulties for your students. Review the process of determining an instantaneous rate on a graph, by determining the slope of the tangent line at the point of interest (used in Lab 2-4). The purpose of this question is to show students that the number of atoms producing a certain radioactivity can be estimated. It is impossible to count the radioactive

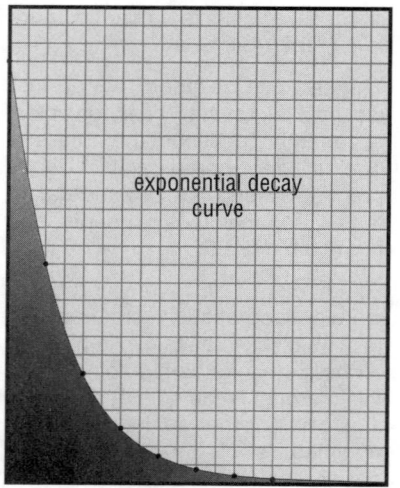

exponential decay curve

Figure 1

$$N_0(1/2)^{\Delta t/t_{1/2}} = N_0 e^{-\lambda \Delta t}$$

$$\cancel{N_0}(1/2)^{\Delta t/t_{1/2}} = \cancel{N_0} e^{-\lambda \Delta t}$$

$$\ln(1/2)^{\Delta t/t_{1/2}} = \ln e^{-\lambda \Delta t}$$

$$(\Delta t/t_{1/2})[\ln(1/2)] = -\lambda \Delta t(\ln e)$$

$$(\Delta t/t_{1/2})(-0.693) = -\lambda \Delta t(1)$$

$$(\cancel{\Delta t}/t_{1/2})(\cancel{-0.693}) = \cancel{-\lambda} \cancel{\Delta t}$$

$$0.693/t_{1/2} = \lambda$$

When discussing a statistical process, exact numbers cannot be predicted for any particular instant in the process. In any half-life time interval, a nuclide atom can either decay or not decay, and while the probability exists that half of the atoms will decay, there is no guarantee that any specific atom will decay. This aspect of radioactive decay is random. Therefore, the actual number of atoms decaying in a half-life interval may be more or less than the number predicted by probability alone. The larger the initial population of atoms, the more closely the change in the number of atoms will follow the statistical behavior predicted by probability. You should also realize that the probability of decay continuously applies to every radioactive atom. At any given instant, the probability of decay is 50% over the ensuing half-life time interval.

The number of nuclear decays per second in a sample is called the **activity** of the sample. From the above discussion, you should expect the nuclide activity to be related to the total number of nuclide atoms present. As the number of nuclides declines with time, the activity also decreases. Mathematically, the proportionality can be written

$$\frac{\Delta N}{\Delta t} \propto N,$$

where $\Delta N/\Delta t$ is the rate of change in the number of particles and N is the number of particles *at any particular time*. To make this relationship an equation, a proportionality constant is included:

$$\frac{\Delta N}{\Delta t} = -\lambda N, \tag{1}$$

where λ is the **decay constant.** Notice that the rate of change, $\Delta N/\Delta t$, is a negative quantity, indicating that N *decreases* over time. However, the activity of a nuclide sample is only the *magnitude* of $\Delta N/\Delta t$ because it represents decays per second.

If you plot the remaining number of radioactive nuclide atoms versus time, the resulting graph will follow a decreasing function called an exponential decay curve. The corresponding equation is

$$N_t = N_0 e^{-\lambda \Delta t}, \tag{2}$$

where N_t is the number of nuclide atoms at time t after some reference time t_0, N_0 is the number of nuclide atoms at the reference time, e is the base of natural logarithms ($e \approx 2.718$), λ is the decay constant with units of inverse seconds (s^{-1}), inverse hours (h^{-1}), or some other inverse time units, depending on the units of Δt, and Δt is the elapsed time $t - t_0$. Figure 1 shows a typical decay curve. In another course of study, you may have used the following equation to express radioactive decay based on half-lives:

$$N_t = N_0(1/2)^{\Delta t/t_{1/2}}, \tag{3}$$

where the exponent $\Delta t/t_{1/2}$ is the number of half-lives that have passed since the time N_0 was determined. Equations (2) and (3) are equivalent. In fact, you can derive the value of λ by substituting Equation (3) for N_t in Equation (2). See the adjacent box for the derivation.

In this lab you will begin the radioactive decay simulation with a known number of radioactive nuclide "atoms." Then for each sequential "half-life," you will determine how many of the radioactive atoms remain from the previous half-life "decay." After enough half-lives have passed that all of your atoms have decayed, you will plot the number of nuclide atoms versus half-lives on a graph and analyze the properties of the graph. In order to illustrate the statistical nature of the simulation, the number of "decayed" atoms will be determined using a randomization process.

Procedure

1. Obtain a bag of M&M's Milk Chocolate Candies and a covered box, such as a shoe box or a plastic refrigerator storage container.

2. Count out 64 candies into the box. (Your teacher may have you use more.) Set aside any candies that are irregular or that have an obvious difference in shape from the average candy. The box should be large enough that there is plenty of room for all of the candies to lie scattered on the bottom of the box. Record your starting number (N_0) in Table 1.

3. Cover the box. To begin a data trial, hold the box horizontally and shake it rapidly up and down several times.

4. Set the box on the table and uncover it. If any candies are resting on top of others, tap the box until they form a single layer on the bottom of the box.

5. Remove all candies that show the M&M's candies logo and set them aside. Count the candies remaining in the box and record the number in Table 1.

6. To complete the first trial, repeat Steps 3–5 for each shake until there are no more candies remaining. Record the number of candies remaining for each shake under the appropriate column in Table 1.

7. Obtain two additional trials by repeating Steps 2–6. Record the results in the appropriate rows of Table 1.

8. When you have finished collecting data, you may eat the M&M's candies!

nuclides directly. Using radiometric spectroscopy, the kind and energies of the decays can be determined, and the isotopes producing the decays can be identified. Scientists determining carbon-14 dates must use a similar process.

Data

Table 1
Radioactive Decay Simulation Data

Shake	Start	1	2	3	4	5	6	7	8	9	10
Number Remaining	N_0	N_1	N_2	N_3	N_4	N_5	N_6	N_7	N_8	N_9	N_{10}
Trial 1											
Trial 2											
Trial 3											
Average											

Postlab Exercises

1. Find the average of the three trials for each shake. Record the averages in Table 1.

2. Plot the ordered pairs of shake number (*x*-axis) versus average number of candies remaining (*y*-axis) on Graph 1. Adjust the scales so that you use as much of the graph area as possible. Label the axes appropriately.

3. Carefully sketch a smooth, best-fit curve as close as possible to the data points.

4. For each shake number on Graph 1, plot the greatest and least number of candies in the three trials for that shake number from Table 1. Connect the two dots with a vertical line. This kind of graph is called an **error graph.**

5. Using a different colored pencil or pen, mark points on Graph 1 representing the number of candies remaining for each shake, based on *mathematical probability*. Use fractional numbers when appropriate and continue the graph to the right-hand edge of Graph 1. If you started with 64 candies, they will decrease in the order 64, 32, 16, 8, and so on. Sketch a smooth, thin, sharp line through these probability points, using the contrasting color.

Graph 1
Radioactive Decay Simulation

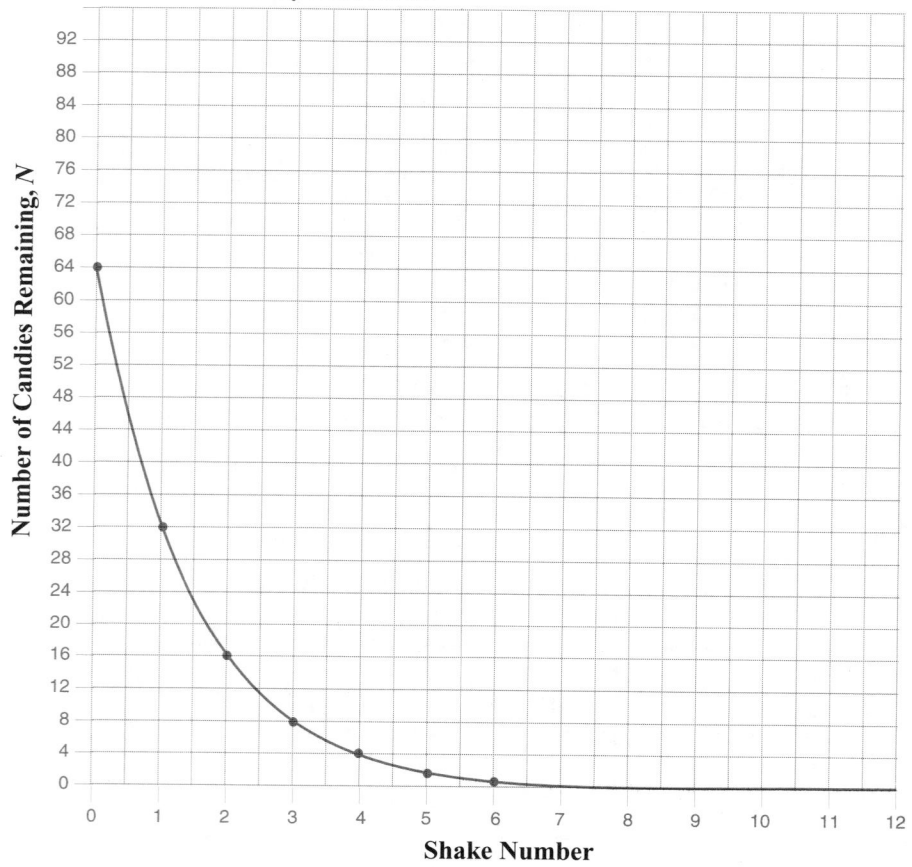

The curve in Graph 1 is a mathematical decay curve. Student data may vary.

Postlab Analysis

1. Inspect Graph 1. What is the approximate fraction of candies remaining after each shake?

   Answers will vary, but students should note that approximately half

   of the candies remain after each shake.

2. How many shakes are required to reduce the number of remaining candies by half?

   Only one shake is required to reduce the number of remaining

   candies by half.

3. What does one shake correspond to in terms of radioactive decay?

   One shake corresponds to one half-life.

4. <u>0.693 shake^{-1}</u> If a shake is one half-life, what is the decay constant (λ) for your "nuclides"? Show your work.

    Given: $t_{1/2}$ = 1 shake; λ = ?

    Formula: $\lambda = \dfrac{0.693}{t_{1/2}}$

    Solution: $\lambda = \dfrac{0.693}{1 \text{ shake}} = 0.693 \text{ shake}^{-1}$

5. In the Postlab Exercises, you were required to develop an error graph on Graph 1, using the maximum and minimum number of candies remaining for each shake. Describe how the ideal probability curve compares to the upper and lower data limits for each shake.

    <u>Answers will vary. If the shakes were performed correctly and no</u>

    <u>errors were made recording the data, the ideal probability curve</u>

    <u>should fall within the upper and lower limits of the error graph.</u>

6. Choose three data points on your graph (other than the first or last) and determine the slope of the curve at those points, using a tangent line the way you did in Lab 2-4. The slope of the curve approximates the instantaneous change in the number of candies per unit time (1 shake) or $\Delta N/\Delta t$. After calculating the slope at the three points, use Equation (1) to mathematically determine the number of candies at that point. Compare the calculated number and the experimental average for each point.

    <u>Answers will vary, but careful students should obtain calculated</u>

    <u>values for N within 10% of the experimental average number for</u>

    <u>each point. Remind them that they must calculate λ for this experi-</u>

    <u>ment (see Question 4).</u>

7. Will a sample of a radioactive nuclide always be radioactive? Explain.

    <u>No. At some point in the future, all of the original atoms will have</u>

    <u>decayed away. (This assumes that the products of decay are not</u>

    <u>radioactive themselves.) See Question 9 in the Prelab Homework.</u>

8. Is hazardous radioactive material safe once it has been stored beyond its half-life? Explain.

    <u>No. After the first half-life there is still half of the hazardous material</u>

    <u>remaining.</u>

9. Using Equation (2), determine how many *full* half-lives must pass in order to eliminate more than 95% of the radioactive nuclides. Does your graph support this conclusion?

    Given: $\dfrac{N_t}{N_0} < 0.05$; Δt = ?

    Formula: $N_t = N_0 e^{-\lambda \Delta t} \Rightarrow \Delta t = -\dfrac{1}{\lambda} \ln\left(\dfrac{N_t}{N_0}\right)$

    Solution: $\Delta t = -\dfrac{1}{0.693/\text{shake}} \ln(0.05) \doteq 4.3$ shakes (or half-lives)

    <u>Therefore, at least 5 full half-lives are required to pass in order to re-</u>

    <u>move more than 95% of the radioactive nuclide. The graph supports</u>

    <u>this conclusion in that, at the fifth shake, the 2 candies remaining rep-</u>

    <u>resent only 3.1% of the original 64.</u>

Name _____

Date _____ Hour _____

PRELAB HOMEWORK

1. Name the three common types of radiation resulting from nuclear decay.

   The three types of radiation are gamma rays, alpha particles, and beta particles.

2. Discuss the typical nuclear conditions that produce the emissions named in Question 1.

   Alpha particles are emitted from nuclei that are too large for stability. Beta particles (electrons and positrons) are emitted from nuclei that have n/p ratios that are too large or too small (respectively) for stability. Gamma rays are emitted from nuclei that have too much energy.

3. Review the graph of neutron number vs. proton number in your textbook. Do the *stable* nuclides have equal numbers of neutrons and protons, or is stability associated with some other relationship of neutrons and protons? Explain.

   The graph shows that as atomic number increases, stable nuclei have more neutrons than protons and that the ratio increases with Z.

4. What is the probability of a radioactive nuclide decaying during any half-life time interval?

   The probability for a radioactive nuclide to decay during any half-life interval is 50%.

5. What is the proportionality constant that relates decay activity to the number of radioactive nuclides in a sample? Give its mathematical equivalent based on half-life.

   The proportionality constant is called the decay constant (λ). $\lambda = \dfrac{0.693}{t_{1/2}}$

6. ___**1.84 h**___ If the decay constant (λ) for the positron (β^+) emission from a fluorine-18 nuclide is 0.377 h^{-1}, what is half-life of fluorine-18? Show your work.

   Given: $\lambda = 0.377$ h^{-1}; $t_{1/2} = ?$

   Formula: $\lambda = \dfrac{0.693}{t_{1/2}} \Rightarrow t_{1/2} = \dfrac{0.693}{\lambda}$

   Solution: $t_{1/2} = \dfrac{0.693}{0.377 \text{ h}^{-1}} \doteq 1.84$ h

7. ___**373 decays/s**___ If 3.56×10^6 atoms of radioactive fluorine-18 are present in a sample of air, what is their *activity* in decays per second? Show your work.

   Given: 3.56×10^6 atoms ^{18}F; $\lambda = 0.377$ h^{-1}; $\dfrac{\Delta N}{\Delta t} = ?$

   Formula: $\left|\dfrac{\Delta N}{\Delta t}\right| = |-\lambda N|$ (Activity is the magnitude of the $\dfrac{\Delta N}{\Delta t}$ term.)

   Solution: $\left|\dfrac{\Delta N}{\Delta t}\right| = \left|-\dfrac{3.56 \times 10^6 \text{ atoms}}{} \dfrac{0.377 \text{ decay}}{\text{h}} \dfrac{1 \text{ h}}{3600 \text{ s}}\right| \doteq 373 \dfrac{\text{decays}}{\text{s}}$

8. ___**1.74×10^5 atoms**___ How many of the 3.56×10^6 atoms of fluorine-18 will remain after 8.00 h? Use Equation (2).

   Given: $N_0 = 3.56 \times 10^6$ atoms ^{18}F; $\lambda = 0.377$ h^{-1}; $\Delta t = 8.00$ h; $N_{8\,h} = ?$

   Formula: $N_t = N_0 e^{-\lambda \Delta t}$

   Solution: $N_{8\,h} = (3.56 \times 10^6 \text{ atoms } ^{18}\text{F})e^{-(0.377\,\text{h}^{-1})(8.00\,h)} \doteq 1.74 \times 10^5$ atoms ^{18}F

9. _____40.0 h_____ How many hours must pass until only 1 atom of fluorine-18 is left? Show your work.

Given: $N_0 = 3.56 \times 10^6$ atoms ^{18}F; $\lambda = 0.377$ h^{-1}; $N_t = 1$; $\Delta t = ?$

Formula: $N_t = N_0 e^{-\lambda \Delta t} \Rightarrow \Delta t = -\dfrac{1}{\lambda} \ln\left(\dfrac{N_t}{N_0}\right)$

Solution: $\Delta t = -\dfrac{1}{0.377 \text{ h}^{-1}} \ln\left(\dfrac{1 \text{ atom}}{3.56 \times 10^6 \text{ atoms}}\right) \doteq 40.0$ h

10. Is it possible to know exactly how many radioactive nuclide atoms will remain after a certain amount of time elapses? Explain.

No. Radioactive decay is a statistical process. Due to the random nature of

radioactive decay, it is not possible to know exactly how many nuclides will remain

at any given time. For statistically large populations, however, close approxima-

tions are possible.

Name _____

Date _____ Hour _____

ELEMENTARY NUCLEAR PARTICLES

Purpose

One area of intense interest in physics is the study of the ultimate particles that form the matter of creation. The purpose of this lab is to

- apply the knowledge obtained from earlier studies in a theoretical analysis of elementary nuclear particles.
- use graphic and mathematical techniques to analyze data.
- demonstrate that the laws of conservation function at the subatomic level.

Prelab Discussion

The concept of momentum and the law of momentum conservation should be valid for microscopic objects as well as macroscopic objects. You should be able to apply these ideas to molecules (such as gas molecules), to atoms, and even to the elementary particles that are the constituents of atoms (electrons, protons, and neutrons). The protons and neutrons of atoms are made up of yet smaller particles. When they collide, they should behave just as billiard balls, cars, and football players do. This is an area of intense study known as high-energy physics (HEP).

How do you see the collisions of these tiny particles? The answer to that is much like watching a jet plane fly high in the sky. Often, the plane will leave a vapor trail. The hot exhaust gases from the combustion of the jet fuel condense and allow you to see where the jet has been. With small subatomic particles, the same thing can happen. If a charged particle passes through a fluid (such as liquid hydrogen), the particles leave a "vapor" trail. The trail is actually small bubbles of hydrogen gas. Thus, you can see where the charged particle has been. Figure 1 is a hydrogen bubble chamber photograph from a particle accelerator at the Lawrence Berkeley National Laboratory located in Berkeley, California.

Understandably, the masses, momenta, and energies of these particles in standard metric units are very small. (A proton's mass is 1.67×10^{-27} kg!) This number, if used in calculations, would constantly produce answers with similar powers of ten. Physicists often prefer to work with quantities that are not very small nor very large. To simplify the data, mass, momentum, and energy can be expressed in units that are more comfortable to work with. As chemists use the atomic mass unit to represent very small masses, physicists use the unit **mega-electron volt (MeV)** for very small energies. One MeV is equivalent to 1.60×10^{-6} J. Working with mass and energy at the elementary particle level requires a relationship that should be familiar to all, $E = mc^2$, which is Einstein's famous equation from special relativity. With these conventions in place, the following list of units for energy, mass, and momentum can be developed:

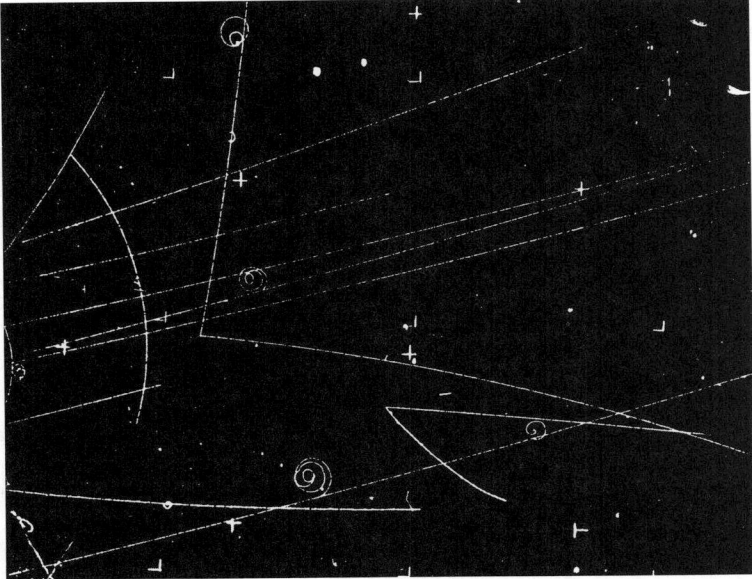

Figure 1

Prelab Discussion

- Review the prerequisites for Lab 5-2 in the back of this manual.

- Momentum and energy are basic concepts in physics. The laws of momentum and energy conservation make up the basis of our mechanical universe and form the backbone of Newtonian mechanics. Much can be learned by studying the effects of macroscopic collisions and applying the conservation laws to macroscopic interactions (such as two automobiles colliding). However, in order for students to appreciate the full power of these conservation laws, they need to see how these laws are applied to areas

of physics not normally included in the standard high-school curriculum. The activities contained in this

This laboratory activity is based on a lesson developed by Jim Gormley with the assistance of Dr. Alan Jackson, Dr. Didar Qadir, and Dr. Stan Hirschi, professors at Central Michigan University. Used by permission.

lab are intended to demonstrate this principle to the students with minimal extra learning (or teaching).

- This exercise incorporates many topics covered throughout this course. In preparation, you should direct your students to review vector analysis and right-triangle trigonometry, mechanics (circular motion, momentum, and kinetic energy), electric potential theory, and magnetism (field theory and movement of charges). You should also have them review geometric construction of perpendiculars, circumscribing three points in a circle, and the proportional properties of chords and secants of a circle.

- The discussion of nuclear particle families and their properties can be found in the textbook and is not repeated in this lab in order to save space.

- Demonstrate to your students that the relativistic units are actually equivalent to the SI units they represent. Work out several of the SI equivalents, using unit analysis. Students prove this in their Prelab Homework. One key identity that they will require is that 1 V = 1 J/C.

Procedure

- This lab is a desktop exercise in which all of the raw experimental data has been provided and the student must extract new information and arrive at some conclusions.

$$\frac{mv_t^2}{r} = qv_t B$$

$$m = \frac{qr \cancel{v_t} B}{v_t^2} = \frac{qrB}{v_t}$$

Recall that $p = mv$.

$$p = \left(\frac{qrB}{\cancel{v_t}}\right)\cancel{v_t} = qrB$$

Variable	SI Unit	Relativistic Unit
energy	$\dfrac{\text{kg·m}^2}{\text{s}^2}$	MeV
mass	kg	$\dfrac{\text{MeV}}{c^2}$
momentum	$\dfrac{\text{kg·m}}{\text{s}}$	$\dfrac{\text{MeV}}{c}$

Elementary Particle Momentum

Before continuing further, study the tracks in the hydrogen bubble chamber in Figure 1. The lines extending from side to side are the tracks of projectile particles. The points where the tracks split are either collisions between the projectiles and protons (the nuclei of liquid hydrogen) or the decay of particles into more elementary particles. If you lay a straight edge along the tracks, you will notice that none are straight. If the photograph displayed a larger area, you could see that the curved tracks form segments of circles or large spirals. They form these arcs because there is an external force acting on the charged particles that is oriented perpendicular to the direction of the particle's motion. This force is also perpendicular to the plane of the photograph. Recall from your study of circular motion (including Lab 2-6) that the formula describing circular motion is

$$F_c = ma_c = \frac{mv_t^2}{r}, \tag{1}$$

where F_c is the centripetal force, m is the mass of the revolving object, a_c is the centripetal acceleration, v_t is the object's tangential velocity, and r is the radius of the circle of motion.

The external force exerted on the particles in this case is a magnetic force produced by a magnetic field that is generated around the bubble chamber. Recall from your study of magnetic fields that the magnetic force ($\mathbf{F_m}$) can be calculated by using the formula

$$\mathbf{F_m} = q(\mathbf{v_t} \times \mathbf{B}),$$

where q is the fundamental charge (usually $\pm e$, the charge of 1 electron, in coulombs, or C) and $\mathbf{v_t} \times \mathbf{B}$ is the vector product of the tangential velocity and the magnetic field strength. (Vector products were introduced in the study of torque.) If the velocity of a particle is perpendicular to the magnetic field, as it is assumed to be in Figure 1, then $\mathbf{v_t} \times \mathbf{B}$ becomes simply $v_t B$, and the *magnitude* of the force on the particle can be calculated by the expression

$$F_m = qv_t B. \tag{2}$$

The charges and other properties of selected elementary particles are provided in Appendix H.

If you equate F_c from Equation (1) and F_m from Equation (2), you can obtain the particle-momentum formula:

$$p = qrB. \tag{3}$$

The derivation of Equation (3) is shown in the box in the margin. For singly charged particles, such as protons and electrons, Equation (3) may be simplified to

$$p = (0.3)rB, \tag{4}$$

where the particle momentum p is measured in MeV/c, r is measured in centimeters, and B is measured in kilogauss, or kG (1 gauss = 10^{-4} tesla).

In HEP, as in classical mechanics, momentum must be conserved during a collision. Therefore, the vector sum of the momenta of all of the particles before the collision must equal the sum of the momenta of the particles after the collision, assuming that the collision was elastic. For the particles in Figure 1, the momenta vectors are tangent to their circular paths. Recall from geometry that a line tangent to a circle is perpendicular to the radius at the point of tangency. This concept will help you determine the direction of the particle momentum vectors later in this lab.

Energy and the Collision of Elementary Particles

In classical mechanics, the total mechanical energy of an object is determined by the sum of its kinetic and potential energies

$$E = K + U.$$

This relationship is true within 1% for speeds less than 10% of the speed of light. However, the particles that produce the hydrogen bubble chamber tracks possess tremendous amounts of kinetic energy and momentum because they are traveling near the speed of light. The momentum of a particle under these conditions is determined by the equation $p = \gamma mv$, where γ (Greek letter gamma) is the factor that accounts for the relativistic change in mass of an object at high speeds (see your textbook for a discussion of the effect of γ). For this reason, the relationship between total energy (E) and momentum (p) needs to be adjusted for relativistic speeds. Einstein showed that the relativistic **energy-momentum equation** is

$$E^2 = (pc)^2 + (mc^2)^2, \qquad (5)$$

where pc represents the energy due to momentum and mc^2 is the *rest energy* of the particle (in MeV). You should note that a particle at rest has no momentum, and Equation (5) then reduces to Einstein's equation. Just as momentum is conserved in a collision, so must the total energies of the particles entering a collision equal the total energy of the particles after the collision, or

$$E_A + E_B = E_C + E_D, \qquad (6)$$

where E_x is the total energy of a designated particle.

In this "desktop" lab you will follow the same procedure that a high-energy physicist uses to identify the particles in a particle accelerator collision. Given a hydrogen bubble chamber image of a particle collision, and the magnetic field strength passing through the chamber, you will

1. geometrically determine the radii of the tracks;

2. calculate the magnitude of the momenta of the particles from their track radii;

3. determine the direction of the particle momentum vectors;

4. assess whether momentum was conserved during the collision by comparing the net momentum before the collision to the net momentum after the collision;

5. attempt to determine the identity of the particles produced from the collision by identifying their charge and estimating their energies, based on hypothetical rest masses.

• When observing the tracks in the photos, it is assumed that the particles are moving parallel to the plane of the paper in circles. However, in the actual chamber, the particle tracks usually describe a spiral or helix around an axis perpendicular to the paper.

• Students should be allowed to attempt various methods for measuring the radii of curvature of the particle tracks. Here are several approaches.

$$\gamma = \frac{1}{\sqrt{1 - \left(\frac{v}{c}\right)^2}}$$

1. Mark dots at the endpoints of an arc and mark a third one in the middle of the arc. Connect the middle dot and the endpoints with line segments. Construct perpendicular bisectors to the line segments and extend them until they intersect. The intersection is the center of the circle containing the arc, and the radius can then be easily determined.

2. Connect the endpoints of the arc with a line segment forming a chord. Construct a perpendicular bisector to the chord. Mark a point on the bisector inside the arc and assume that it is located at the center of the arc. Draw a line segment from the center mark to an endpoint of the arc. Assume this line segment is the radius (r). Accurately measure the segment of the perpendicular bisector between the chord and the arc (a), and the length of the chord (b). See the following diagram.

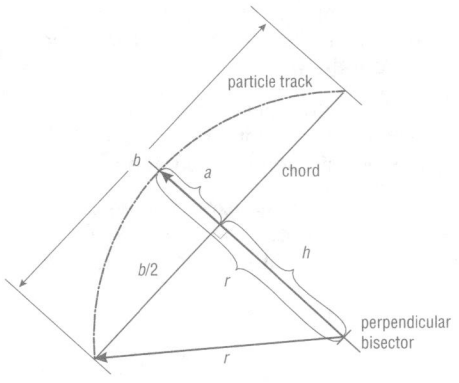

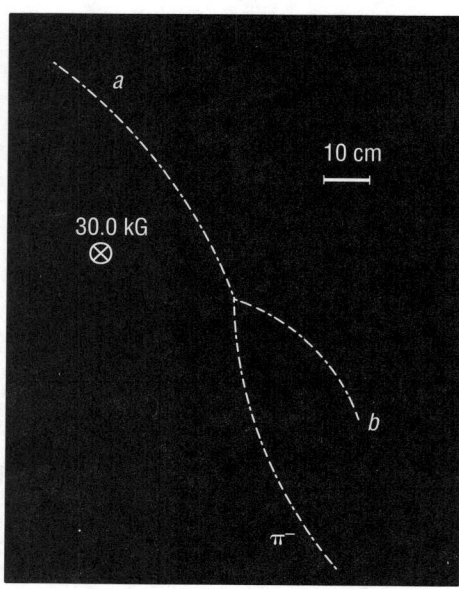

Figure 2

The Pythagorean theorem is required to develop the equation

$$r^2 = (b/2)^2 + h^2.$$

Eliminating h gives you

$$r^2 = (b/2)^2 + (r - a)^2.$$

Solving for r yields the following formula:

$$r = \frac{a^2 + (b/2)^2}{2a}.$$

When the known values of a and b are substituted into the equation, r is readily calculated.

The derivation of the radius formula by students will be left to your discretion. This derivation may be an excellent source of extra credit for them.

3. The least precise method is the guess-and-check approach. Students should, as a minimum, construct the perpendicular bisector of the chord of the arc as in Method 2, then use the bisector to position the compass point as trial radii are tested to trace out the arc.

Have your students discuss the advantages and disadvantages, including the precision, of each method attempted.

• Students should expect some differences between the various computations of total energies due to the inaccuracies of the initial measurements of the radii.

Procedure

Conservation of Momentum

Figure 2 is the image of a single collision isolated from a liquid hydrogen bubble chamber photograph for analysis. The projectile is a negative pion (π^-), which is one of the mesons of the hadron family of elementary particles. The target particle is the nucleus of one of the liquid hydrogen atoms, a proton (p), which is at rest. The magnetic field strength (**B**) is 30.0 kG oriented *into* the page (represented by the $\otimes$ symbol). The scale size of the bubble chamber is indicated on the photo. In order to facilitate the analysis of the collision, an enlarged "negative" of the image is provided in Figure 3.

1. Determine the radii of the tracks for the pion and particles a and b, using the scale shown in Figure 3. (At this point, the identities of a and b are unknown.) The precision of this determination is extremely important to the accuracy of the results for the remaining sections of this procedure.

   a. There are several methods that you can use.

      (1) You can make a geometric construction that inscribes three points on the track arcs in a circle (whose radius is the radius of the arc).

      (2) You can construct the perpendicular bisector of the chord connecting the endpoints of the track arc. You know that the center of the arc lies on the bisector. If you select an arbitrary point on the bisector and draw a line representing the radius of the arc from that point to one of the endpoints of the arc, you form a right triangle. By measuring the length of the chord and the segment of the bisector between the chord and the arc, you can calculate the length of the radius. Write an equation expressing the Pythagorean theorem in terms of the radius, the chord, and the segment of the bisector between the chord and the arc. Then substitute the known quantities and solve for the radius.

      (3) You can also guess and check.

   b. To ensure maximum accuracy in your constructions, use a sharp pencil and a sharp chisel point on your compass. Your teacher can give you guidance on the use of auxiliary lines and arcs to produce accurate constructions.

   c. For each particle, measure the arc radius from your construction and record the measurement (in centimeters) in Table 1. Recall that the proton was at rest at the time of collision, so there is no arc associated with it.

   d. A 10.0 cm scale line is provided in Figure 3. Rather than using a compass to find the scale track radius by marking off that distance on the constructed radius, it is far more accurate to use a scale factor. Determine the scale factor by dividing 10.0 cm by the actual length of the 10.0 cm line on Figure 3 and record this value in the blank above Table 1.

   e. Multiply the measured arc radius for each particle by the scale factor and record the track radius in Table 1 in centimeters. This is the actual radius of the particle track inside the bubble chamber.

2. Calculate the magnitude of momentum (p) for each particle, using Equation (4), and enter your results in Table 1. The units will be MeV/c.

3. Construct or draw a coordinate axis (x-y axis) positioned at the vertex (center) of collision. The axes need to be perpendicular, but their orientation relative to the particle tracks does not.

4. Determine the direction of the momenta for each particle *at the instant of collision*. Recall from the Prelab Discussion that the direction of momentum is tangent to the track arc. Express the angular direction as a positive *reference angle* (<90°) measured with respect to the *x*-axis. Record the angle to the nearest 0.1° for each particle in Table 1.

5. Using appropriate analytical methods, determine the *x*- and *y*-components of the particle momenta and record them in Table 1. Be sure to observe correct sign conventions based on your coordinate system.

6. Calculate the total momentum before and after the collision by adding the momenta components. Record your results in Table 1. For these entries, measure the angle of the momentum vectors from the positive *x*-axis of your coordinate system.

Conservation of Energy

7. Using the momenta determined in Step 2, calculate the total energies for the four particles involved in this collision, using Equation (5).

   a. Rest energies (mc^2) for the known particles may be obtained from Appendix H. Therefore, you can compute the total energy for these particles. Write out the energy-momentum equation containing the applicable values; then compute the total energies (in MeV) for the pion and the proton. Enter the results in Table 2 for Particle Total Energy. Add their total energies and enter the sum as Energy In in Table 2.

   b. You do not know the rest energies for the unknown particles. In the Energy-Momentum Equation column in Table 2, write an expression for total energy based on Equation (5) that includes what is known (momentum). Leave the remaining cells in the last two rows of Table 2 blank for now.

Since you do not know the rest energies (masses) of the *a* and *b* particles, which is the case in most HEP experiments, you need to make a guess at the rest energies so that you can complete the calculations for total energies. If you select the correct rest energies for the unknown particles, total energy should be conserved, and you can be relatively sure that those are the rest energies of the unknowns. From Equation (6), energy conservation for the pion-proton collision requires that

$$E_{\pi^-} + E_p = E_a + E_b. \tag{7}$$

The total energy entering an interaction must equal the total energy produced.

Before calculating the total energies of candidate unknown particles, you can restrict the particles being considered by determining their charge properties. Note from Figure 3 that *a* curves to the left in the magnetic field and *b* curves to the right. You should be able to conclude that neither *a* nor *b* is a *neutral* particle. (Why?) Therefore, you may eliminate considering species of particles that are neutral.

8. Refer to the table of elementary particles in Appendix H. Enter the name symbol of each species of charged particle and its rest energy in the appropriate columns of Table 3 under both *a* and *b*. Note that protons are positive and antiprotons ($\overline{p}$) are negative.

9. Determine the charges of *a* and *b* by noting the direction of curvature of their tracks in Figure 3. Recall from your textbook that according to the right-hand rule for magnetic fields, the direction of the magnetic force vector is the direction in which a *positive* charge is deflected. Write the appropriate superscript beside each symbol listed in the Candidate Particles columns under particles *a* and *b* in Table 3.

Postlab Analysis

- The following additional activities are presented to build on the foundations developed in this lab.

  1. If the expression γmv is substituted for p in Equation (5) (including the expression for γ given in the Prelab Discussion) and the equation is simplified with some algebra, the equation $E = \gamma mc^2$ results—the total energy of an object is the product of gamma and its rest energy. Have students prove this identity.

  2. The velocities of the particles in Figure 3 before and after the collision can be determined by equating γmc^2 to their total energies calculated in Table 2. Expand the γ factor and solve for v.

  3. Determine the lifetime of the pion. Of the two particles involved in the collision, only the proton is stable. The pion has an accepted lifetime of 2.60×10^{-8} s and the bubble chamber track ends when it decays.

     a. Obtain the velocity of the pion before and after the collision from Activity 2.

     b. Determine the length of the pion's track segment *before* the collision and its track segment length *after* the collision. This can be done by finding the central angle of each track arc, dividing the angle by 360°, and multiplying the result by $2\pi r$, where *r* is the radius of the arc.

     c. Using the formula $t = d/v$, calculate the time intervals for each segment of the pion's track by dividing the track length by the associated velocity. Sum the two time intervals to obtain the pion's lifetime in the photo. Compare the result with the accepted value.

10. Using the incomplete energy-momentum equations for *a* and *b* from the last two rows of Table 2, substitute the values of rest energy listed in Table 3 in order to find the total energies of *a* and *b* for each candidate particle listed. Write the calculated total energy in Table 3 for each particle.

11. Select a positive particle and a negative particle from the applicable lists in Table 3 whose total energies, when added together, equal the Energy In recorded in Table 2.

12. Write the identities and total energies of *a* and *b* in Table 2. Record the sum of their energies as Energy Out in the last column of Table 2.

Data

Table 1
Particle Momentum Data and Calculations

Scale factor ___8.00___ $\dfrac{\text{cm scale}}{\text{cm photo}}$

Particle	Arc Radius	Track Radius, *r*	Particle Momentum, *p*	Momentum Reference Angle, θ	Momentum *x*-component (observe sign)	Momentum *y*-component (observe sign)
π⁻	12.50 cm	100.0 cm	900. $\frac{MeV}{c}$	89.7 ¡	+4.5 $\frac{MeV}{c}$	+899.9 $\frac{MeV}{c}$
p	0 cm	0 cm	0 $\frac{MeV}{c}$	— ¡	— $\frac{MeV}{c}$	— $\frac{MeV}{c}$
a	15.13 cm	121.0 cm	1089 $\frac{MeV}{c}$	70.8 ¡	−358.1 $\frac{MeV}{c}$	+1028.4 $\frac{MeV}{c}$
b	5.38 cm	43.0 cm	387 $\frac{MeV}{c}$	19.9 ¡	+363.9 $\frac{MeV}{c}$	−131.7 $\frac{MeV}{c}$
Total Momentum	Before Collision	900. $\frac{MeV}{c}$ at 89.7 °		After Collision	897 $\frac{MeV}{c}$ at 89.6 °	

Data and results in Table 1 are typical. Student answers will vary.

Table 2
Total Energies

Particle	Symbol	Charge	Energy-Momentum Equation	Particle Total Energy, *E*	Interaction Energies	
Pion	π⁻	−	$E^2 = (900.\text{ MeV})^2 + (139.6\text{ MeV})^2$	911 MeV	Energy In	1849 MeV
Proton	p	+	$E^2 = (0\text{ MeV})^2 + (938.3\text{ MeV})^2$	938 MeV		
a Proton	p	+	$E^2 = (1089\text{ MeV})^2 + (x\text{ MeV})^2$	1437 MeV	Energy Out	1848 MeV
b Pion	π⁻	−	$E^2 = (387\text{ MeV})^2 + (y\text{ MeV})^2$	411 MeV		

Data and results in Table 2 are typical. Student answers will vary.

Table 3
Candidate Particle Total Energies

Particle *a*			Particle *b*		
Candidate Particles	Rest Energy	Total Energy	Candidate Particles	Rest Energy	Total Energy
e⁺	0.511 MeV	1089 MeV	e⁻	0.511 MeV	387 MeV
μ⁺	105.7 MeV	1094 MeV	μ⁻	105.7 MeV	401 MeV
τ⁺	1777 MeV	2084 MeV	τ⁻	1777 MeV	1819 MeV
π⁺	139.6 MeV	1098 MeV	π⁻	139.6 MeV	(411) MeV
K⁺	493.7 MeV	1196 MeV	K⁻	493.7 MeV	627 MeV
p	938.3 MeV	(1437) MeV	p̄	938.3 MeV	1015 MeV
Σ⁺	1189 MeV	1612 MeV	Σ⁻	1189 MeV	1250 MeV
Σ̄⁺	1197 MeV	1618 MeV	Σ̄⁻	1197 MeV	1258 MeV
Ξ⁺	1321 MeV	1712 MeV	Ξ⁻	1321 MeV	1377 MeV
Ω⁺	1672 MeV	1995 MeV	Ω⁻	1672 MeV	1716 MeV
	MeV	MeV		MeV	MeV

Rest energies are taken from Appendix H. Total energies in Table 3 are typical. Student answers for total energies will vary.

Postlab Analysis

1. State your conclusions regarding the identities of the particles resulting from the interaction shown in Figure 2.

   Answers will vary. Students who worked carefully will conclude that

   the two particles were the original pion and the target proton.

2. Is your answer to Question 1 reasonable, considering the conservation principles you are studying?

   Answers will vary depending on the response in Question 1. Careful

   work will show that taking into account a proton at rest, momentum

   was conserved during the interaction, eliminating the possibility of a

   simple decay. The only particles that could show conservation of total

   energy are a proton and a pion.

3. If you knew the speed of the particles, how could you determine the length of time represented by each of the tracks?

   If the track length were determined by any one of several methods,

   the length of time represented by the tracks could be determined

   from the simple formula $t = d/v$.

4. If the track of a particle in a bubble chamber is an inward spiral, what can you conclude about the momentum of the particle during the time period in which the track was created? Explain your answer.

Based on Equation (4), the momentum must have been decreasing

during that interval because the radius was decreasing.

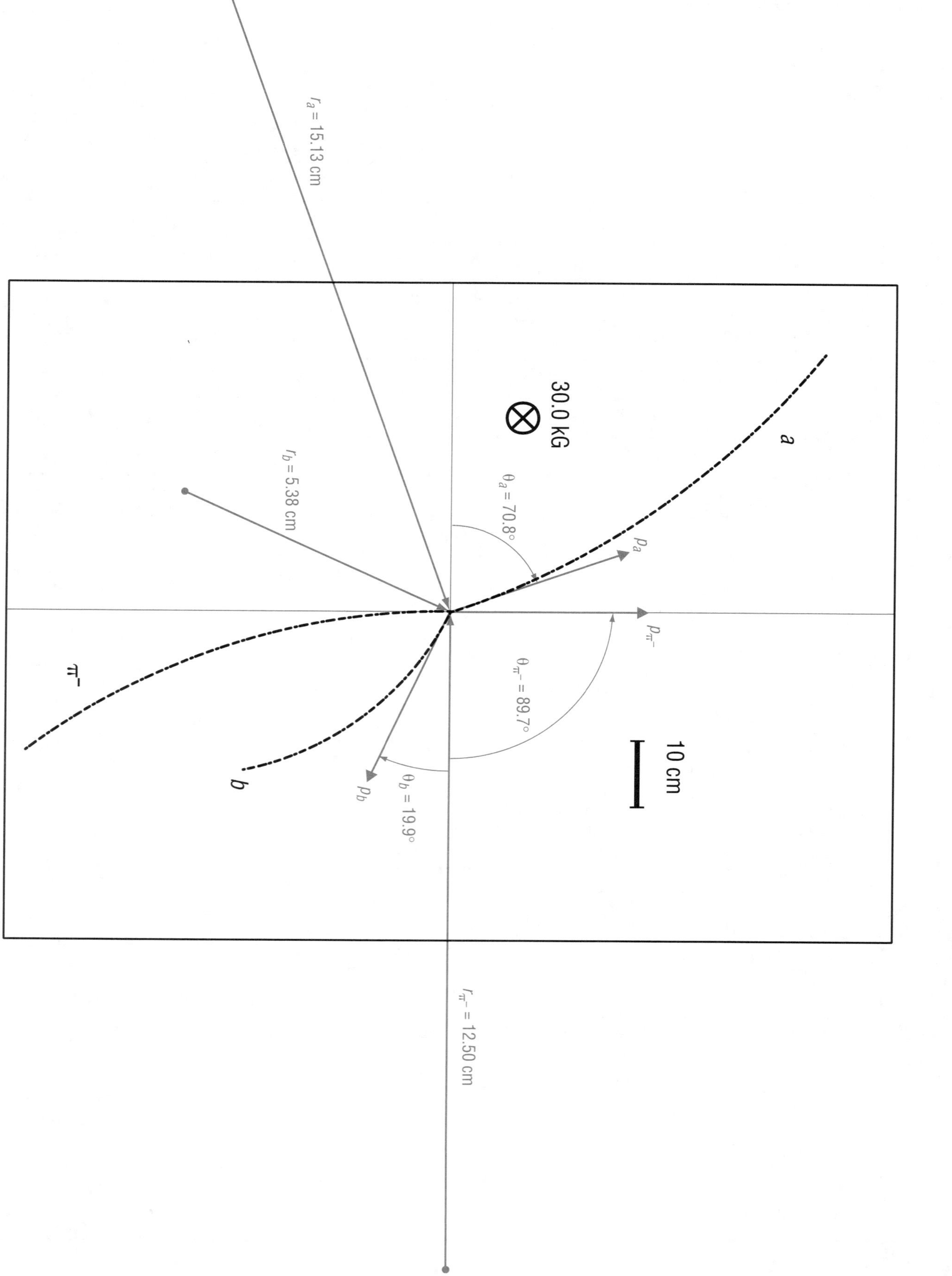

Figure 3

$r_a = 15.13$ cm

$r_b = 5.38$ cm

30.0 kG

$\theta_a = 70.8°$

$\theta_{\pi^-} = 89.7°$

$\theta_b = 19.9°$

p_a

p_{π^-}

p_b

10 cm

a

b

π^-

$r_{\pi^-} = 12.50$ cm

Name _____

Date _____ Hour _____

PRELAB HOMEWORK

1. What kind of device can show the paths of subatomic particles involved in collisions and nuclear decays?

   A bubble chamber can show these paths. (Accept cloud chamber also.)

2. How do scientists simplify working with very small quantities, such as the masses, energies, and momenta of elementary nuclear particles?

   Scientists often define new units based on standard units in order to make

   working with extremely small (and large) quantities easier.

3. What is the SI equivalent of 1 MeV?

   The SI equivalent of 1 MeV is 1.6×10^{-6} J.

4. Using the equivalence in Question 3, prove through unit analysis that the relativistic units given in the Prelab Discussion are identical to their SI units. Show your work.

   relativistic energy: MeV $\Rightarrow$ J (energy), which can be expressed in base units as $\dfrac{kg \cdot m^2}{s^2}$

   relativistic mass: $\dfrac{MeV}{c^2} \Rightarrow \dfrac{(kg \cdot m^2)/s^2}{m^2/s^2} = kg$ (mass)

   relativistic momentum: $\dfrac{MeV}{c} \Rightarrow \dfrac{(kg \cdot m^2)/s^2}{m/s} = \dfrac{kg \cdot m}{s}$ (momentum)

5. What characteristic of the tracks of charged particles in a bubble chamber photograph assists in the identification of the particles?

   The tracks curve to the right or to the left, depending on the charge of the particle.

6. Using Equation (6), prove that the units of momentum, p, can be obtained from the product of elementary charge, q, (in coulombs), the radius of a circular track, r, (in meters), and the magnetic field strength, B, (in teslas). You will have to convert all units into equivalent SI base units, where applicable, in order to complete this exercise.

   Given: 1 esu = 3.335×10^{-10} C; 1 T = $1 \dfrac{V \cdot s}{m^2}$; 1 V = $1 \dfrac{J}{C} = \dfrac{kg \cdot m^2}{s^2 \cdot C}$

   Solution: $p = qrB \Rightarrow \dfrac{C}{} \Big| \dfrac{m}{} \Big| \dfrac{V \cdot s}{m^2} = \dfrac{C}{} \Big| \dfrac{m}{} \Big| \dfrac{[(kg \cdot m^2)/s^2 \cdot C)]s}{m^2} = \dfrac{C}{} \Big| \dfrac{m}{} \Big| \dfrac{[(kg \cdot m^2)s}{(s^2 \cdot C)m^2} = \dfrac{kg \cdot m}{s}$

7. Write the expression that is represented by the variable γ in a relativistic equation.

   $\gamma = \dfrac{1}{\sqrt{1 - \left(\dfrac{v}{c}\right)^2}}$

8. Using Equation (4), what is the *momentum* of a singly charged particle in a bubble chamber if the radius of its track is 20.0 cm and the magnetic field strength is 25.0 kG.

   Given: $r = 20.0$ cm; $B = 25.0$ kG; $p = ?$

   Formula: $p = 0.3rB$ (Assume that 0.3 is a pure number.)

   Solution: $p = (0.3)(20.0 \text{ cm})(25.0 \text{ kG}) = 150. \dfrac{MeV}{c}$

9. In classical (Newtonian) mechanics, total mechanical energy is dependent only on kinetic and potential energy; a body at rest with no potential energy has no mechanical energy. The total energy of a body measured according to Einstein's theory of relativity is always greater than zero, even at rest. What term in Equation (5) guarantees this?

The term $(mc^2)^2$ guarantees that the total energy of a physical body is greater than zero.

10. In the high-energy physics (HEP) interaction studied in this lab, what particle is the projectile and what particle is the target?

The projectile is a negative pion (π^-), and the target is a proton (p).

11. What would you look for in your analysis to show that the interaction depicted in Figure 2 was the nuclear decay of a single particle rather than a collision? What would disprove your hypothesis that it was a decay?

If the tracks recorded a decay, the total energy of the particles produced by the decay visible in the bubble chamber should be equal to or less than that of the original particle. If the sum of the total energies of the residual particles is much greater than the total energy of the original particle, the discrepancy indicates that another particle was involved (which would be the case in a collision with a stationary particle).

12. Why is the point of interaction the most convenient place to measure momentum before and after the interaction?

The direction of the momenta vectors are continually changing in a curved path. In order to combine the momenta of two or more particles to find total momentum, you must know their speed and direction at the same instant. The most convenient point to do this is the instant of the collision.

13. ___1850 MeV___ Calculate the *total energy* of a negative tauon in the bubble chamber described in the procedure if it has a particle track radius of 54.5 cm. You will need to refer to Appendix H for additional information. Show your work.

Given: $r = 54.5$ cm; $B = 30.0$ kG; $mc^2 = 1784$ MeV; $E = ?$

Formulas: $p = 0.3rB$; $E^2 = (pc)^2 + (mc^2)^2$

Solution: $p = (0.3)(54.5 \text{ cm})(30.0 \text{ kG}) = 491 \dfrac{\text{MeV}}{c}$

$E^2 = (491 \tfrac{\text{MeV}}{\cancel{c}} \times \cancel{c})^2 + (1784 \text{ MeV})^2$

$E^2 = 3\,423\,737 \text{ MeV}^2 \Rightarrow E = 1850 \text{ MeV}$

Appendix A

Precision, Accuracy, and Estimating

I. Numbers in Science

Science involves the systematic observation and description of creation. Scientific observations go beyond just listing qualitative characteristics such as "The sky is blue" or "Sound waves move fast." Science is characterized by quantifying nearly every property of an object or phenomenon and showing predictable relationships through mathematical formulas. Quantitative observations involve numbers, which may be obtained by one of two methods. You can *count* individual objects, or you can perform some kind of *measurement*. After data from an observation is recorded, scientists often must perform calculations with the numbers in order to obtain new information. Explicit rules exist that must be followed during calculations so that their results do not imply accuracy or precision that is not warranted by the original data. This appendix explains how to treat different kinds of numbers you use in this course and how to correctly complete calculations using the data that you obtain.

II. Data—The Raw Material

A. Counting

1. The simplest kind of quantitative data obtained in scientific studies is counted data. Counting is accomplished using integers, and it accounts for all occurrences of the items being counted that are observable by the counter. If you counted the students in your physics class, you would obtain an integer number of students. There would be no uncertainty about your result. For relatively small numbers, counting can produce an exact quantity.

2. When large numbers of items are counted, errors begin to creep into results because of the inherent limitations of the powers of human observation. If every student in your class were required to count the number of jelly beans in a 5-gallon jug, there would probably be as many different results as there are students. Scientists who study populations of organisms, analyze the molecular composition of materials, and determine the distribution of stars in the heavens deal with extremely large numbers. The errors introduced by the instruments, the counting methods, and the scientists themselves must be evaluated so that accurate counts can be obtained.

3. Refining counting results is accomplished through the science of **statistics.** Mathematical techniques allow a prediction to be made with a known degree of confidence regarding the **accuracy** of the count compared to the original number. It is not the intent of this course to include statistical methods in the analysis of data obtained in experiments. *ALGEBRA 2 for Christian Schools,* Second Edition, and *PRECALCULUS for Christian Schools* introduce statistical concepts and methods, and the interested student should refer to them. In this course, you may have the opportunity to perform graphic modeling and a statistical process called regression analysis, using an advanced graphing calculator. These techniques are discussed in Appendix D.

B. Measuring

1. The other method for obtaining numerical data is through measurement. Measuring is comparing the dimension or another characteristic to be measured against a known standard for that parameter. For instance, if you want to determine the length of an archery arrow, you place a ruler along the shaft and note the arrow's length as the sum of whole and fractional units marked on the ruler. The same process is true for measuring time, volume, and a host of other quantities.

2. Every measurement consists of two parts—the unit of measure (e.g., grams, centimeters, or seconds) and the number of units, which is a pure number. The measurement can be viewed as the product of a pure number and the named unit. This is the reason that you can multiply, divide, and cancel units just like numbers in nearly every kind of mathematical operation.

3. Every measurement requires (1) an instrument, which contains the measuring standard, and (2) a person to make the measurement. Both the instrument and the person performing the measurement are subject to limitations. There is no such thing as a perfect measuring instrument, and there are certainly no perfect human beings. Therefore, any measurement is subject to error. A scientist is interested in knowing how much error exists in a measurement and how that error will affect calculations made using that data. These concerns center around the accuracy and precision of data.

III. Accuracy and Precision

A. Accuracy

1. The **accuracy** of both counted and measured quantities can vary. What is accuracy? Accuracy is a *qualitative* term that indicates how close a measured quantity is to the actual value. The accuracy of data is *quantitatively* indicated in various ways, such as percent error. The U.S. National Institute of Standards and Technology (NIST) cooperates with similar international organizations in establishing detailed guidelines for determining the accuracy of instruments and measurements.

2. An instrument's accuracy is determined by its design and how well it is built. Correct use of a well-designed and well-built instrument will consistently provide measurements that are statistically close to the actual value being measured. The instrument error is often expressed as a tolerance (a $\pm$ value) of the scale being read.

3. Most instruments experience mechanical wear or other forms of deterioration with time that may affect their accuracy. In order to ensure that precision instruments are working correctly, they are frequently checked against a known standard called a **prime standard.** This may be as simple as the zero mark on a triple-beam balance or as complex as a cesium atomic frequency standard. Some accuracy checks verify that the instrument is accurate at only the zero point (zeroing the instrument), while other checks involve testing correspondence at several points over the full range of the instrument.

4. In this course, you will zero an instrument if it has such an adjustment, or you will assume that it is accurate within the limits of its precision.

B. Precision

1. The **precision** of a measurement is a *qualitative* description of a measurement's *repeatability* (or an instrument's ability to produce a measurement that is repeatable within certain limits). In other words, if ten students make a given measurement under the same conditions, using the same instrument, the collective results will be within a certain narrow range of readings determined by the smallest scale calibrations on the instrument.

2. Every measuring instrument has a scale calibrated in units and fractions of units of measure. A metric instrument's scales, for example, are subdivided into tenths of the major scale divisions. These subdivisions are called minor subdivisions. Any measurement using such an instrument is limited by the size of the smallest minor subdivisions because the person doing the measuring will have to estimate where the measurement falls between marks on the scale. The practical effect that the smallest subdivisions have on measurements is that they limit the number of decimal places allowed in a measurement.

3. The precision of measurements depends not only on the scale calibrations of the instruments used, but also to a great extent on experimental conditions and the human measurers. Recall that precision indicates repeatability. If a set of similar experimental quantities (such as the acceleration due to gravity) is obtained using several similar instruments (possibly having different individual accuracies) by several students of variable skill, the results may vary over a greater range than indicated by only the instrument's scale subdivisions. For this reason, sophisticated statistical methods developed by organizations such as NIST have been established to determine the actual repeatability of a given measurement.

4. Statistical methods for accurately determining precision are beyond the scope of this course. A simpler method, determining the *mean absolute deviation,* is acceptable for the level of work in this manual, and the process is provided here.

    a. Step 1—Collect and tabulate the measurements or results to be evaluated $(x_1, x_2, \ldots, x_n)$.

    b. Step 2—Find the average or *mean* of the group of numbers $(\bar{x})$.

    c. Step 3—Find the absolute value of the difference of each number and the group mean $(|x_i - \bar{x}|)$.

    d. Step 4—Find the average of the differences found in Step 3 $\left(\dfrac{1}{n} \sum\limits_{i=1}^{n} |x_i - \bar{x}| \right)$.

    e. Step 5—The mean absolute deviation is plus or minus the average of the differences for the group, found in Step 4.

C. Usage of Accuracy and Precision

You may have been in the habit of using *accuracy* and *precision* interchangeably, but you should now see that they mean two distinctly different things. You should strive to use the terminology properly.

IV. Measurements and Significant Digits

A. Process

1. The process of measuring involves comparing the quantity to be measured against an appropriate standard calibrated in the units required. Length is measured with a linear ruler, volume is measured with a graduated cylinder, time with a stopwatch, temperature with a thermometer, and so on.

2. The quantity is measured against the instrument's scale, and normally the edge or indicator falls somewhere between two subdivisions. *Whenever a metric instrument is used, the person measuring must estimate where the indicator lies to the nearest 1/10 of the smallest decimal subdivision on the instrument's scale. (Decimal* implies a power of 10.) Note that calibrations representing 0.2, 0.5, 2, and 5 units are commonly found on instruments. These are not powers of 10; they are provided to improve estimating to 1/10 of the next larger decimal subdivision.

3. The measurement to be recorded consists of all of the digits that are known from the instrument's scale plus the last digit that you estimated. These numbers are the **significant digits,** or **SDs,** of the measurement. No scientific measurement may have more SDs than are permitted by the precision of the instrument from which it was obtained.

B. Significant Digits

1. Using SDs in scientific reports ensures that all scientists understand the precision of the measurements. Not using SDs or reporting a measurement to a greater precision than is possible is dishonest. The practice has other consequences. When a scientist attempts to use a measurement that has too many SDs in a calculation, the result will be incorrect in that it will appear to have a greater precision than it warrants. Incorrect conclusions are possible as a result.

2. Some simple rules for determining SDs follow:

    a. The determination of SDs applies *only to measurements*. They do not apply to pure numbers or definitions, such as 60 s/min.

    b. All digits in a *counted number* are assumed to be significant unless a statistical method is used to limit its precision.

    c. All nonzero digits are significant.

    d. All zeros between nonzero digits are significant.

    e. All zeros to the right of the rightmost nonzero digit in a measurement *containing a decimal point* are significant. Lacking a decimal point, they are not significant.

    f. All zeros to the left of the leftmost nonzero digit in a measurement containing a decimal point are **not** significant.

    g. All digits in the decimal portion of scientific or engineering notation are significant.

3. The number of SDs in the following quantities are determined as examples.

  a. π (3.14159. . .)   N/A   Rule 2a
  b. 143.5 cm   4 SDs Rule 2c
  c. 1005 mL   4 SDs Rule 2d
  d. 3.50 m   3 SDs Rule 2e
  e. 0.0075 km/h   2 SDs Rule 2f
  f. 3500 cm   2 SDs Rule 2e

4. Take a closer look at Example 3f. Note that you cannot tell whether the estimated digit is the 5 or one of the 0s. Therefore, only the nonzero digits may be counted as significant in this situation. If the zero in the tens place were significant, then the number should be written 3.50×10^3 cm (Rule 2g). If all digits are significant, then the number could be written 3500. cm (Rule 2e). This convention is used throughout this manual.

V. Calculations Using Measurements

A. Consequences of Calculations with Measurements

1. When measurements are combined using basic arithmetic operations, you must be aware of the relative precision of the quantities involved. For example, if you add 10 cm to 5000 m you might conclude that the sum is 5000.10 m. However, the 5000 m distance is estimated to the nearest 1000 m, so the 10 cm is inconsequential, considering the potential error of the larger number.

2. In a similar fashion, when finding the area of a rectangle whose width is 4.5 cm and length is 130 cm, the product of the two numbers is 585 cm². However, the 130 cm measurement was estimated to the nearest 10 cm. The actual length could be anywhere between 125 cm and 135 cm, which means the true area could be between 562.5 cm² and 607.5 cm²! Notice that the tens place in the product is uncertain due to the uncertainty of the original measurement.

B. Rules for Math Operations Using Measurements

1. **Addition and Subtraction**

The sum or difference of two measurements cannot have greater precision than the least precise measurement.

  a.
$$\begin{array}{r} 27 \quad \text{m} \\ + \quad 1.65 \text{ m} \\ \hline 28.65 \text{ m} \approx 29 \text{ m} \end{array}$$

  b.
$$\begin{array}{r} 0.083 \text{ m/s} \\ -1.4 \quad \text{m/s} \\ \hline -1.317 \text{ m/s} \approx -1.3 \text{ m/s} \end{array}$$

2. **Multiplication and Division**

  a. The product or quotient of two or more measurements cannot have a greater number of SDs than the factor, divisor, or dividend with the least number of SDs. Note that this rule may produce results that have less precision than the circumstances warrant, but it is easier to apply than calculating computational precision for every calculation you make.

   (1)   (2 cm)(6.57 cm) = 13.14 cm² ≈ 10 cm²   (1 SD allowed)
   (2)   (1.69 g)/(1.2 mL) $\doteq$ 1.408$\overline{3}$ g/mL ≈ 1.4 g/mL (2 SDs allowed)

  (Note that the $\doteq$ symbol indicates a rounded or truncated calculator result without considering SDs.)

  b. Multiplication or division by a pure number should not produce a result that has greater or less precision than the original measurement.

$$d = 5.3 \text{ cm}; r = d/2 = (5.3 \text{ cm})/2 = 2.65 \text{ cm} \approx 2.7 \text{ cm}$$
                 (original 0.1 cm precision)

c. When performing simultaneous similar operations, you should complete all calculations before rounding to the correct SDs to avoid introducing rounding errors.

d. When performing complex calculations that involve a mixture of addition or subtraction and multiplication or division operations, you should determine the correct number of SDs following one type of operation before proceeding to the other type of operation because the rules are different. Note that some educators advocate completing the entire mixed calculation first and then rounding the result. The difficulty with this approach is that you may have a conflict between rounding the answer to the least precise term and rounding to the least number of SDs, using the rules discussed here.

3. **Manufacturer's Tolerances**

a. A measurement or quantity defined by a manufacturer's tolerance requires a modification to the rules discussed above. A 1 MΩ resistor with a 5% tolerance has a resistance between 1 050 000 Ω and 950 000 Ω. This range of uncertainty is not indicated by the nameplate value of the resistor. (The value 1 MΩ printed or coded on the resistor has only 1 SD, but the uncertainty of the resistance value is in the 10 000 Ω digit, giving the resistance value 3 SDs of precision.)

b. Consequently, when performing operations using quantities that have tolerances, it is recommended that all calculations be completed first without rounding. Then the result should be multiplied by the *largest tolerance* expressed as a decimal. The position of the leftmost SD in this result is the position of the uncertain or estimated digit in the answer, and the answer must be rounded to that digit's position.

Example: Calculate the voltage drop from a measured current of 0.1253 mA ($\pm 1\%$) through a 10 kΩ ($\pm 5\%$) resistance.

Solution: $V = IR = 1.253$ V. The larger tolerance is 5%, so 1.253 V $\times$ 0.05 = ± 0.06265 V. The calculated voltage drop must be rounded to the nearest 0.01 V; therefore, the final answer is 1.250 V.

4. **Rounding Rules**

The discussion of rounding may seem to be an elementary topic, but there are several methods in use. Each has its merits and disadvantages, and each produces slightly different results. This lab manual uses the following simple rounding method, which is adequate for the work included in this course.

a. Determine the position of the digit to which the number must be rounded. This digit will be referred to as the "last SD."

b. Note the digit to the right of the last SD and round accordingly.

(1) If the number is 0 through 4, drop all digits to the right of the last SD. If necessary, substitute the dropped numbers with zeros as placeholders to locate the decimal point. Do *not* add the decimal point in this case.

(2) If the number is 5 through 9, add 1 to the last SD and drop the remaining digits, replacing them with zero placeholders if required.

c. Avoid rounding to the left from the rightmost digit. This error often results in rounding up the last SD.

Appendix B

Preparation of Formal Lab Reports

In this lab manual you will usually summarize your work in data tables that have been provided for you. In addition, the discussion of the experimental setup and significance of the results has been largely provided for you by the authors of the lab manual. Occasionally, however, your teacher may require you to prepare a formal lab report in order to give you some exposure to the kind of reports you will be expected to write in college science courses. Your formal reports should follow the standardized format detailed below.

The sections in a formal report should include the following: Heading, Introduction, Data, Results, Graphs, Discussion, and Conclusions. Although you may work with one or more other students in gathering data, each student must write his own report.

Heading

List the number and title of the experiment, the date, your name, and the name of any partner(s) you worked with when collecting the data.

Introduction

1. Purpose—An explanation of the reason for the experiment is required. You should include a summary of the theory that you intend to verify and the design of the experiment.

2. Procedure—The procedural steps used to acquire and analyze the data should be summarized in your own words. Do not repeat the detailed steps contained in the lab manual procedure.

3. Diagrams—Sketches of the experimental apparatus used, if any, should be included. Complete electrical circuit diagrams should also be included (where applicable). The polarities of all DC meters and power sources should be clearly labeled. Ranges of instruments such as spring scales should also be indicated on the diagram. Each diagram should have a clearly marked title.

Data

This section should consist of clearly labeled tables containing the raw data recorded during the experiment. Be sure the data is recorded with the proper number of significant digits and the correct units.

Results

1. The results section should contain any intermediate values calculated from the raw data as well as the final results. A sample calculation should be included to show how any intermediate and final numerical values were obtained from the raw data. Each sample calculation should include an

   a. equation in a familiar form.
   b. algebraic solution of the equation for the desired unknown quantity.
   c. example of substitution using known values with units, such as the following:

$$d = \frac{1}{2}at^2$$

$$a = \frac{2d}{t^2} = \frac{2(10 \text{ cm})}{(2 \text{ s})^2} = 5 \tfrac{\text{cm}}{\text{s}^2}$$

2. If more than one trial was performed, the numerical values should be recorded in a table.

3. All tables must have titles. Each column and row should be clearly labeled.

4. Extra notes can be included if necessary to make the results clearer to the reader.

Graphs

1. Graphs should contain a title that clearly states how the two axes are labeled (for example, Distance vs. Time).

2. The axes should be labeled to match the title, including units [e.g., Distance, d (m)].

3. The dependent variable should be placed on the y-axis and the independent variable on the x-axis.

4. Mark the axes in logical increments that will allow you to produce a graph as large as possible on your available space.

5. Include a labeled table in unused space on the graph, giving the coordinates of the points. Draw a small circle around each plotted point, but do not label each point with its coordinates.

6. Draw the curve or line that best fits the data. A best-fit curve should be a smooth curve or a straight line that passes through as many points as possible or has about the same number of data points scattered on both sides of the graph.

7. If more than one variable is plotted against another variable on the same graph, use a different colored pen or pencil for the second graph. In the second color, label the appropriate axis including the scale, fill in a second coordinates table, and draw the points and the curve.

Discussion

In this section you should evaluate whether the experiment worked the way it was supposed to and whether the results were what you expected. You should relate your results to the purpose of the experiment stated in the introduction. If the experiment didn't work well, try to explain why. You should comment on possible sources of error and suggest possible improvements in the procedure or apparatus, if applicable.

Conclusions

This section should consist of one or two concise paragraphs drawing together the main results and their significance in relationship to the data you gathered. The conclusions should be written by each student without assistance from the other members of his laboratory team.

1. Discuss all of the purposes for the experiment stated in the introduction.

2. Base your summary clearly on the results of the experiment.

3. When referring to any table or graph for the first time in the conclusions, be sure to use its complete title. Instead of "the distance graph," write "Graph 1, Distance vs. Time."

4. Although the use of "I" or "we" can be appropriate in the discussion when mentioning experimental procedures, avoid it in the conclusion.

It may seem at first that the Conclusions section is merely a repetition of the Discussion section. The purpose is different, however. This section should provide a quick summary for a reader who is interested in knowing the main results and their significance without having to read the details usually included in the discussion.

Appendix C

Physical Constants

Constant	Symbol	Value
Absolute zero	0 K	-273.15 ¡C
Avogadro s constant	N_A	6.022×10^{23} mol^{-1}
Coulomb s constant	k	8.988×10^9 N·m^2/C^2
Earth		
Equatorial radius		6.378×10^6 m
Mass		5.974×10^{24} kg
Orbital radius		1.496×10^{11} m
Elementary charge	e	$\pm 1.602 \times 10^{-19}$ C
Electron rest mass	m_e	9.109×10^{-31} kg
		5.49×10^{-4} u
Electron specific charge	e/m_e	-1.759×10^8 C/g
Gas constant	R	0.0821 (L·atm)/(mol·K)
		8.315 J/(mol·K)
Gravitational acceleration, standard	$|g|$	9.807 m/s^2
Mechanical equivalent of heat	J	4.187 J/cal
Molar volume of ideal gas at STP	V_m	22.414 L/mol
Moon		
Equatorial radius		1.738×10^6 m
Mass		7.35×10^{22} kg
Orbital radius		3.844×10^8 m
Neutron rest mass	m_n	1.675×10^{-27} kg
		1.009 u
Permeability of vacuum	μ_0	$4\pi \times 10^{-7}$ N/A^2
Permittivity of vacuum	ε_0	8.854×10^{-12} C^2/(N·m^2)
Pi	π	3.142
Planck s constant	h	6.626×10^{-34} J·s
Proton rest mass	m_p	1.673×10^{-27} kg
		1.007 u
Speed of light in vacuum	c	2.998×10^8 m/s
Speed of sound in air at STP	v_{air}	331.45 m/s
Sun s mass		1.989×10^{30} kg
Triple point of water		273.16 K (0.01 ¡C)
Universal gravitational constant	G	6.673×10^{-11} m^3/kg·s^2)

Units and Conversion Factors

Unit Name	Symbol	Value
Ampere	A	1 C/s
Astronomical unit	ua	1.496×10^8 km
Atmosphere	atm	1 atm
		101 325 Pa
		1.0133 bar
		1013.3 mb
		14.696 lbf/in.^{2}
		760.002 mm Hg
		760.002 torr
		29.921 in. Hg
Atomic mass unit	u	1.661×10^{-27} kg
Bar	bar	1.000×10^5 Pa
British thermal unit	Btu	1055.87 J
Calorie	cal	4.184 J
Dyne	dyn	1.000×10^{-5} N
Dyne-centimeter	dyn·cm	1.000×10^{-7} N·m
Electron volt	eV	1.602×10^{-19} J
Energy equivalent of 1 u	—	931.5 MeV/c^2
Erg	erg	1.000×10^{-7} J
Farad	F	1 C/V
Gauss	G	10^{-4} T
Henry	H	1 (V·s)/A
Hertz	Hz	1 s^{-1}
Horsepower (550 ft·lbf/s)	hp	745.70 W
Inch	in.	2.540 cm
Joule	J	1 (kg·m^2)/s^2
Light-year	l.y.	9.461×10^{12} km
Mile, U.S. statute	mi	1609.3 m
Newton	N	1 (kg·m)/s^2
Ohm	Ω	1 V/A
Ounce, fluid	fl oz	29.574 mL
Parsec	pc	3.0857×10^{13} km
Pascal	Pa	1 N/m^2
Pint	pt	0.4732 L
Pound, force	lbf	4.448 N
Pound, mass	lbm	0.4536 kg
Quart	qt	0.9464 L
Tablespoon	tbsp	14.79 mL
Teaspoon	tsp	4.929 mL
Tesla	T	1 (V·s)/m^2
Torr	torr	133.322 Pa
Volt	V	1 J/C = 1 (kg·m^2)/(s^2·C)
Watt	W	1 J/s
Weber	Wb	1 V·s
Yard	yd	0.9144 m

Appendix D

Modeling with the TI-83 Plus Graphing Calculator

Many of the lab exercises in this manual require you to validate some principle of physics by plotting the data on a coordinate plane and evaluating the resulting graph. The best-fit curve that you draw may or may not be the best representation of the data trend, depending on your graphing skill and the quality of data. Modern graphing calculators, such as the Texas Instruments TI-83 Plus, provide the capability to analyze data to a high degree of precision. With this hand-held tool you can evaluate how well a particular relationship or model accounts for the data, and you can apply various tools to help you assess the quality of your data and the experimental process itself.

This appendix is not intended to be an exhaustive instruction manual for the TI-83 Plus. Texas Instruments supplies an excellent user's manual with the calculator, and you need to be familiar with its statistical functions before attempting the operations discussed below. The principle modeling technique you will use is a statistical methodology called **regression analysis.** The calculator determines a best-fit curve based on the kind of function you choose (linear, quadratic, exponential, logarithmic, etc.). A statistical evaluation is provided for the "fit" of the proposed curve. The calculator can also display a plot of **residuals,** which is a graph of the differences between the best-fit curve's y-values and the data y-values. This graph can indicate whether the differences appear to be random errors or reveal a pattern, which can imply that the basic functional relationship of the model you chose did not conform to the data.

In this course, there are eight steps you will find useful to complete these modeling operations:

1. Prepare the calculator to input the data.

2. Input the data into a table.

3. Draw a scatterplot of the data.

4. Evaluate the functional relationship of the data.

5. Prepare the calculator for diagnostics.

6. Choose a mathematical model from a list of potential models.

7. Graph the model.

8. Evaluate the model.

1. Prepare to input the data.

Usually, you can bypass this step and proceed directly to Step 2. However, if someone else has been using the calculator, perform the following steps:

a. Initialize the data editor by keying in the following. This takes the data editor back to the default settings.

$\boxed{\text{STAT}}$

`5:SetUpEditor` $\boxed{\text{ENTER}}$ (You could just press $\boxed{5}$ instead of highlighting the whole command.)

$\boxed{\text{ENTER}}$

b. Delete any existing data.

$\boxed{\text{STAT}}\boxed{1}$ (selects `Edit`)

If you see values in any of the lists, delete them one at a time. Or, if only L_1 and L_2 have data, you can delete them like this:

$\boxed{\text{STAT}}\boxed{4}$ (selects `ClrList`)

$\boxed{\text{2nd}}\boxed{1}$ **,** $\boxed{\text{2nd}}\boxed{2}$ (The comma is required.)

$\boxed{\text{ENTER}}$

Similarly, you could clear data lists from L_3, L_4, and so on.

c. Press Y= and delete all of the functions in the screen. Place the cursor to the *right* of any equal signs followed by functions and press the DEL key until all entries are removed. It is possible to deselect the equal signs to turn off a graph, but for now delete the functions.

2. Input the data.

In order to demonstrate the modeling capabilities of the TI-83 Plus, you will use the typical data from an experiment that verifies the relationship of the period of a pendulum to the pendulum's arm length (Lab 3-7). Table 1 lists the data.

Table 1
Pendulum Arm Length and Period

Trial	Pendulum Arm Length, l	Pendulum Period, T
1	0.100 m	0.64 s
2	0.200 m	0.90 s
3	0.400 m	1.27 s
4	0.800 m	1.78 s
5	1.600 m	2.52 s

Input the data from Table 1. Be sure to double-check your entries.

a. Enter the data for one of the variables into L_1. Normally, L_1 holds data for the independent variable (the *x*-values). For this model, the independent variable is *l*, the pendulum arm length.

STAT 1 (selects **Edit . . .**)

Key in the numerical values (no units) for the first data point and press ENTER; then enter the next list value and press ENTER. Continue until all of the *x*-values are entered.

b. Use the arrow keys to move the cursor under L_2. Enter the data for the second variable—normally the dependent variable (the *y*-values). For this example, it will represent the period values, *T*.

```
L1      L2      L3      1
.1      .64     ------
.2      .9
.4      1.27
.8      1.78
1.6     2.52
------  ------
L1(1)=.1
```

3. Draw a scatterplot.

This step creates a graph of the plotted raw data.

a. Open the statistical scatterplot menu. A scatterplot is a graph of just the data points.

2nd Y= 1 (selects **STAT PLOT** and **Plot1 . . .**)

b. Press ENTER to turn **Plot1 On**. Later, you can choose **Plot2** or **Plot3** to show other plots.

c. On the next line, select the first **Type** of graph. While the other five types have their uses, only the first type (⊹⃛) is a scatterplot.

d. Set the **Xlist** to L_1. (This is probably already done for you. If not, press 2nd 1.)

e. Set the **Ylist** to L_2. (This also might already be done. If not, press 2nd 2.)

f. If you like, choose a marker to represent the data. The last choice, a dot, clutters the screen the least, but any of the choices are fine.

g. Display the data graph. While you normally have to set the display parameters at the WINDOW command, Z o o m S t a t will automatically set the display scales and show your data.

· ZOOM 9 (selects Z o o m S t a t)

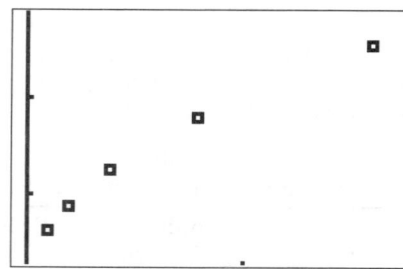

4. Evaluate the functional relationship of the data.

Before you continue, study the scatterplot. Here are some questions you might consider:

a. What general trends do you see in the data? For instance, does the data generally fit a straight line?

b. If the data does not appear to be linear, does it follow another recognizable pattern?

c. If the data generally follows a straight line (or another recognizable trend), are there exceptions? If so, what kinds of exceptions?

5. Prepare for diagnostics.

a. Before you obtain a model for the data, turn on the diagnostic feature.

2nd 0 (selects C A T A L O G)

b. Scroll down the list to D i a g n o s t i c O n. Press ENTER twice.

This will permit the TI-83 Plus to display r and r^2 values for most models. The value r is called the *correlation coefficient,* and it can be any value from $+1$ to -1. The closer r is to either $+1$ or -1, the better the data will fit the model curve. If you square the correlation coefficient, you obtain r^2, the *coefficient of determination*. The coefficient of determination is a measure of the extent to which the variation in the data can be explained by the model. Thus $r^2 = 1.00 = 100\%$ means that the model is a perfect fit, while $r^2 = 0.00$ means that the model is entirely useless. Generally, you will focus on the value of r^2 to assess the fit of your model.

6. Choose a model.

Now you are ready to select a model for the data.

a. View the available models.

STAT ▶ C A L C

You will see thirteen options. The first three are of little concern here. The command for linear regression, L i n R e g, is the one you will use most frequently to check the linearity of various data sets. However, this plot is clearly concave downward, suggesting that the function may be a power of the independent variable. Each of the models listed works especially well in certain situations, but the power regression permits analyzing situations in which the independent variable is raised to some power other than 1 (linear), 2 (quadratic), or 3 (cubic). The model is expected to fit the function $y = x^{1/2}$, because the period of a pendulum is proportional to the *square root* of the length of the pendulum.

b. Choose the command for power regression, A:PwrReg, from the list and assign the required arguments.

PwrReg L₁, L₂, (Commas are required.)

[VARS]

[▸] Y−VARS

1:Function [ENTER]

Y₁ [ENTER]

The command line should now look like this:

PwrReg L₁, L₂, Y₁

The L₁ and L₂ tell the calculator where to find the *x*- and *y*-variables. Of course, you could use other lists if you like, but be sure to tell the calculator where they are when you use the regression commands. The Y₁ selected from the Y−VARS list tells the calculator where to save the model function in the [Y=] list. You will then be able to view the mathematical equation for the model along with the model.

Press [ENTER] to view the regression parameters, *r*, and r^2. Of course, higher r^2 values are better.

```
PwrReg
y=a*x^b
a=1.994020608
b=.4938440182
r²=.9999846546
r=.9999923273
```

7. Graph the model.

The model was saved in [Y=] when the regression was performed, so you can view the model graph along with your data. Since you already used ZoomStat, the graphing window is ready to use. To graph the model, just press [GRAPH].

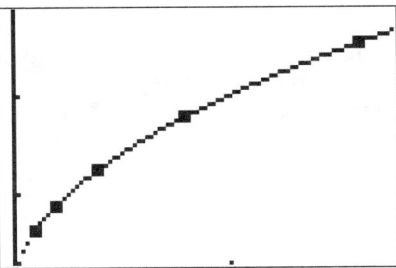

To obtain the coordinates of a point, you can trace the data by pressing [TRACE] and using the arrow keys.

8. Evaluate the model.

With all of the information that you have gathered, how should you evaluate the model? The model curve seems to fit the data for this example very closely, but this may not always be the case if your data contains significant systematic or random errors. There is another tool that will help you to decide whether the model you chose is correct or another would be more appropriate. The difference between the *y*-value of the data and the *y*-value of the corresponding point on the model curve is called the **residual**. If you plot the residuals versus the corresponding values of the independent variable, you can answer the questions "How closely does the data fit the model over the range of the data?" and "Do the residuals vary in a pattern that would indicate that a different model should be tried?" The model should be considered a good one if the magnitude of the residuals is small, the residuals are random in sign, and there is no apparent trend in the residual plot.

Prepare the residual plot as follows:

a. Enter the residual data in the variable list by keying in the following:

STAT 1 (selects **Edit**)

L$_3$ ENTER (highlights the L$_3$ **Name** editor at the bottom of the screen)

2nd STAT 7 (selects **RESID**)

ENTER

Now, you should see the residuals listed under L$_3$.

b. Prepare the residual plot by keying in or selecting the following.

2nd Y= 2 (selects the second **stats plot**)

On (turns on the second **stats plot**)

Type: ⊾ (scatterplot)

Xlist:L$_1$ (selects the independent variable list)

2nd STAT 7 (selects **Ylist:RESID**)

Mark +

c. Turn off the original model and data graph.

Y=

◄ ENTER (selects **Y$_1$** and turns it off)

▲ ENTER (selects **Plot1** and turns it off)

d. Observe the residual plot by pressing ZOOM 9 (selects **ZoomStat**).

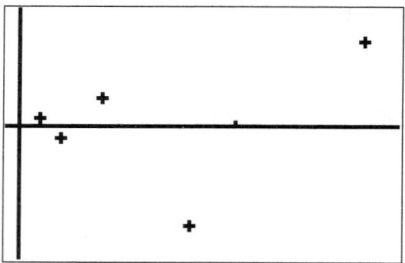

Note that the residuals are relatively small and randomly arranged around the horizontal line. This indicates that the model is useful. Also observe that the residuals increase in magnitude with the length of the pendulum arm. This suggests a systematic error, which may indicate a problem with the experimental design.

Appendix E

Rules for the Use of Electrical Test Instruments

Introduction

Electrical meters, as used in this appendix, are instruments designed to indicate electrical resistance, voltage, or current. They may stand alone and be used for a single purpose, or they may be **multimeters** that can serve all three functions as well as other purposes. In the following discussion, the usage and precautions for each kind of meter is presented.

Electrical meters are precision instruments, and they must be handled with great care. The most common causes of damage are dropping or incorrect electrical connections, which result in excessive current flow through the instrument. **Analog meters** require special care. (An *analog* meter movement provides a continuous indication throughout its range, so the indication is *analogous* to the actual parameter being measured—hence the name analog.) These meters have pointers attached to delicate galvanometer mechanisms. They are typically designed for use in either AC or DC circuits and are not usually interchangeable. Many meters of this kind are designed for a specific range of values. The galvanometer mechanism is very delicate, and it can burn up if it is exposed to excessive current. Protective fuses are usually provided by the manufacturer to prevent damage to the meter.

Blowing a fuse should be avoided. A blown fuse can at best delay completion of a lab exercise and can at worst make a meter unavailable, possibly for days or weeks, until the fuse is replaced. Several things can be done to prevent blowing a fuse. First, whenever possible, insert a switch into the circuit to allow you to quickly open the circuit if the current is too high for the instrument. Second, if the meter has selectable ranges, choose the highest range to make an initial reading and then adjust the range scale downward until you obtain readings that fall in the middle of the scale (for analog meters) or provide the greatest possible number of significant digits (for digital meters). Third, for analog meters, ensure that the connection polarity is correct; this will prevent the pointer from being forced the wrong direction into the meter stops and potentially damaging the mechanism.

The following discussion describes the features of analog meters, but their operation and precautions pertain to both analog and digital meters.

Voltmeters

Voltmeters are used to determine the potential difference between two points in a circuit. They are connected in parallel with the component to be measured. Analog voltmeters use the potential difference across the component to generate the indication. If you have correctly connected the voltmeter into the circuit, you should be able to remove it without breaking the circuit path.

The terminals of a voltmeter are marked with plus and minus signs. The red test probe is usually connected to the positive terminal, and the black probe to the negative terminal. To avoid negative voltage readings on digital meters or backward pointer movement with analog meters, always connect the positive terminal of the voltmeter to the end of the component closest to the positive terminal of the voltage source (via the circuit) and the negative meter terminal to the negative end of the component.

Some meters have several ranges from which to choose. If the voltage is unknown and the possibility exists that it may be hazardously high, select the highest scale (the scale with the largest value) to begin checking. If the voltage exceeds the nameplate capacity of the voltmeter, the meter could be permanently damaged. **Caution:** Never plug a voltmeter's test probes into a wall socket or any other electrical outlet unless you know the voltmeter is designed to measure 110 volts AC or higher.

Ammeters

Ammeters are used to determine the amount of current flowing in a circuit. In order to be accurate, the resistance within an ammeter is very low. For this reason, ammeters should always be inserted in series with the load and other resistances in the circuit. If it were connected in parallel with a load, essentially all of the current would pass through the meter, possibly damaging it. Analog ammeters use the current flowing through the circuit to generate the indication. *In order to connect the ammeter correctly, you must break the circuit.*

As with the voltmeter, ensure that the positive and negative terminals on the instrument are connected with the corresponding terminals on the voltage source. For unknown currents, always start your measurements on the highest scale and work down. **Caution:** Never connect an ammeter directly across the terminals of a battery.

Galvanometers

A galvanometer is essentially an extremely sensitive ammeter that is used to measure only very small currents (often measured in microamps). As with regular ammeters, it must be connected in series in a circuit. It can measure the presence of a current, its direction, and its relative magnitude. Some galvanometers may have a low-resistance wire across the terminals to protect the instrument from being exposed to currents that are too high. Most modern meters have a sensitive protective fuse.

Ohmmeters

Ohmmeters measure the resistance of an element in a circuit. An ohmmeter contains a battery and a very precise voltage regulator circuit to generate a current through the component in proportion to its resistance. For this reason, the component should be disconnected from the circuit before measuring the resistance. If an ohmmeter is connected to an energized circuit, it can be damaged or destroyed.

Multimeters

Multimeters are convenient because you can switch from one function to another very easily by plugging one of the test leads into a different terminal on the meter or just by selecting a different function. Many basic models include a voltmeter, an ammeter, and an ohmmeter, and most can test both AC and DC circuits. An analog multimeter will typically have three or more scales on the meter face. The better meters have a mirror embedded in the scale to help you eliminate pointer parallax when making a reading. Digital multimeters have a single liquid crystal display that automatically changes with the meter mode. Multimeters may also measure signal level (in decibels), electrical continuity, transistor or diode function, and temperature.

The same operating considerations apply to both single-function meters and multimeters. When taking readings, care must still be taken to maintain the same polarity as the power source. If a digital meter is exposed to too much current, you may have to replace a blown fuse. When using both analog and digital instruments, you should begin with the highest range on the selector switch and adjust downward. For analog meters, you should adjust the range until you obtain a reading that is close to midscale. When using a digital meter, the final display should contain at least three significant digits. Some digital meters have a feature that automatically selects the optimum range of operation for a particular mode. This feature is often called "autoranging." Be sure to read the instructions included with your multimeter before using it.

Rheostats

A rheostat (also called a variable resistor or potentiometer) is a device inserted into the circuit that allows you to vary the resistance and the current flow in a circuit. High resistance wire in the instrument is not greatly affected by temperature changes, which makes it useful for laboratory experiments. A slide or a rotary wiper allows the resistance to be changed gradually. A rheostat is not technically a meter, but it is a delicate electrical device that requires care in use.

Common Electrical Component Symbols

AC voltage source		relay contact	
ammeter		resistor	
antenna		speaker	
battery, 1.5 V cell		switch, knife	
battery, 9 V		switch, pushbutton	
capacitor, polarized		transformer	
diode		transistor, NPN	
diode, light-emitting (LED)		transistor, PNP	
electrical ground		variable capacitor	
fuse		variable resistor	
inductor		voltmeter	
lamp		wire or conductor	
motor		wire, connected	
ohmmeter		wire, not connected	

Appendix G

Electrical Resistor Color Codes

Color	Significant Digit	Multiplier		Tolerance
Black	0	1		—
Brown	1	10		1%
Red	2	100		2%
Orange	3	1 000	1 K	3%
Yellow	4	10 000	10 K	4%
Green	5	100 000	100 K	—
Blue	6	1 000 000	1 M	—
Violet	7	10 000 000	10 M	—
Gray	8	—		—
White	9	—		—
Gold	—	0.1		5%
Silver	—	0.01		10%
(No Color)	—	—		20%

The color bands printed on the end or middle of a resistor indicate the resistance. The first two bands are the two significant digits of the resistance. The total resistance is determined by multiplying the two-digit number by the multiplier (indicated by the third band color). The fourth color band indicates the range of resistance that may be observed under actual use (tolerance). See the sample resistor below.

First band	(first SD)	Red	2
Second band	(second SD)	Green	5
Third band	(multiplier)	Gold	0.1
Fourth band	(tolerance)	Gold	$\pm 5\%$

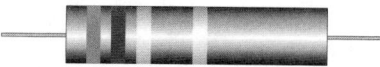

The resistance is $(25 \ \Omega \times 0.1) \pm 5\% = 2.5 \ \Omega \pm 5\%$, or a range of $2.38 \ \Omega$ to $2.63 \ \Omega$.

Appendix H

Characteristics of Selected Elementary Nuclear Particles[1]

Family Name	Particle Name	Particle Symbol	Antiparticle Symbol	Rest Energy (MeV)	Particle Lifetime
Lepton	Electron	e^-	e^+	0.511	4.2×10^{24} y
	Muon	μ^-	μ^+	105.7	2.20×10^{-6} s
	Tauon	τ^-	τ^+	1777	291×10^{-15} s
	Electron neutrino	ν_e	$\overline{\nu}_e$	0	
	Muon neutrino	ν_μ	$\overline{\nu}_\mu$	0	
	Tauon neutrino	ν_τ	$\overline{\nu}_\tau$	0	
Hadron					
Mesons	Pions (light, unflavored)	π^-	π^+	139.6	2.6×10^{-8} s
		π°	π°	135.0	8.4×10^{-17} s
	Kaons (strange)	K^+	K^-	493.7	1.2×10^{-8} s
		K°	$\overline{K}^\circ$	497.7	8.9×10^{-10} s or 5.2×10^{-8} s
Baryons	Proton	p	$\overline{p}$	938.3	1.6×10^{25} y
	Neutron	n	$\overline{n}$	939.6	886.7 s
	Lambda	Λ	$\overline{\Lambda}$	1116	2.6×10^{-10} s
	Sigma	Σ^+	$\overline{\Sigma}^-$	1189	0.80×10^{-10} s
		Σ°	$\overline{\Sigma}^\circ$	1193	7.4×10^{-20} s
		Σ^-	$\overline{\Sigma}^+$	1197	1.5×10^{-10} s
	Xi	Ξ°	$\overline{\Xi}^\circ$	1315	2.9×10^{-10} s
		Ξ^-	$\overline{\Xi}^+$	1321	1.6×10^{-10} s
	Omega	Ω^-	Ω^+	1672	0.82×10^{-10} s

[1]D.E. Groom *et al.*, The European Physical Journal **C15** (2000) 1 and 2001 off-year partial update for the 2002 edition available on the PDG WWW pages (URL: http://pdg.lbl.gov/)

To the Teacher

Teaching Philosophy

The foremost aim of this laboratory manual is to help you reach your primary goal, to help your students become more Christlike. This goal is achieved in this science course by appealing to the whole student. There should be no artificial barriers between knowing and doing in a Christian school. In all areas of his life, the Christian student must realize that he should act upon what he knows to be true. Science can reveal to the student the wonders of God's creation. It can teach him how to make objective observations and analyze information. But you, the teacher, will teach him how to apply what he learns to his daily life by the way you teach and live.

Features

The laboratory activities in this manual are divided into units according to the sequence of presentation in *Physics for Christian Schools,* Second Edition (in development). Consequently, teachers using the first edition (and eventually the second edition) should refer to the Laboratory Prerequisites list immediately following this section in order to determine which material must be covered to prepare for each lab. In most cases, the prerequisite information resides in a single (but not the same) chapter in both the first and second editions, so determining the sequence of the labs will be relatively easy.

Student Edition Features

Each lab activity is printed on perforated pages for easy removal from the manual. The Student Edition labs are generally organized into the following areas:

1. Purpose—A list of the objectives for the lab is provided.

2. Required Equipment—The required equipment and materials are listed so that the student knows what he will need in order to perform the lab. The teacher should refer to the Frequency Lists in the Teacher's Edition for a more complete description of equipment and materials.

3. Prelab Discussion—The necessary background information is provided, including key terms, definitions of variables, and important formulas. The discussion often goes into more detail on a topic than can be afforded in the textbook.

4. Procedure—This section provides detailed, step-by-step instructions to successfully complete the experiment. Explicit data collection steps ensure that the exercise can produce meaningful results.

5. Data—Most labs include this section for recording data and performing calculations in an organized manner.

6. Postlab Exercises—This section provides instructions for completing calculations and graphing the results when required. Steps in this section can normally be performed outside class.

7. Postlab Analysis—This material should normally be assigned immediately after the lab is completed, but you may choose to wait a day to evaluate the results of the class. Many assignments include thought-provoking questions that extend what was learned during the lab.

8. Prelab Homework—Assignment of Prelab Homework should be considered mandatory to ensure proper preparation for the lab. It is printed on a separate page so that the homework can be collected separate from the lab report itself. All skill steps unique to the lab are practiced in the Prelab Homework. Prelab Homework should be graded before performing the lab.

The lab manual also provides a series of useful appendices to which the student can refer in order to complete the experiments.

Teacher's Edition Features

The Teacher's Edition incorporates the following additional features:

1. Complete alphabetical equipment and materials frequency lists are provided in the back of the manual. The numbers listed are the suggested items per lab team unless otherwise noted.

2. Detailed answers are overprinted on the lab report and homework assignment pages. Free-response answers are always given as complete sentences, a standard that you should encourage your students to adhere to. Mathematical solutions list the quantities given, the unknown, the required formula(s), and a complete solution. The methodology is proven and is recommended. This manual also encourages the use of *unit analysis notation* in order to give structure to complex calculations and facilitate unit cancellation. It is most often employed when two or more terms involving ratios are multiplied or divided. The notation consists of a horizontal line representing the fraction bar and vertical lines representing multiplication operations. Cancellation of units is easily and reliably accomplished using this notation. See the solution to Prelab Homework Question 1 in Lab 2-4 for an example of its use.

3. Many labs include typical data and results obtained when students or teachers actually performed the experiments. These results are provided to help you evaluate the results of your class.

4. Thorough notes to the teacher are overprinted in the margin. The notes are organized in the same order as the lab sections.

5. The teacher's notes include a section called Home School Notes, where applicable, which provides numerous suggestions to the home school and small Christian school teacher for equipment substitutions and instructions for building equipment.

Safety and Teacher Responsibility

The labs contained in this lab manual are inherently safe. No hazardous chemicals requiring special safety precautions are used, and the only electrical voltages required are less than 12 volts DC. No labs testing AC voltages or current are performed at all. For safety as well as good stewardship, it is recommended that you store lab equipment and chemicals in a locked cabinet or in a room that can be locked. Many Christian school classrooms are also used for church-related activities. Easy access to laboratory materials could result in damage to your equipment or serious injury to curious, unsupervised children.

Propane, butane, or natural gas burners (often collectively called Bunsen burners) are preferred for regular laboratory use. Alcohol burners are also available. However, alcohol burns with an almost invisible flame, and this characteristic has resulted in many laboratory accidents. Therefore, they are *not* recommended.

Because you may have made substitutions in the recommended equipment or because of other unexpected factors, experiments do not always go as planned. You should become thoroughly familiar with the labs before assigning them to the students and alert students to any changes that you will be making. It is also essential that you *perform* the experiments in advance so that you will know what results to expect and what kind of assistance your students might need during the lab period.

Scheduling and Materials

Scheduling

This manual contains enough labs to perform approximately one lab per week when school is in session. Most teachers will be challenged to complete all of the labs. Therefore, you will have to choose the labs that best suit your students, your facilities, your time, and your budget. To help you schedule these activities, refer to the Introduction to the Teacher's Edition of *PHYSICS for Christian Schools,* First Edition. Use the appropriate suggested teaching plan in conjunction with the Laboratory Prerequisites list to schedule each lab.

A decision that teachers commonly face is how much credit to give for laboratory activities. Most states require that 20% of the classroom time in high-school science courses be devoted to hands-on activities. If your state makes this requirement, the laboratory activities should compose about 20% of the students' final grades.

Equipment and Materials

Following the Laboratory Prerequisite list, you will find an important tool that will help you prepare for the activities in this course. An alphabetized frequency list of the equipment and materials necessary to perform all of the experiments in this lab manual will give you an idea of how your lab will need to be stocked before the beginning of the year. *The numbers of items in the equipment list are per lab team.* Quantities for optional items are listed in parentheses. Items that can or must be shared among teams can be determined from each lab's procedures. See the teacher's notes for each exercise for possible substitutions and detailed requirements.

General sources for the labs are indicated in the equipment list following this section. Local sources are indicated by *L,* and those items usually available only through science suppliers are indicated by *S*. Where both are listed together, the first letter indicates the preferred source. Your most convenient source for physics lab equipment and materials is Bob Jones University Press. Visit the BJUP website at www.bjup.com to obtain the latest information about equipment, materials, and resources for this course. A science lab materials order form can be obtained from BJUP Customer Service by calling 800-845-5731, ext. 3300.

Laboratory Prerequisites

The following table shows the pages containing the minimum information required for successful completion of the lab. Students are expected to be familiar with information from preceding chapters.

Lab	Title	Applicable First Edition Pages	
1-1	Measurement	pp. 11–30	(Ch. 2)
1-2	Vectors	pp. 55–65	(Ch. 4)
2-1	Balanced and Unbalanced Forces	pp. 88–92	(Ch. 6)
2-2	The Recording Timer	pp. 35–44	(Ch. 3)
2-3	Transmitted Forces	pp. 131–34	(Ch. 8)
2-4	Displacement, Velocity, and Acceleration	pp. 35–52	(Ch. 3)
2-5	Horizontal Projection	pp. 69–76	(Ch. 5)
2-6	Circular Motion	pp. 104–5	(Ch. 7)
2-7	Mechanical Advantage—Efficiency	pp. 181–83	(Ch. 10)
2-8	Conservation of Energy—Spring Constant	pp. 149–66	(Ch. 9)
2-9	Conservation of Momentum	pp. 187–95	(Ch. 11)
3-1	Length of a Molecule	pp. 221–33	(Ch. 13)
3-2	Latent Heat of Fusion	pp. 261–77	(Ch. 15)
3-3	Coefficient of Thermal Expansion	pp. 235–38	(Ch. 14)
3-4	Specific Gravity and Buoyancy	pp. 301–10	(Ch. 17)
3-5	Boyle's Law	pp. 240–48	(Ch. 14)
3-6	Charles's Law	pp. 240–46	(Ch. 14)
3-7	Period of a Pendulum	pp. 205–22	(Ch. 12)
3-8	Speed of Sound in Air	pp. 212–17	(Ch. 12)
4-1	Electrostatic Charges	pp. 326–29	(Ch. 18)
4-2	Resistance	pp. 350–58	(Ch. 20)
4-3	Series Circuits	pp. 359–68	(Ch. 20)
4-4	Parallel Circuits	pp. 359–68	(Ch. 20)
4-5	Series-Parallel Circuits	pp. 359–68	(Ch. 20)
4-6	Mapping a Magnetic Field	pp. 375–99	(Ch. 21, 22)
4-7	Electrical Work	pp. 399–406	(Ch. 22)
4-8	Capacitors, Diodes, and Transistors	pp. 342–46, 427–36	(Ch. 19, 23)
4-9	Special Transistor Applications	pp. 399–414, 427–36	(Ch. 22, 23)
4-10	Plane Mirror Reflections	pp. 449–50	(Ch. 24)
4-11	Curved Mirror Reflections	pp. 451–59	(Ch. 24)
4-12	Refraction	pp. 465–70	(Ch. 25)
4-13	Reflected Diffraction	pp. 485–95	(Ch. 26)
5-1	Radioactive Decay Simulation	pp. 567–70	(Ch. 30)
5-2	Elementary Nuclear Particles	pp. 526–35, 561–79	(Ch. 28, 30)

Frequency List for Equipment

Description	Source*	1-1	1-2	2-1	2-2	2-3	2-4	2-5	2-6	2-7	2-8	2-9	3-1	3-2	3-3	3-4	3-5	3-6	3-7	3-8	4-1	4-2	4-3	4-4	4-5	4-6	4-7	4-8	4-9	4-10	4-11	4-12	4-13	5-1	5-2
ammeter	S																										0								
balance, lab	S		X						X			X		X		X																			
ball bearing, large	S/L						X																		X	X									
battery, dry cell, 1.5 V (with holder)	S			0											0											0	X								
battery, dry cell, 6 V	S/L										X	X		X		X																			
beaker, 50 mL	S										X	X		X	X																				
beaker, 250 mL	S														X	X																			
beaker, 500 or 1000 mL	S											2																							
board, leveling	L										0																								
board, leveling (or table)	L																																		
book, generic	L							X										2							2										
Boyle's law apparatus	S/L														0		X	X																	
Bunsen burner and lighter	S														0			0																	
buzzer, DC	S/L													X																					
calorimeter	S															X																			
can, overflow	L						X					X																							
carpenter's level	L							2																											
C-clamp	L					2		2																											
clamp, flask	S																										X								
clamp, pulley	S					X																													
clamp, right-angle	S					X																				X									
compact disc, standard-sized	L																																X		
compass, drawing	S/L																								X										
compass, magnetic, small	S/L					X						2																							
dynamics cart, with bumper	S																			X															
Elenco Electronics Learning Center kit	L																					X	X	X				X	X						
eyedropper	S/L			X																		X	X	X											
force board and accessories (including 3 pulley clamps)	S/L												X																						
friction rod kit	L/S					X															X											4-12=X			
glass square (crown glass), 5 cm × 5 cm	S																																		
graduated cylinder, 10 mL	S												X																						
graduated cylinder, 25 mL	S															X																			
graduated cylinder, 100 mL	S		X											X																					
graduated cylinder, large (500 or 1000 mL)	L							0												0															
hose (1 or more)	L														X																				
hot mitt	L																	2																	
inclined plane or board	L/S					X													X																
laser pointer (or other laser source)	L/S																															X			
linear expansion apparatus	S																							X											
magnet, bar	S																									2									
magnet, odd-shaped	S/L																		0							(2)									
mallet, rubber	L																			0															
marble, shooting	L							0																											
meter stick	S/L					X		X	0	X	X	X			X		3	X	X	X		X	X	X											
metric mass set	S			0	X																									2			X		
metric mass, 200 g	S			X	X																	X	X	X											
metric mass, 1 kg	S				3																														
metric measuring tape	L/S																		0												X	X			
metric ruler (12 in. or 30.5 cm)	L	X	X		X		X	X		X			X		X	X	X				X				X	X				X	X	X			
mirror, concave	S																														X				
mirror, plane	S/L																													X		X			
motor, electric, DC	L/S																				X														
multimeter, Elenco M-1000B	S/L			X	X		X								X		X					X	X	X				X	X		2		X		
ohmmeter	S/L																										0								
optical bench stands	S/L																														X				
optics candle or lamp and support	S/L																													X		X			
optics dish, semicircular	S																															X			
optics focusing screen and support	S/L																														X				
pan, large, shallow	L												X																						
pith ball	L/S							X																											
plumb line and bob	L																										X								
potentiometer or rheostat	S/L																										X								
projectile track	S					X		X																											X

*S = science supplier, L = local source, in order of preference   X = required, 0 = optional

Description	Source*	1-1	1-2	2-1	2-2	2-3	2-4	2-5	2-6	2-7	2-8	2-9	3-1	3-2	3-3	3-4	3-5	3-6	3-7	3-8	4-1	4-2	4-3	4-4	4-5	4-6	4-7	4-8	4-9	4-10	4-11	4-12	4-13	5-1	5-2
protractor	L		X																																	
pulley, dual-tandem	S																																			
recording timer and accessories	S				X	X				2																										
s.g. specimen, brass or other object	S	X													X																					
s.g. specimen set	S																																			
scissors	L										X																									
sewing pins, round-headed	L																																			
spool, sewing	L																																			
spring	S/L																														X		X			
spring scale, metric	S								X	X																										
steam generator and heat source	S																																			
stopper, rubber, one-hole	S																																			
stopper, rubber, two-hole (or other mass)	S						X	X	X																											
stopwatch	L/S													(3)																						
support rod, horizontal	S/L					X			X	X								X	X	X																
support stand, heavy-duty, and clamps	S					X			X	X								X	X	X																
switch, electrical knife	S/L																	0	X									7								
test lead, with alligator clips	S/L																									0	X									
thermocouple and multimeter	S																																			
thermometer, lab	S												0					X	X	X																
tongs, beaker	S												X					X	X																	
tube, glass resonance	S																																			
tubes or rods, metal	S/L							X							X																					
tubing, glass, 0.25 in. or 6 mm	S														X				X																	
tuning forks, 512 Hz and 1024 Hz	S																																			
voltmeter	S/L																			2+																
washer, metal	L		0						30								0											0								
wire gauze (beaker support accessory)	S																																			
wire hanger and support	L																			X																
wire, insulated	L																										X									
wire leads, electrical test	S/L											X		0													X	X								

Description	Source*	1-1	1-2	2-1	2-2	2-3	2-4	2-5	2-6	2-7	2-8	2-9	3-1	3-2	3-3	3-4	3-5	3-6	3-7	3-8	4-1	4-2	4-3	4-4	4-5	4-6	4-7	4-8	4-9	4-10	4-11	4-12	4-13	5-1	5-2
alcohol, isopropyl	L											X			0																					
alcohol, rubbing	L													0																						
box, with cover	L																																	X		
cardboard, corrugated sheet	L																																			
cardboard, thin sheet	L																																			
corn oil	L													0		0										X						X	X			
corn syrup	L													0		0																				
cover, insulated (for calorimeter cups)	L													(2)		0	0																			
cup, polystyrene	L															0	0																			
ethanol, denatured	L															0	0																			
glycerin or soap	L													X																						
ice, crushed	L																X													X						
liquid detergent	L															0																				
lycopodium powder (or chalk dust)	S/L																																			
M&M's Milk Chocolate Candies, 1 bag	L																																	X		
marker, felt-tipped	L				X			X										X												X						
oleic acid solution, 0.50%	S							X																								X	X			
paper, carbon, standard-sized	L																																X			
paper clips	L			0	X		X																										X			
paper, graph, standard-sized	L													X																						
paper towels	L																																			
paper, unlined, legal-sized	L																															3				
paper, unlined, standard-sized	L					X								X			X									X				X		X				
string, various weights	L	X			X	X	X	X					X		X			X	X							X				X		3	X	X		
tape, masking	L	X			X	X	X	X	X	X	X	X	X		X			X	X	X																
thread	L											X	X		X																					
water, tap, various temperatures	L																	X								X										
wood block	L																									X				X		X	X			
wooden sticks (or pencils)	L																																X			2

*S = science supplier, L = local source, in order of preference

X = required, 0 = optional